Occupation: Writer

By the Same Author

ooooooooooooooooooooooooooooooooooooooooooooooooooooooooooooooooooooooooooooooooooooooooo

I, CLAUDIUS · CLAUDIUS THE GOD
COUNT BELISARIUS · WIFE TO MR. MILTON
SERGEANT LAMB OF THE NINTH · PROCEED, SERGEANT LAMB
HERCULES, MY SHIPMATE · KING JESUS
THE WHITE GODDESS · THE ISLANDS OF UNWISDOM
POEMS, 1938-1945

ooooooooooooooooooooooooooooooooooooooooooooooooooooooooooooooooooooooooooooooooooooooooo

ROBERT GRAVES

Occupation: Writer

CREATIVE AGE PRESS
NEW YORK : 1950

Introduction

RECENTLY I revised and published, under the title *The Common Asphodel,* all my essays on poetry written since the early 'Twenties. Here is a companion volume: a collection of my short stories, plays, and miscellaneous essays, similarly revised.

First comes 'Lars Porsena, or The Future of Swearing'; and this is its history. I had been a soldier in the First World War and early in 1919 was demobilized with a temporary pension, later made permanent, for neurasthenia. In January, 1926, after seven difficult years, during which I got a degree at Oxford and wrote poetry and essays on poetry, I took a job at Cairo as Professor of English Literature at the Royal Egyptian University. My salary was high, but I did not like Egypt. As the year drew on, the weather grew very hot; then I had difficulties with my French colleagues, the students went on strike, and swarms of offensively large and queer insects appeared in the flat where I was staying. My language soon recovered much of its wartime foulness, and for want of anything better to do with my spare time — the students still being on strike and my colleagues having decided to hold their faculty meetings in secret — I wrote a critical monograph on the subject of swearing. It was published that autumn; a revised and enlarged edition appeared in 1936, and I have now added a few paragraphs here and there, enclosed in brackets, to bring it up to date.

I resigned my appointment at the end of the academic year, determined never to take another job of any sort, and returned to England. There, in 1927, after another difficult time complicated by my open defiance of social conventions, I wrote a biography of T. E. Lawrence which put me in funds again. The next essay, the venomous 'Mrs. Fisher, or The Future of Humour,' was written, like 'Lars Porsena,' for the *Today and Tomorrow* series, which, beginning with J. B. S. Haldane's *Daedalus, or Science and the Future,* had already reached seventy volumes. Several more were in preparation. I wrote 'Mrs. Fisher' in London, a few months before my valedictory autobiography *Goodbye to All That;* then I retired to a mountain village in Majorca where I hoped to avoid the more shocking sights and sounds of pluto-democratic civilization. Little apology is needed for the republication of 'Mrs. Fisher.' Even the calamities of the Second World War have not put it seriously out of date. Though life in Great Britain is no longer quite so 'goddawful' in the exuberantly anti-poetic sense defined in the essay, it has grown more so in the United States. If, as the Americans assert, this is to be the American Century, millions now living may yet witness the outrageous theophany of Mrs. Fisher, which I predicted.

'The Shout' had been written in 1926, but I could not find a publisher until 1929, when it appeared in a signed limited edition as one of *The Woburn Books*. Unfortunately, the publisher insisted that it should be reduced from eight thousand to five thousand words, which was too drastic a condensation, and I have since lost the original version. Richard in the story is a surrogate for myself: I was still living on the neurasthenic verge of nightmare. 'Old Papa Johnson' is a true story; I omitted it from *Goodbye to All That* partly because it was too long for an incidental anecdote and partly because 'Papa Johnson' himself might have objected. 'Desolation Island' was South Georgia. 'Avocado Pears' is also a true story. The narrator was T. W. Harries of Balliol College, Oxford, who died soon afterwards while on a visit to India. The four short essays that follow are extracts from a 'Journal of Curiosities' which I kept at this period.

'But It Still Goes On' was written in Majorca early in 1930, in answer to a request for a play by Mr. Maurice Browne, who had recently staged R. C. Sheriff's successful *Journey's End. Goodbye to All That* had brought me a lot of notoriety and my name was being coupled with Sheriff's. The play came back by return of post with a curt note that its subject prevented it from ever being staged in England. It now interests me less as a period piece of the late 'Twenties than as a tactful reshuffling of actual events and situations in which I had been more or less closely concerned.

Majorca had the calming effect on my nerves that I had hoped, and, after one short visit to England in 1930, I remained there until 1936 (the year I wrote 'The Cult of Tolerance,' hitherto unpublished), when the outbreak of the Spanish Civil War set me on the move again. I returned to England for a while, then lived in Switzerland, France, and the United States. I wrote 'Horses' on the liner that brought me back to England from the States a few days before the outbreak of World War II; I shall not contradict anyone who reads it as a self-satire. I remained in England throughout the War.

By this time I had realized that my best way to earn a living without loss of poetic independence was by writing history disguised as novels; and the rest of the essays included here are byproducts of this activity. 'Colonel Blimp's Ancestors' was suggested in 1942 by the uneasy feeling that the British Army still contained far too many pigheaded officers, leftovers from the First World War, whose prototypes I had come across while reading up English military history of the seventeenth and eighteenth centuries for my *Wife to Mr. Milton,* and my two *Sergeant Lamb* novels. 'The Search for Thomas Atkins' was provoked by a letter in *The Times* during the fighting at Arnhem in 1945, which claimed that the original Thomas Atkins was a private soldier in the 33rd Foot, killed there in 1797. As a Royal Welch Fusilier I recalled the regimental tradition that he had been one of our men, and my researches proved (to my own satisfaction, at least) that Atkins had served for a time with Sergeant Lamb in the American War of 1775-83. I wrote in the serene confidence that Atkins' battalion, which had recently been all but wiped out by the Germans at Calais and again by the Japanese in Burma, would before long be quartered in Berlin; as they are, in fact, now. 'It Was a Stable World' was my answer to a request from *Life* magazine for a description of the Roman world at the time

of Jesus. My novels *I, Claudius, Claudius the God,* and *King Jesus*
had covered this period, so I knew something about it; but the
essay came back by return of post with the hint that it was not
in line with editorial policy. It appeared in *The Cornhill* instead.
'Caenis on Incest' (hitherto unpublished) is a recent consideration
of the series of dynastic murders recorded in my *Claudius* novels:
a confession that I missed the hidden motive for most of them.
'Pharaoh's Chariot Wheels' develops a theory propounded in
King Jesus; it was originally intended as part of the argument
of my *White Goddess.* 'How Mad Are Hatters?' is evidence of
my etymological obsession: if the accepted derivation of a word
or phrase does not convince me, I cannot help hunting through
half a dozen dictionaries in search of the true one. 'Dead Man's
Bottles' is written in self-criticism of my absent-minded habit
of pocketing pencils and match boxes. 'Está en su Casa,' 'founded
on fact,' as the Victorians used to say in the days before writers
had to worry about libel actions, records my happy return to
Majorca in 1946.

Deyá
Majorca
1949   R. G.

Contents

Occupation: Writer

'Lars Porsena,' or the Future of Swearing and Improper Language

(1926; revised 1935)

OF recent years there has been a noticeable decline of swearing and foul language in England; and this, except at centres of industrial depression, shows every sign of continuing indefinitely until a new shock to our national nervous system — such as war, pestilence, revolution, fire from Heaven, or whatever you please — revives the habit of swearing, together with that of praying. Taking advantage of the lull, I propose to make a short enquiry into the nature and necessity of foul language: a difficult theme and one seldom treated with detachment.

To begin with a few necessary commonplaces. It is the chief strength of the oath that its use is restricted by both ecclesiastical and legal authority to the most solemn occasions only. The Mosaic injunction against taking the name of Jehovah in vain had a double force. It recorded a primary taboo against the mention, except on solemn occasions, of the tribal god's holy name, for fear that foreigners might learn it and use it mischievously.

1

It also recorded a secondary taboo against the misuse of even a periphrasis of the name: for the act of calling the godhead to witness any vow or contract, or to injure a personal enemy, necessarily involved elaborate purifications and sacrificial offerings. Any appeal to Jehovah to witness or punish a triviality was forbidden as both diminishing divine prestige and depriving of their perquisites the priestly commissioners for oaths. But that is ancient history. Now the vain oath is no longer punishable with stoning or the stake — it is regarded not as blasphemy but merely as a breach of the peace. 'Goddam you, sir, for an impertinent jack-in-office,' growled at a London ticket-inspector, is liable to no greater penalties than 'To the pigs with dirty ould King William!' bawled in Belfast outside an Orange Lodge. If a riot results, the original Goddam (or whatever) may be cited as a provocation when the case comes up for trial; but the only oath that a court of law can take seriously is the oath sworn by the witness before giving evidence. The Almighty is expected to take personal vengeance on vain oaths sworn out of court; yet should the witness, after kissing the Book, fail to tell the truth, the judge will assume responsibility to the Almighty for 'perjury' and commit the offender to prison; because the dignity of the court has also been offended. The judge is impartial, and will be as zealous on behalf of the Jewish God — if the witness is a Jew — or the Mohammedan, Buddhist, Parsee, or any other sort of deity, as on behalf of the God of his state religion. But only the breach of an oath sworn in the due course of legal proceedings (whether by Bible, Koran, Book of Mormon, lighted candle, or a coloured print of the Peacock Pagoda) makes the swearer liable to prosecution for perjury; extrajudicial oaths and blasphemies, however hair-raising, are regarded by the law as mere trumpery.

Since abusive swearing is not a punishable offence, unless calculated to cause a breach of the peace, it is possible in favourable circumstances to call a man a blasted fool without fear of getting into trouble. Yet to call him, plainly and without qualification, a fool is always dangerous: that constitutes a slander and an action lies. 'Favourable circumstances' are those in which 'blasted fool' is accepted as a harmless colloquialism; and the same principle is applied to even harsher phrases, according to local custom. Recently a man charged at Hoxton with 'using language calculated to cause a breach of the peace' complained that at Bethnal Green, where he lived, he could have said all that and more with impunity. What was wanted, he protested, was a swearing directory for the London districts which would indicate precisely what he might say where.

Every minister of religion is expected to protest against the taking in vain of God's name, and his cloth protects him against active resentment of his protests; but he has no legal authority to support them by force. Officers of the law have an advantage over him: if they feel so inclined they can always construe a merely blasphemous remark as an illegal act of incitement.

One of the most violent of the early nineteenth-century street ballads is that of 'Sam Hall,' the unrepentant criminal who cares for neither God nor man:

> My name it is Sam Hall,
>   Damn your eyes!
> My name it is Sam Hall,
>   Damn your eyes!
> My name it is Sam Hall
> And I hate you one and all,
> And I curse you one and all,
>   God damn your eyes!

Knowing that he will hang in any case, he makes the best possible use of his last hours:

> Oh, His Lordship he did stare
> For to hear me curse and swear,
> And himself I did not spare,
>   God damn his eyes!

and this defiance of the judge in his own courtroom must, even in those methodistical days, have caused still greater dismay than persistent defiance of his Creator.

The taboo on the vain mention of God or gods extends to

the sacred mysteries, sacraments, and writings, and finally to the saints, called to mediate between God and man. In Catholic countries these friendly representatives of Heaven offer rich facilities for swearing in a low key; in Protestant countries, where God is approached directly on all occasions, the swearer, deprived of the saints, is forced into blasphemy. In Catholic countries, too, the reading of the Bible is a prerogative of the priesthood, and an oath sworn by the Great Sealed Word of God remains resonant and effective; in Protestant countries the prolific output of sixpennyworths and even penn'orths of the Holy Scriptures from secular presses has further impoverished the swearer's vocabulary. The triumph of Protestantism is best shown by the decline into vapidity of the proudest oath an Englishmen could once swear: 'By George!' We have long lost all interest in our patron saint. It has been stated with persistence and circumstantial detail that in the late summer of 1918 an Australian mounted unit sensationally rediscovered the actual bones of St. George in Palestine — not George of Cappadocia but the other George who slew the dragon. The remains were brought to light by the explosion of a shell in the vault of a ruined church. The officer in command cabled the Dean and Chapter of Westminster, inviting them to provide sanctuary for the holy relics. After some delay he received a formal reply regretting the serious overcrowding of the Cathedral. To accept the gift would have meant an elaborate ceremony of translation, too Popish by far for this century, as well as a tacit acceptance of the dragon myth. The saint was lost again by the disgusted Australians, this time beyond rescue.

Undistinguished as the oath by St. George has become, he has at any rate had the glory of outlasting all his peers. What Protestant cobbler still swears by his patron St. Crispin? What huntsman or whipper-in by St. Hubert? The breach with Rome has taken all the sting out of religion in England. 'Oh, to hell with the Pope!' amiably remarked an Englishman in the course of a political argument in a saloon bar. 'And to hell,' replied the furious Italian, upsetting the glasses with a blow of his fist, 'and to hell with your Archbishop of Canterbury!' The Englishman laughed immoderately.

Bound up with the taboo on the mention of God, of Heaven his throne, and Earth his footstool, and of all his other charges and minions, is the complementary taboo on the Devil, his ministers, and his sulphurous prison house. At one time the vain invocation of the Devil was even more dangerous than the breach of the Third Commandment. God, though he would not hold him guiltless who took his name in vain, might forgive an occasional lapse — as he forgave St. Peter his cursing and swearing in the high priest's courtyard; but the Devil, if called in professionally, would not fail to charge dearly for his visit. However, since the great Victorian day when an excited workingman came rushing out of the City church where Dean Farrar was preaching the gospel, and shouted to his friends at the public-house corner: 'Good news! Good news, mates! Old Farrar says there ain't no 'ell!' the taboo has weakened year by year. 'That dreadful other place,' as Christina respectfully calls it in the deathbed scene of Butler's *Way of All Flesh,* is now seldom dwelt upon in the English pulpit. Parts of Scotland and Wales remain loyal to their terrors, but the threat of Hell's quenchless flames and the satyromorphic view of Satan are now chiefly used as exports to foreign mission schools. Practically speaking, the demand in the English market is limited to industrial reformatories, Boys' Brigades, and homes for fallen women.

There is no surer way of testing the current of popular religious opinion than to examine the breaches of the taboos in swearing. The most important result of the great religious controversies of the nineteenth century was the overturning of the theocratic despotism of the Puritan First Person of the Trinity, and the institution of a liberal oligarchy, the Benefactors of the Human Race, under the omnipresent regency of the Second Person. An irreverent appeal to the Second Person is thereby expressive of far greater exasperation than a similar one to the First Person, who has been left with only the barren attributes of power.

'O God!' has indeed become an inferior oath and crept into the legitimate vocabulary of the drawing room and the stage, as 'O Jesus!' and 'O Christ!' have not. 'By God!' is stronger than 'O God!', and expresses fierce determination: but 'By Jesus Christ!' expresses perfect indomitability. The Third Person of the Trinity is never appealed to, except disguisedly as 'Holy Smoke!', either because the sin against the Holy Ghost is known to be the one unforgivable offence, or because the Dove seems to the ordinary, hard-headed Protestant an unnecessary encumbrance to his religion — part of the Virgin-birth mystery about which he does not like to think. God, for him, is a benevolent abstraction; Jesus Christ, a hero towards whom he has warm, friendly feelings; while the Holy Ghost remains a shadowy doctrinal formula.

The legitimization of 'O God' and 'By God' has made old-fashioned such euphemisms as 'Gog' (By Gogges bones), 'Cock' (Yea, by Cock), 'Cod' (I'cod), 'Ad' (Adzooks, i.e., 'God's hooks' — the nails of the cross), 'Bob' (Swelp me Bob), 'Odd' (Odds Bobs), and 'Gad'; whereas 'Crimes,' 'Cripes,' 'Crickey,' 'Christmas,' and various 'Gee' formations such as 'Gee whiz,' 'Jeeze,' and 'Jeepers creepers' are still current.

It is only a short step from blasphemy and near-blasphemy to secular irreverence. Many secular objects that symbolize deep-seated class loyalties are held in the highest reverence. The Crown and the Union Jack are, for the governing classes, enthroned beside Altar and Chalice. To call the smallest King's ship a 'boat,' let alone a 'wretched tub' or 'lousy hencoop,' or to mistake a pack of hounds in full cry for a 'horde of howling dogs' are still social crimes. The ingenious General Gambier, who had been a gunner, used this form of profanity with the happiest result. Once, when inspecting the famous 'Z' Battery of the Royal Horse Artillery, he was dissatisfied with its response to his order 'Dismount!' He bellowed at them: 'Now *climb back again,* you pack of consumptive little Maltese monkeys!'

Nowadays, to curse effectively one cannot rely merely on breaches of religious or semireligious taboos: a reality or at least a plausibility must be evoked. If, for example, a taxi-driver deliberately takes you out of your way to put another twopence on the clock, and then gets held up in a traffic jam and makes you lose your appointment, the sensible way to curse him (if you are the cursing type) is not to start with 'What the blazes!' and 'Who the hell?', and end with blasting his bleeding neck; but by using frequent obscene intensives in 'f' and 'b': 'May your gears seize up and your tyres burst, and may you get pitched through the windscreen, break both your absurd legs against a lamppost, and have your licence cancelled by the worst-tempered magistrate in London!' Hells, Blazes and Blasts are mere fiddle-faddle to a taxi-driver.

No form of humour is more boring than such nonalcoholic substitutes for the true wine of swearing as 'Great jumping beans!', 'Ye little fishes!', 'Snakes and ladders!', and 'Jam and butter your whiskers, you irregular old Pentagon!' If Sinclair Lewis has done nothing else in *Arrowsmith*, he has at least branded Cliff Clawson, the medical student who perpetually indulged in this form of heartiness, as a menace to society.

Among the working classes one of the unforgivable words of abuse is 'bastard' — because they take bastardy seriously; though in the governing classes, where bastards, under the courtesy title of 'natural sons and daughters,' have contributed largely to our ancestral splendours, the word has only a playful sense. Illegitimacy carries no penalties with it nowadays; recent history has shown that a bastard can become prime minister, or be offered an earldom. About the only disadvantage a bastard suffers now is that if he wishes to take holy orders he has to apply for a special licence from the Archbishop of Canterbury; and this is never refused.

So much for 'bastard.' But the other common word in 'b,' which originally meant a Bulgarian heretic, but later, by association, implied 'one addicted to unnatural vice,' is not a serious insult among the working classes, who are comparatively free from the homosexual habit. Dr. Johnson correctly defined the word as 'a term of endearment among sailors.' In the governing classes the case is reversed. When the word was written up nakedly on a club notice-board some thirty years ago as a charge against one of the members, a terrific social explosion followed, the dust of which has not yet settled even now. Had the accusation been 'Mr.

Wilde is a bastard,' shoulders would only have been shrugged at the noble lord's quixotic ill-temper. As it was . . .

[*I have made a mistake here, I find. Mr. Christopher Millard has written as follows in correction of the preceding paragraph:*

Your account of the libellous card left at Wilde's club is not quite accurate. Queensberry wrote on his own visiting card 'Oscar Wilde posing as a somdomite' — the words 'posing as' were inserted on legal advice and 'somdomite' was the marquess's quaint spelling of a word, with which he was apparently unfamiliar, suggested to him by his lawyers in lieu of the word that you credit him with using. Queensberry handed the card to the porter of the Albemarle Club, who put it into an envelope and handed it to Wilde on his next visit to the club. So there was only technical 'publication'; but if Wilde had not taken action when he did, Queensberry would have gone on until he compelled Wilde to do something to protect himself.]

This brings us to the sex and lavatory taboo; mention even of the less private parts of the body is forbidden by a convention which has lost little of its rigidity since mid-Victorian times. The soldier, shot through the buttocks at Loos, who was asked by a visitor where he had been wounded, could only reply: 'I'm sorry, ma'am, I don't know: I never learned Latin.' Public reference to a man's navel, thighs, or armpits, even, is scandalous; by which the size of the 'breeches of fig leaves' tailored in Eden may be measured.

The wounded soldier situation has given rise to a whole anthology of prettily turned jokes, an education in perfect gentlemanliness. One popular version runs: 'If you had been shot where I was shot, lady, you wouldn't have been shot at all.' Another: 'Pretty close it came, and if I didn't have happened to be thinking of my sister-in-law at the time . . .'

The taboo in polite society on the harmless word 'bottom' dates from the eighteenth century. Boswell, in his *Life of Dr. Johnson*, writes (1781):

Talking of a very respectable author he told us a curious circumstance in his life, which was, that he had married a printer's devil.

Reynolds: 'A printer's devil, sir! Why, I thought a printer's devil was a creature with a black face and in rags.'

Johnson: 'Yes, sir. But I suppose he had her face washed and put clean clothes on her. (Then looking very serious and earnest.) And she did not disgrace him; the woman had a bottom of good sense.' The word *bottom* thus introduced was as ludicrous when contrasted with his gravity, that most of us could not forbear tittering and laughing; though I recollect that the Bishop of Killaloe kept his countenance with perfect steadiness, while Miss Hannah More slyly hid her face behind a lady's back who sat on the same settee with her. His pride could not bear that any expression of his should excite ridicule, when he did not intend it; he therefore resolved to assume and exercise despotick power, glanced sternly around and called out in a strong tone, 'Where's the merriment?' Then collecting himself and looking awful to make us feel how he could impose restraint, and as it were searching his mind for a still more ludicrous word, he slowly pronounced, 'I say that the *woman* was *fundamentally* sensible' as if he had said 'Hear this now and laugh if you dare!' We all sat composed as at a funeral.

The recent phenomenon of nudism has done nothing to relax the rigour of these taboos. Previously, public nakedness was restricted to savages, French chorus girls, ships' stokers in the Red Sea, and the Doukhobors, a fanatical Russian sect who, when they became unpopular in their own country, emigrated to the Canadian West at the beginning of the present century. Nudism has now gained quite a following in America especially, where nudist marriages have been performed and nudist garden parties given — their code of propriety permits the officiating priest to come undressed but forbids the waiters at the garden parties to undo so much as a single button. It has been less popular in England, perhaps because the climate is not so favourable. I have never visited a nudist camp, but those who have agree that in England, at least, the proprieties are maintained so strictly that any direct reference to a tabooed part of the body, however freely exposed, or the least particularized prying, would be enough to have the offender expelled. Nudism has been sentimentalized in much the same way as the use of contraceptives by Dr. Marie Stopes. The body is regarded as holy and a holy silence must be

observed about it: conversations in nudist camps, I am told, tend
to run on stark philosophical lines.

'Whore' and 'harlot' are swear words of power in all ranks of
society. Among the working classes they are taken realistically.
Among the governing classes they are an accusation of aesthetic
coarseness: for a woman to have a *liaison* is almost always par-
donable, and occasionally, when the lover chosen is sufficiently
distinguished, even admirable; but in love, as in sport, the amateur status must be strictly maintained. Yet the accusation against
a man that he consorts with harlots ranks as a serious insult in
neither class; though 'pimp,' 'ponce,' and 'procurer' do because
it is considered unsporting to live off women.

I am not qualified to write about American swearing, but I
understand that, though the words are used as in England, they
are governed by different conventions. 'Bastard,' for example, and
'son of a bitch' are mere friendly terms of reproach. This recalls
the experience of Mrs. Beech, an American tourist who was staying in Paris after the War. An elderly Frenchman who was introduced to her greeted her delightedly: 'Ah, Mrs. Beech, Mrs.
Beech, you are one of ze noble muzzers who gave so many sons
to ze War.'

'Son of a bitch' is something of a philological rarity, being 'common in gender' like the Latin words *dies* and *margo*. Feminine,
for example, in the well-known low-life ballad: 'The Fly Flew
into the Grocery Shop,' here quoted in a bowdlerized version:

> Mother, mother, my heart's so sore!
>   (*Sing dodie-eye doo-doo!*)
> Then, you son of a bitch, don't sin no more!
>   (*Sing dodie-eye doo-doo!*)
> She tossed her arms and she slapped her knees,
> 'And I'll sin,' she said, 'as I goldarned please,'
>   (For the son of a bitch had nothing else to do).

'Son of a bitch' is the modern equivalent of the Elizabethan
'whoreson,' which was also common in gender. Both mean 'son
of a whore,' yet neither carries the same sting as 'son of a whore'
itself, which remains as deadly an insult as it was in Elizabethan

and Jacobean days. As Middleton's Captain Ager said in tragic monologue:

> . . . Son of a whore!
> There is no such another murdering-piece
> In all the stock of calumny; it kills
> At one report two reputations —
> A mother's and her son's.

Except perhaps in Glasgow. A recorded conversation between two small Glasgow boys in wartime ran:

> 'Your mither's a hoor.'
> 'She's no a hoor.'
> 'She's a hoor tae the sojers.'
> 'Och aye, mebbe tae the sojers.'

The prevalence of perversion in well-to-do society has added 'Nancy-boy,' 'fairy,' 'pansy,' and 'poof' to the list of unforgivable synonyms. It is noteworthy that all these words are of modern origin. In England male homosexuality became popular in Tudor times together with Italian and Spanish fashions in dress and deportment — the words 'pathic' and 'catamite' (a word derived from 'Ganymede,' Juppiter's cupbearer) were then in current use but declined again until their reintroduction from the Continent nearly three centuries later, this time sponsored by French artistic decadence and Prussian military *esprit de corps*. An anecdote of historical interest concerns the old Empire Lounge, a resort of the late Victorian and Edwardian ladies of the town. Directed by the squire, a worried country clergyman arrived there one evening, in search of his schoolboy son who had run off with money from the Parish Organ Fund. A white-stockinged woman swooped down on him at once: 'Are you looking for a naughty little girl?' The old clergyman beamed gratefully at her. 'No, madam, I thank you kindly all the same: I am looking for a naughty little boy.' She threw up her hands. 'I don't know what's to become of us poor women these days!' Those were the days 'when men were men and pansy was still a flower name.'

In England the shame of cuckoldry has abated: the very word 'cuckold' has dropped out of the popular vocabulary and I know of no synonym in current use. Husband morale is not what it used to be, and the ease with which one can get a divorce in non-Catholic countries has taken the sting out of the word. [*In Spain, where no divorce is allowed,* cornudo *or* cabron, *both meaning 'cuckold,' are still very offensive words and used in the Army without relevance by one young unmarried recruit to another.*] The chastity of sister or daughter has become a more serious consideration than the faithfulness of a wife. When once the master of a Thames tug, bawled at for fouling a pleasure boat and breaking an oar, leaned over the rails and shouted hoarsely: 'Oh, I did, did I, Charley? And talking of oars, 'ow's your sister?', he did so only in detestation of the leisured classes and the confidence of a quick getaway.

In Hindu India the insult 'brother-in-law,' carrying with it the implication 'I have been familiar with your sister,' is the one unforgivable insult, and the first word therefore that, in pre-Curzon days, the British soldier picked up. In Mohammedan India a man is best insulted paternally: 'O you father of sixty dogs!' This is because Hindus lay most stress on the decencies of family life in a large household, Mohammedans on the passing down of male perfection from father to son. Chinese swearing is well illustrated by this quotation from *Kai Lung's Wallet:* 'May the principles of your warmth and cold never be properly adjusted; may hate defile your ancestral tablets; and may your hamstrings snap in the moment of achievement.'

The Chinese, it should be noted, seem to be the only people who have openly cultivated the social art of swearing, and a treatise on the subject is included in the Chinese classics. Their theory is that from the very earliest times man has sworn at man; that to abstain from the exercise of this natural function of the tongue is to court some physical malady; but that it requires a high degree of intellectual ability to exercise it to the full, and that swearers should therefore ask themselves first whether they would not be wise to use moderation. To attempt too much, with insufficient technique, is, they say, to run the risk of a slap on the mouth, a lawsuit, or a humiliating reverse at the hands of an adept in the art. The advice given in the treatise is:

Keep obscene or indecent language as a last resort. Avoid reflections on the chastity of your opponent's female relations or on any physical infirmity from which he may be suffering. Once you have gone so far it is impossible to retrace your steps and resort to minor forms of vituperation. Be careful whom you swear at: to swear at a man who has justly earned a reputation for virtue and integrity is to make yourself ridiculous; to swear at a man of no reputation at all is to honour him by assuming that he has one. The most suitable victim is someone a little more virtuous than yourself, but with vices differing from your own; if, for example, you are a drunkard or glutton, choose one who is a gambler and frequenter of brothels, and contrariwise. Avoid any appearance of passion. Never shout as if your opponent were deaf. A single intemperate expression, a flushed face or twitching hands, will alienate the sympathy of the bystanders to whom you should appeal as if you were their chosen spokesman. And if these feel themselves in the least degree involved by the reflections you have made on your opponent, you will find yourself carrying on a dozen verbal duels at once, which can be very troublesome. Be calm, and swear at your opponent as though the outcome were a matter of little importance to yourself. Begin with a great show of courtesy so that he does not suspect your intentions, then gradually unmask your fire. As you proceed, use subtle expressions, note well the sort of replies he makes, and modify your style of swearing accordingly. Your object is to force him to the defensive by correct and logical statements that nevertheless contain hidden meanings which one by one reveal themselves; to offer him false targets for the arrow-flights of his counter-accusation so that he presently loses control of himself, and gives you wild, absurd and untrue replies. The highest art of swearing consists in thus bringing your opponent to a dead stop. His colour will go from pale to red, from red to purple, from purple to ashen. When you have reached this point, stop, otherwise the bystanders will regard you as a bully and you will forfeit their admiration.

But to return to this country. In all classes one can change an opponent's face from pale to red by accusing him of venereal infection. Though there have been times when this was considered a mark of manliness, a fashionable martyrdom, the disastrous results of the disease are now generally realized, so 'pox-ridden' and 'clap-stricken' are yearly gaining force as adjectives of abuse.

It is only a minor taboo that prevents reference to human excrement, but major swearing is greatly strengthened by lavatory metaphors implying worthlessness or offensiveness — the word lavatory itself is a euphemism, and as offensive as the euphemism w.c. which it displaced. It is only a minor taboo again that forbids mention of lice, fleas, and bugs. But the imputation of lousiness (except in the trenches, where it was a joke) carries serious implications with it; and the metaphorical 'You louse!' is ripe with hatred. [*This is no longer true. The American general-utility adjective 'lousy,' which means no more in the United States than 'rotten' does in England, has now infiltrated into British idiom by way of the cinema, and taken all the bite out of 'louse.' 1949*]

The possible combinations that a swearer with a high degree of intellectual ability can contrive from the simultaneous breach of several of these taboos are far more numerous than appears at first sight. The man who can go on swearing, without repetition, for an hour or more is highly esteemed in low society, especially among seamen; but consider for a moment. It takes nine hours or more to exhaust the combinations of a full peal of church bells: and while there remain so many major or minor taboos that the daring tongue may outrage, with such an ancient wealth of vituperation lying within the territory of each of them, and so constant an enrichment of this ancient wealth by new pathological research, by religious sectarianism, and the general march of time, that the recourse which most celebrated swearers take to foreign tongues or dialects can only be considered a confession of imaginative failure.

Add to this positive art of foulmouthedness that of negative swearing, and the possibilities grow even larger. The sequel to General Gambier's inspection of 'Z' Battery is to the point here. He had been given to understand that one more instance of foul or abusive language on parade would lose him his command. Then the day came when he was not inspecting but being himself inspected by the commander-in-chief. His brigade had assembled on the parade ground half an hour before the C.-in-C.

was expected, and General Gambier had posted a trumpeter at the gate where the beflagged staff car was expected to pull up. The boy's orders were to sound the call for 'Steady!' when he saw the car approaching; or to sound it three minutes before the hour if it did not. He was to watch the church clock. Time passed, no staff car came, no call was sounded, and then the hour chimed. The infuriated general spurred his charger and thundered down to the gate. Passion choked him, his face grew scarlet. Reining up close to the terrified trumpeter and pointing down at him with his finger, he spoke in ogreish tones:

'Oh, you naughty, naughty, naughty little trumpeter!' And at that moment, under cover of a hedge, having left their cars on the main road, up came the commander-in-chief and his staff on foot.

Before the War a physical-training expert at Aldershot knew the value of negative swearing, the sarcastic Balaam's blessing where a curse is expected, the whispered triviality more impressive than the thunder and whirlwind that went before it. Many of this staff sergeant's best extempores have since been learned by rote and repeated by his pupils in season and out. Once, failing after vigorous efforts in positive swearing to induce in his squad the supple gymnastic style he expected, he moodily gave the 'Stand easy!' and beckoned the men up to listen to a story. 'When I was a little nipper,' he began, 'my dear old Granny gave me a little box of wooden soldiers on my seventh birthday. Oh dear, you wouldn't imagine how pleased I was with them! I drilled them up and I drilled them down, and then one day I took them to the seashore and lost them. Bless my soul, how I cried! My little handkerchief was soaked. And when I came home to tea that night, blubbering and late, my dear old Granny — God bless 'er, her hair was white as snow and her soul whiter still — she says to me: "Little Archie, cheer up!" she says. "For God is good and one day you'll find your little wooden soldiers again." And oh, good God, she was right; *I have*. YOU WOODEN STIFFS WITH THE PAINT SUCKED OFF YOUR FACES!'

At another time, more simply and despairingly: 'Now men,

I've done my best for you, and it's all so much labour in vain. Now I say to you solemnly — solemnly, mind: "May the blessed Lord Jesus Christ take you into his merciful and perpetual keeping"; for I've finished with you. Class, dismiss!'

By old tradition, the soldier is the expert in cursing. The cavalry more so than the infantry; hence, 'to swear like a trooper.' Shakespeare, in his seven ages of man, characterized the soldier as 'full of vain oaths and bearded like the pard.' The discharged Elizabethan soldier often turned his command of language into a means of livelihood. There was a regular profession, that of 'roaring,' or 'ruffling,' which meant the extortion of money, food, or other goods from civilians by means of threats and angry curses. In *A Fair Quarrel*, written by Middleton and Rowley in the year after Shakespeare's death, we find a discharged soldier, 'The Colonel's Friend,' earning forty pounds by instructing Chough, a provincial gentleman, and his servant Trim-tram in the art of roaring. Chough first practises on Vapour, a tobacco-seller.

Chough: I'll tell thee, tutor, I am to marry shortly; but I will defer it a while till I can roar perfectly, that I may get the upper hand of my wife on the wedding-day; 't must be done at first or never.
Col.'s Fr.: 'T will serve you to good use in that, sir.
Vap.: I can stay no longer indeed, sir: who pays me for my tobacco?
Chough: How? pay for tobacco? away, ye sooty-mouthed piper! you rusty piece of Martlemas bacon, away! May thy roll rot, and thy pudding[1] drop in pieces, being sophisticated with filthy urine!
Trim.: May sergeants dwell on either side of thee, to fright away the twopenny customers!
Chough: And for thy penny ones, let them suck thee dry!
Trim: When thou art dead, mayst thou have no other sheets to be buried in but mouldy tobacco-leaves!
Chough: And no strawings to stick thy carcase but the bitter stalks!
Trim: Thy mourners all greasy tapsters!
Chough: With foul tobacco pipes in their hats, instead of rotten rosemary;[2] and least of all, may my man and I live to see all this performed, and to piss reeking even upon thy grave! So, are you paid now, whiffler?

[1] Roll and pudding were tobacco made up in particular forms. But there is a double meaning here.
[2] Rosemary was worn at funerals.

Later they roar a certain Captain Albo, a cowardly Irishman, out of his protection of two women of the town, Priss and Meg.

Trim.: Peace, sir; here's practice for our roaring, here's a centaur and two hippocrenes.
Chough: Offer the jostle, Trim.
                    [*Trim-tram* jostles *Captain Albo.*]
Cap. Albo: Ha! What meanest thou by that?
Trim.: I mean to confront thee, cyclops.
Chough: I'll tell thee what 'a means — is this thy sister?
Cap. Albo: How then, sir?
Chough: Why, then, I say she is a bronstrops;[3] and this is a fucus.[4]
Priss: No, indeed, sir; we are both fuc-usses.
Cap. Albo: Art thou military? — art thou a soldier?
Chough: A soldier? no, I scorn to be so poor; I am a roarer. Deliver up thy panagron to me.
Trim.: And give me thy sindicus.
Cap. Albo: Deliver?
Meg: I pray you, captain, be contented; the gentlemen seem to give us very good words.
Trim.: 'Sault the women; I'll pepper him till he stinks again: I perceive what countryman he is; let me alone with him.
Cap. Albo: Darest thou charge a captain?
Trim.: Yes, and discharge upon him too.
Cap. Albo: I yield; the great O'Toole[5] shall yield on these conditions.
Trim.: Then thus far we bring home conquest. — Follow me, captain; the cyclops doth command.
Chough: Follow me, tweaks,[6] the centaur doth command.

Infatuated with the charm of their new language they address the women in it:

Chough: Melodious minotaur!
Trim.: Harmonious hippocrene!
Chough: Sweet-breasted bronstrops!
Trim.: Most tunable tweak!
Meg: We shall never be able to deserve these good words at your hands, gentlemen.

[3] Prostitute.
[4] Bawdmistress.
[5] Notorious for his romantic bravery, vanity and eccentricity. But his name had a comically obscene ring even in the seventeenth century.
[6] Prostitutes.

Chough: For thee, O pander, mayst thou trudge till the damned soles of thy boots fleet into dirt, but never rise into air.

Trim.: Next, mayst thou fleet so long from place to place, till thou be'st kicked out of Fleet Street! [7]

Chough: As thou hast lived by bad flesh, so rotten mutton be thy bane!

Trim.: When thou art dead, may twenty whores follow thee, that thou mayst go a squire[8] to thy grave!

Chough: For thee, old sindicus, may I see thee ride in a caroch with two wheels, and drawn with one horse.[9]

Trim.: Ten beadles running by, instead of footmen!

Chough: With every one a whip, 'stead of an Irish dart! [10]

Trim.: Forty barbers' basins[11] sounding before, instead of trumpets!

Meg: This will be comely indeed, sweet gentlemen roarers.

Chough: Mayst thou have two ruffs torn in one week!

Trim.: May spiders only weave thy cobweb-lawn!

Chough: Mayst thou set up in Rogue-lane —

Trim.: Live till thou stinkest in Garden-alleys —

Chough: And die sweetly in Tower-ditch!

Priss: I thank you for that, good sir roarer.

Private Frank Richards, D.C.M., M.M., who served with me in France, has contributed the following interesting notes on swearing in the British Army before the First World War.[12]

One of my best pals in India was a Signaller, whom we called the Prayer-wallah. He had studied the Bible as much as most parsons and used to curse like an Old Testament prophet in beautifully worded language. I remember once, on the line of march, at a place called Kalsi, my company was sleeping in the open one hot night and a man near us commenced to grind his teeth in his sleep. I don't think that there is any sound in Nature more horrible than a sleeping man grinding his teeth — unless it is a sleeping woman when she grinds hers. I thought I was the only man awake and began wondering if I would ever drop off . . . The man ground his teeth more

[7] Fleet Street was famous as a seat of prostitution as early as the sixteenth century.

[8] Pimp.

[9] With two wheels and one horse, meaning—may you be carted as a bawd.

[10] An allusion to the darts carried by Irish running footmen.

[11] When bawds were carted, a mob preceded them, beating metal basins. The hiring of their basins for this purpose was a source of profit to the barbers.

[12] They appear in his *Old Soldier Sahib* (Faber & Faber).

desperately than ever and the Prayer-wallah, who was lying with his head not far from my feet, began to pray in a low but distinct voice. He earnestly requested the Almighty of His Infinite Goodness and Mercy to send down from on high a first-class lightning-dentist with strict orders not to report back at the Orderly Room of Heaven until he had painfully extracted every blasted tooth, sound and rotten, single and double, upper and lower, from the grinding-teeth wallah's head, so as to give His faithful flock the blessings of deep and peaceful sleep so long despaired of. Half a dozen of us said, 'Amen, Amen!' 'Christ, I thought I was the only poor unfortunate swaddy awake,' he replied.

When we were in the Hills at Chakatra the Prayer-wallah spent his leisure time in learning the *crab-bat,* as it was called, which was all the swear-words in the Hindoostani language and a few more from the other Indian dialects to help these out. He had picked up a fair knowledge of the *crab-bat* at Meerut, but he now studied it seriously and used to curse the natives to such order that they looked upon him with veneration. One day he and I were in a native bazaar bargaining for a table cloth with an old white-bearded shopkeeper. When the price had come down to a sum that was practically what we were prepared to pay and then stuck fast, the shopkeeper swearing by the Beard of the Prophet that he would not take a pice less, the Prayer-wallah suddenly opened fire with his battery of *crab-bat.* By the time he had finished, the shopkeeper was trembling like an aspen-leaf and gazing at him with an awed look on his face. He double-salaamed three times before saying: 'Sahib, sahib, me mallam (know) you twenty years ago in Connaught Rangers. You young soldier then, now you very old soldier in other regiment, but me mallam you just the same, Sahib.' The Prayer-wallah was only in his twenties, but his fierce upturned moustache made him look a bit of a veteran and the old shopkeeper could not believe that any man could have learned to sling the *crab-bat* to such order in less than twenty years in the East. The *crab-bat* was a useful investment in India. A native was more afraid of a good cursing in his own tongue than what he was of a boot in his backside or a punch in the belly.

We had an old cleaning-boy at Agra who one day brought along as his assistant a native who proved a thorough scoundrel and nearly cost one of our corporals his life. When the assistant's villainy came out, our old cleaning-boy swore by all his gods that he would do battle that evening with the man who had introduced the assistant to him as a pukka cleaning-boy. He was in such a fierce mood all day that the natives working about the bungalow gave him a wide berth. The Prayer-wallah and I knew what the battle would be like, having been present at one or two similar ones before, so ten minutes

after he had left for home we walked down to the Regimental
Bazaar, which was built on one side of a very wide road. Soon a
crowd of natives collected in a ring on the road, and our old cleaning-
boy and his opponent took up their positions inside it, standing four
paces apart, each with his arms folded on his chest. It was at this
distance that they began and finished their battle. I had by now
picked up a fair knowledge of the *crab-bat,* but I could not by any
means understand all they said. The Prayer-wallah had to do a little
quick interpreting, now and then. First the old cleaning-boy let loose
his broadside and banged away until he temporarily ran short of
ammunition. Then his opponent replied, with shot for shot. Then it
was the old cleaning-boy's turn again. They called each other all
manner of far-fetched names and used swear-words and oaths that
made the Prayer-wallah tremble with admiration. He memorized
great strings of execration for his own future use.

As this fierce battle went on and on, the spectators were worked up
to a terrific pitch of excitement and ecstatically applauded each foul
spurt of angry abuse. They each went along the other's pedigree,
generation by generation, making more and more loathsome discoveries, until our cleaning-boy was finally acclaimed the victor. He
had gone back two thousand years in his rival's genealogical line and
given convincing proof that a direct female ancestress had secretly
cohabited for years during her widowhood with a diseased bull-frog,
thus going one better than her mother, who had legitimately married
and cohabited with a healthy pig. The loser slunk away from the
ring, a beaten man.

On the need for swearing there is more than one opinion.
Large numbers both of the educated and the uneducated stand
for self-control and the rigour of the taboo: for them yea must
always be yea, and nay, nay. Yet in practice they will permit a
few sterilized ejaculations, such as 'You silly beggar,' which is
the drawing-room synonym for the double 'b' of the street corner;
'Bother,' 'blow,' and 'dash' have to do service for 'damn,' 'curse,'
and 'blast,' which are just beyond the old-fashioned limit. For
oaths there are 'By Jove!', 'By George!', and 'By goodness!', and
on comic occasions 'Oddsboddikins!', 'Strike me!', 'Swelp me
Bob!', and 'By my halidom!' are dragged out, their blasphemy
purged by the lapse of time. It is one of the curiosities of English
that an oath by 'God's little bodies' — that is, by the Host — is
a Christmas-annual jest, and 'blimey!' — which stands for the

terrible 'God blind me!' — is kitchen comedy; but 'bloody' is still disallowed, though only a simple intensive of the general type as 'awfully' or 'fearfully,' and originally quite polite. So Swift could write to inform Stella on May 28, 1711, that it was 'bloody hot walking today.'

Another section of the community swears luxuriously, from anti-institutional conviction. But a middle course is, as usual, the most popular one: bad language is permitted only under great provocation, and even then must stop short of complicated invention.

The late Sir Walter Raleigh once discussed with me the deep-rootedness of the instinct to blaspheme. He had overheard a conversation between the young and well-behaved children of an Oxford theologian. The little girl said she wasn't afraid of God and wasn't even sure that God existed. 'Let's say something awful and see what happens.' 'He might bang out on us from a cloud,' said the little boy nervously, 'and frighten us to death.' But the little girl did not care. She looked up into the sky, put out her tongue, and said provocatively: *'Piggy* God!' Sir Walter said that Sam Hall himself could not have done better. The obscenity of children is interesting. Words that 'mustn't be used' have a natural fascination, as of magical power. Hence the refrain that nasty little East-enders sometimes sing in the streets to embarrass passing clergymen and old ladies:

> Pa's out and Ma's out, let's talk dirt!
> Pee-poh-belly-bottom-drawers!

Swearing as a gentlemanly art probably reached its high-water mark in the late eighteenth century. The aristocracy was as careful in its protection of a corrupt Church as it was cynical about religion; and swearing as a weapon of assault on a coffee-house rival and a preliminary to a duel demanded a nice refinement of oratorical blasphemy; as the contemporary sermon demanded a nice refinement of oratorical euphemy. The Elizabethan Age may have been richer in farfetched profanities and wild roaring conceits than the Augustan Age. (Kent's swearing at Oswald in

King Lear is in the true Elizabethan vein: 'Thou whoreson Zed, thou unnecessary letter! My Lord, if you will give me leave, I will tread this unbolted villain into mortar, and daub the wall of a jakes[13] with him.') But the Augustan Age swore with greater deliberation and method, as clearly appears in Sheridan's *Rivals*:

Acres: If I can find out this Ensign Beverly, odds triggers and flints! I'll make him know the difference o't.

Absolute: Spoken like a man! But pray, Bob, I observe you have got an odd kind of a new method of swearing.

Acres: Ha! ha! you've taken notice of it — 'tis genteel, isn't it? — I didn't invent it myself though; but a commander in our militia, a great scholar I assure you, says that there is no meaning in the common oaths and that nothing but their antiquity makes them respectable — because, he says, the ancients would never stick to an oath or two, but would say, by Jove! or by Bacchus! or by Mars! or by Venus! or by Pallas! according to the sentiment; so that to swear with propriety, says my little major, the oath should be an echo to the sense; and this we call the *oath referential* or *sentimental swearing* — ha! ha! 'tis genteel, isn't it?

Absolute: Very genteel and very new indeed! — and I daresay will supplant all other figures of imprecation.

Acres: Ay, ay, the best terms will grow obsolete — Damns have had their day.

Swearing has a useful physiological function. After childhood, relief in tears and wailing is discouraged, and groans are permitted only in cases of extremity; yet silence under suffering is sometimes impossible. The nervous system demands some expression that does not imply mere acquiescence; and, as a nervous stimulant in a crisis, swearing is unequalled. It is a bold defiance of Destiny. Where rhetorical appeals to Patriotism, Honour, Duty, Self-respect, and similar idealistic abstractions fail, the well-chosen oath often saves the situation. At the beginning of the War peacetime soldiers advised me never to swear at my men; and I was hurt by the suggestion that I should ever feel tempted to do so. But I changed my opinion after putting the matter to a practical test in trench warfare, and later I used to advise young officers not to restrain their tongues altogether but,

[13] Latrine.

because swearing had become universal, to suit their language carefully to the occasion and to the type of men under their command, and to hold the heavier stuff in reserve for bombardments and panics. Tristram Shandy's father and his Uncle Toby, whose opinions were formed some two hundred years before by trench warfare in the same district, anticipated me here:

'Small curses, Dr. Slop, upon great occasions,' quoth my father, 'are but so much waste of our strength and soul's health to no manner of purpose.'
'I own it,' replied Dr. Slop.
'They are like sparrow-shot,' quoth my Uncle Toby (suspending his whistling), 'fired against a bastion.'
'They serve,' continued my father, 'to stir the humours but carry off none of their acrimony; for my own part, I seldom swear or curse at all — I hold it bad; but if I fall into it by surprise I generally retain so much presence of mind ('Right,' quoth my Uncle Toby) as to make it answer my purpose, that is, I swear on till I find myself easy. A wise and just man, however, would always endeavour to proportion the vent given to these humours, not only to the degree of them stirring within himself, but to the size and ill-intent of the offence upon which they are to fall.'
'Injuries come only from the heart,' quoth my Uncle Toby.

But after this, Tristram Shandy, who was an Elizabethan born too late, treats of contemporary swearing, and protests that the connoisseurs have pushed the formal critical control of swearing too far. He speaks of a gentleman,

who sat down and composed, that is, at his leisure, fit forms of swearing suitable to all causes from the lowest to the highest provocation which could happen to him; which forms being well considered by him and such moreover as he could stand to, he kept them ever by him on the chimney-piece within his reach, ready for use.

This practice Tristram Shandy finds far too academic. He asks no more than a single stroke of native genius and a single spark of Apollo's fire with it, and Mercury may then be sent to take the rules and compasses of correctness to the Devil. He says, furthermore, that the oaths and imprecations which have been lately

'puffed upon the world as originals' are all included by the
Roman Church in its form of excommunication: that Bishop
Ernulphus, who formulated the exhaustive commination which
he quotes (and which later the Cardinal used with such success
on the Jackdaw of Rheims), has indeed brought categorical and
encyclopaedic swearing to a point beyond lay competition. He
asks what is our modern 'God damn him!' beside Ernulphus's:

> May the Father who created man curse him!
> May the Son who suffered for us curse him!
> May the Holy Ghost who was given to us in baptism curse him!
> May the Holy Cross, which Christ for our salvation triumphing
> over his enemies ascended, curse him!
> May the holy and eternal Virgin Mary, mother of God, curse him!
> May all the angels and archangels, principalities and powers, and
> all the heavenly armies curse him!
> ('Our armies swore terribly in Flanders,' cried my Uncle Toby, 'but
> nothing to this. For my own part, I could not have a heart to curse
> my dog so.')

Tristram Shandy wrote at the beginning of the Classical period
of English profanity (1760-1820), which owes a great debt to
Voltaire and his fellow rationalists. The 'Zounds!', 'Icod!', 'Zoodi-
kers!', and 'Pox on you!' of a Squire Western were discarded by
men of fashion, and the 'oath referential' of Acres, facetiously and
indecently blasphemous, succeeded these; it was taken up by the
populace and materially assisted national morale in the difficult
years of the new century.

Coleridge's distinction between the violent swearer who does
not mean literally what he says and the quiet swearer who swears
from true malignity is an essential one. In his apologetic preface
to *Fire, Famine and Slaughter,* he writes:

> The images, I mean, that a vindictive man places before his
> imagination will most often be taken from the realities of life: there
> will be images of pain and suffering which he has himself seen
> inflicted on other men, and which he can fancy himself as inflicting
> on the object of his hatred. I will suppose that we heard at different
> times two common sailors, each speaking of someone who had
> wronged or offended him, that the first with apparent violence had

devoted every part of his adversary's body and soul to all the horrid phantoms and fantastic places that even Quevedo dreamed of, and this in a rapid flow of those outrageous and wildly combined execrations which too often with our lower-classes serve for escape-valves to carry off the excess of their passions, as so much superfluous steam that would endanger the vessel if it were retained. The other, on the contrary, with that sort of calmness of tone which is to the ear what the paleness of anger is to the eye, shall simply say, 'If I chance to be made boatswain, as I hope I soon shall, and can but once get that fellow under my hand (and I shall be on the watch for him), I'll tickle his pretty skin. I won't hurt him, oh, no! I'll only cut the —— to the liver.' I dare appeal to all present which of the two they would regard as the least deceptive symptom of deliberate malignity — nay, whether it would surprise them to see the first fellow an hour or two afterwards cordially shaking hands with the very man the fractional parts of whose body and soul he had been so charitably disposing of; or even perhaps risking his life for him.

Swearing that introduces deliberate acts of aggression or punishment is, indeed, not swearing in the ordinary sense, which is more abstract and comparatively innocent of violent intention. The following passage from Captain Marryat's *Peter Simple* is an even better example of malignant swearing than Coleridge's. We cannot tell what more unprintable words Mr. Chucks used, for Marryat wrote for the family circle:

He would say to the man on the forecastle, 'Allow me to observe, my dear man, in the most delicate way in the world, that you are spilling that tar upon the deck — a deck, sir, if I may venture to make the observation, I had the duty of seeing holystoned this morning. You understand, sir, you have defiled his majesty's forecastle. I must do my duty, sir, if you neglect yours; so take that — and that — and that — (thrashing the man with his rattan) — you d—d haymaking son of a sea-cook. Do it again, d—n your eyes, and I'll cut your liver out.'

. . . I remember one of the ship's boys going forward with a kid of dirty water to empty in the head, without putting his hand up to his hat as he passed the boatswain. 'Stop, my little friend,' said the boatswain, pulling out his frill, and raising up both sides of his shirt-collar. 'Are you aware, sir, of my rank and station in society?'

'Yes, sir,' replied the boy, trembling and eyeing the rattan.

'Oh, you are!' replied Mr. Chucks. 'Had you not been aware of it,

I should have considered a gentle correction necessary, that you might have avoided such an error in future; but, as you *were* aware of it, why then, d—n you, you have no excuse, so take that — and that — you yelping, half-starved abortion. I really beg your pardon, Mr. Simple,' said he to me, as the boy went howling forward, for I was walking with him at the time; 'but really the service makes brutes of us all. It is hard to sacrifice our health, our night's rest, and our comforts; but still more so, that in my responsible situation, I am obliged too often to sacrifice my gentility . . . In the service, Mr. Simple, one is obliged to appear angry without indulging the sentiment. I can assure you, that I never lose my temper, even when I use my rattan.'

'Why, then, Mr. Chucks, do you swear so much at the men? Surely that is not gentlemanly?'

'Most certainly not, sir. But I must defend myself by observing the very artificial state in which we live on board of a man-of-war. Necessity, my dear Mr. Simple, has no law. You must observe how gently I always commence when I have to find fault. I do that to prove my gentility; but, sir, my zeal for the service obliges me to alter my language, to prove in the end that I am in earnest. Nothing would afford me more pleasure than to be able to carry on the duty as a gentleman, but that's impossible.'

'I really cannot see why.'

'Perhaps, then, Mr. Simple, you will explain to me why the Captain and first-lieutenant swear.'

'That I do not pretend to answer, but they only do so upon an emergency.'

'Exactly so; but, sir, their 'mergency is my daily and hourly duty. In the continual working of the ship I am answerable for all that goes amiss. The life of a boatswain is a life of 'mergency, and therefore I swear.'

'I still cannot allow it to be requisite, and certainly it is sinful.'

'Excuse me, my dear sir; it is absolutely requisite, and not at all sinful. There is one language for the pulpit, and another for on board ship, and, in either situation, a man must make use of those terms most likely to produce the necessary effect upon his listeners. Whether it is from long custom of the service, or from the indifference of the sailor to all common things and language (I can't exactly explain myself, Mr. Simple, but I know what I mean), perhaps constant excitement may do, and therefore he requires more "stimilis," as they call it, to make him move. Certain it is, that common parlancy won't do with a common seaman. It is not here as in the Scriptures, "Do this and he doeth it" (by the bye, that chap must have had his soldiers in tight order); but it is, "Do this, d—n your eyes," and then it is done directly. The order to *do* just carries the weight of a cannon-shot, but it wants the perpelling power — the d—n is the gunpowder which sets it flying in the execution of its duty. Do you comprehend me, Mr. Simple?'

Frequent swearing, outside the life of emergency that a bos'n or a sergeant-major leads, may point to debauch and spiritual presumption, but is equally often merely what the psychologists call the 'sublimation in fantasia of a practical antisocial impulse.' Others call it 'poor man's poetry'; yet if this metaphor is accepted, true poets are as rare now in nonliterary as in literary life. Occasionally one hears a labourer use a picturesque ancient, or a lively modern, oath and feels an invigorating thrill course up the jaded spine; but for the most part one must bear patiently and drearily with the repetitious sexual mainstays of lower-class swearing: b——, f——, and c——.

During the War I once or twice heard an anonymous poem recited at singsongs with the simple title *The Australian Poem;* it satirized the unimaginative swearing of the Australian Forces. *Bloody* was their mainstay. [*Admiral Kelly has very kindly traced the authorship for me. The poem was more ancient than I had supposed; it first appeared in the* Sydney Bulletin *in 1899, and is ascribed to W. T. Goodie.*]

'———'

(The Great Australian Adjective)

The sunburnt ——— stockman stood,
And, in a dismal ——— mood,
  Apostrophized his ——— duddy;
'The ——— nag's no ——— good,
He couldn't earn his ——— food —
  A regular ——— brumby,[14]
               ——— !'

He jumped across the ——— horse
And cantered off, of ——— course!
  The roads were bad and ——— muddy;

——————————————
[14] Wild horse.

Said he: 'Well, spare me ——— days
The ——— Government's ——— ways
  Are screamin' ——— funny,
                       ——— !'

He rode up hill, down ——— dale,
The wind it blew a ——— gale
  The creek was high and ——— floody.
Said he: 'The ——— horse must swim
The same for me and ——— him,
  Is something ——— sickenin',
                      ——— !'

He plunged into the ——— creek,
The ——— horse was ——— weak,
  The stockman's face a ——— study!
And though the ——— horse was drowned
The ——— rider reached the ground
  Ejaculating: '——— ?'
                   '——— !'

'Bloody' has as a matter of fact achieved a peculiar position among swear words. I have already remarked that it is merely an intensive of the general type as 'awfully'; yet it corresponds more closely with the Greek *dētā* or *dē* (translated in the dictionaries as *verily,* or *forsooth*) and may be used verbally, adjectivally, adverbially, as an interjection, or as an enclitic, in such interruptive forms as 'of bloody course' and 'abso-bloody-lutely.' There is a memorable couplet in an early poem of the present poet laureate's:

I'll bloody you a bloody fix:
I'll bloody burn your bloody ricks.

And Captain Gunn, writing from the Imperial Service Club, Sydney, has sent me the following poem, ascribed to the year 1915, in which the adjective becomes even more agile grammatically:

Australian Battle Hymn

Shift yer ——— carcases, move yer ——— boots,
Fellers of Australier, blokes an' coves an' coots,

Gird yer ——— loins up, get yer ——— gun,
Set the ——— enermy an' watch him ——— run.

Chorus:

Git a ——— move on, have some ——— sense,
Learn the ——— art of self de———fence!

Have some ——— brains beneath yer ——— lids.
An' swing a ——— sabre for the missus an' the kids.
Chuck supportin' ——— posts an' strikin' ——— lights,
Support a ——— family an' strike for yer ——— rights.

When the ——— bugle sounds 'Ad———vance'
Don't be like a flock er sheep, in a ——— trance
Biff the ——— foeman where it don't agree,
Spifler———cate him to eternity.

Fellers of Australier, cobbers, chaps an' mates,
Hear the ——— enermy kickin' at the gates!
Blow the ——— bugle, beat the ——— drum,
Upper-cut an' out the cow to Kingdom ——— come.

Two men discussing plural votes.
'What I says, is: *one man, one vote.*'
'Whadyer mean?'
'Clear, ain't it? *One man, one vote.* Fair's fair, ain't it?'
'Can't make out whadyer mean, I can't, nohow.'
'Seems to me what you want is your bloody ear-'oles syringed
out! What I mean is: *"one* bloody *man, one* bloody *vote!"*'
'Aow! Now, why didn't yer say so fust of all?'
The point of this old gag is that an intensive is often needed
in English to clarify the accentual emphasis of certain sentences.
There are, for example, a group of elliptical popular sayings whose
familiarity makes us forget that when we first heard them as
children they had to be explained to us. 'Bloody' may well be
legitimized one of these days as the missing intensive which
shows where the accent falls. 'Give a dog a bad name and bloody
hang him'; 'In for a penny, in for a bloody pound'; 'Handsome
is as handsome bloody does'; 'Needs bloody must when the devil
drives.' You don't agree? Then what about: 'Stuff a cold and
starve a fever?' Here popular misunderstanding has had a dele-

terious effect on the nation's health. Though usually read as two
unrelated injunctions, it really means: 'If you stuff a person who
has a cold, he will get a fever and then you will have to starve
him.' But put in a *bloody*: 'Stuff a cold, and bloody starve a fever,'
and nobody could go wrong. *Forsooth* is not bad in the context;
but it is easier to tame a wild word to conventional use than to
revive a dead one. Besides, if not abused in the Australian manner, the adjective 'bloody' has a very precise meaning: 'exciting
feelings of resentful hopelessness.' The difference between a
damned thing and a *bloody thing* is that the first admits of a
humorous and even affectionately tolerant attitude, the second
does not. An exact use of 'bloody' was made by a Balliol under-
graduate when asked by an American visitor to what architectural
period the New Quad belonged — was it late Gothic or Renais-
sance? 'Early Bloody, sir,' he answered.

A dean's sister once wrote to her brother from a holiday in
Devon:

My dear William, this hotel is in a delightful situation. (My window is marked with a cross.) The weather, however, has been perfectly beastly.

But remembering that the postcard would probably be read by
the butler at the Deanery, she crossed out the somewhat vulgar
word *beastly,* and substituted the first and last letters, with a dash
between. Her brother had to send her a note of reproof, reminding her that postcards passed through the hands of domestics.

Orderly-room charges of obscene and blasphemous language
during the late War showed a distressing sameness:

'Sir, the accused called me a f—ing b—,' or 'Sir, the accused
called me a f—ing c—.'

'And what have you to say for yourself, my man?'

'Well, sir, it was because the lance-corporal called me a *double*
f—ing c—, and in reply I called him only the halfth of that.'

The only novelty I remember in a long series of these charges
was: 'Sir, the accused used threatening and obscene language; his
words were "Two men shall meet before two mountains." '

Omne ignotum pro obsceno is the rule among the uneducated. Once in South Wales an old hedge-schoolmaster entered an inn where W. H. Davies the poet happened to be drinking, and sat down in a corner. Presently he cried out twice: 'Aristotle was the pupil of Plato.' After a moment's silence the man at the bar protested: 'Keep silence, you there!' Their wives caught up their skirts tightly: 'We are respectable married women and did not come here to be insulted.' The publican threatened to throw the speaker out if he uttered any further obscenity. However, the old man apologized in the acceptable formula: 'No offence intended; I'm a stranger here,' and was duly forgiven. [*Mr. Fred Hale of the Nelson Inn, Merryvale, Worcester, has cleared up this mystery. He explains that* Aristotle *is rhyming slang for* bottle, *and that* bottle *is short for* bottle and glass, *which is rhyming slang for guess what.* Aristotle *therefore means b—. Mr. Hale gives another interesting example of farfetched derivation. 'Gehout, you berk!' is a really insulting phrase.* Berk *is short for* Berkeley Hunt, *which is rhyming slang again for the female pudenda.*]

As for *Lars Porsena; or The Future of Swearing,* who is going to write it? Not I. To begin with, I cannot believe that it has a future worthy of its past. I must admit, though, that this is the title of my essay, and apologize for the deception, recalling those advertisements in *Snappy Bits* that hint at erotic delights for the schoolboy who will send five shillings and a statement that he is not a minor: only to be jobbed off with smudgy prints of classical paintings and statuary — since to send indecent matter by post is illegal. No doubt the Chic-Art Publishing Company would be glad to deal more honestly with its clients if it could, and perhaps the delight of expectation is worth the inevitable disappointment of getting only the Venus of Milo and a Rubens or two to gloat over. Nevertheless, by including at least a few classically draped forecasts and an enquiry into the taboos which prevent publication of a real *Lars Porsena,* this volume goes as far as it decently can. And this is probably the nearest approach to an undraped *Lars Porsena* that may ever be published. As soon as the taboos weaken sufficiently to permit detailed publication of indecent matter, that will be a sign that swearing and obscenity have no future worth prophesying about, but only a past more or less conjectural because undocumented.

Though Samuel Butler's definition of 'Nice People' as 'people with dirty minds' may easily be misunderstood by critics who refuse to differentiate between the humorously obscene and the obscenely obscene, I like it. No nice person is uncritical; and yet we are all hedged round with an intricate system of taboos against 'obscenity.' To consent uncritically to the taboos, which are often grotesque, is as foolish as to reject them uncritically. The nice person is one who good-humouredly criticizes the absurdities of the taboo in good-humoured conversation with intimates; but does not feel compelled as a proof of his emancipation from taboo to celebrate a black mass or commit a nuisance on the pavement of Piccadilly. This, then, is written for Nice People only. Though to begin with it is a detached treatise on swearing and obscenity, it cannot claim complete innocence of obscenity. Observe, please, with what delicacy I have avoided and still avoid writing the words f— and c—, and how I dance around a great many others of equal popularity. I have yielded to the society in which I move, that is, an obscene society: by which I mean that it aquiesces emotionally in the validity of the taboo, while intellectually objecting to it. I have even let a learned counsel go through these pages with a blue pencil and strike through paragraph after paragraph of perfectly clean writing.

Horace is my idea of a really obscene man. An immoderate liking of his poems is, I believe, a sure proof of obscenity in any person. Catullus, on the other hand, was not obscene: he had greater self-respect. Witness his:

> Caeli, Lesbia nostra, Lesbia illa
> Illa Lesbia quam Catullus unam
> Plus quam se atque suos amavit omnes.
> Nunc in quadriviis et angiportis
> Glubit magnanimos Remi nepotes.

where the filthy word *glubit,* by self-disgust and by the bitter irony of the *magnanimos Remi nepotes,* leaves obscenity looking foolish. Nor is the ithyphallic 'Long Man of Cerne' carved out in chalk on the Dorset Downs obscene in the sense that the modern cinema is obscene with its sudden fade-outs at the crisis of sexual excitement. Undoubtedly the most obscene shot in modern film history (if we except the *Cinéma Bleu*) was that of the heroine's face in the Austrian picture *Ecstasy,* a world release: taken, in the carefully chosen words of the American magazine *Time,* 'while the remaining portions of her anatomy were otherwise engaged.'

Some historian of the future will discuss the social taboos of the nineteenth and twentieth centuries in a fourteen-volume life work. He will postulate the existence of an enormous secret language of bawdry and an immense oral literature of obscene stories and rhymes known, in various degrees of initiation, to every man and woman in the country, yet never consigned to writing or openly admitted as existing. His contemporaries will dismiss the theory as fantastic, and he will write perhaps:

'Shortly before the 'Great War for Civilization" (the first indecisive conflict, 1914-1918, between rival European confederations, to decide which was to have the right of defining Civilization) there was a student at Oxford University famous for his practical joking and for deriding the most sacred taboos of his time. It was he who first defiled a local altar, "The Martyrs' Memorial," by climbing to its very summit at nighttime and planting a chamber pot — a stringently tabooed vessel — on the cross that crowned it. The civic authorities had great difficulty in removing this scandalous object, because climbing the Memorial was no easy feat, and the chamber pot, being made of enamel-ware rather than, as was first thought, of porcelain, could not be dislodged by rifle fire. On another occasion, this same student is said to have impersonated an African potentate and, with a suite of companions in disguise, to have been welcomed officially with a royal salute aboard a battleship of the English Navy, and to have aggravated this quasi-blasphemous performance by the bestowal of mock medals on the ship's officers.

'But the most interesting breach of taboo with which he is credited was a dinner party that he gave at a Cathedral town in the Midlands. He spent over a year and a great deal of money in scraping acquaintance under an assumed name with every person in this town whose surname contained the syllable *bottom*: Ramsbottom, Longbottom, Sidebottom, Winterbottom, Higginbottom, Wethambottom, Bottomwetham, Bottomwallop, Bottomley, Bottome, and plain Bottom; he insinuated himself into the bosom of every one of these families, but separately, not permitting them to meet in his presence, until finally he was able to invite them all to a huge dinner party at his hotel. When each name in turn had been announced by a loud-voiced master-of-ceremonies, he withdrew, begging them to begin dinner without him and promising to return in a few minutes. The meal consisted entirely of rump steak, and the host was already in a railway train bound for London, leaving no address.

'This story is regarded by Roberts and others as a very amusing one, though the point of the joke will need explaining to readers of this thirtieth century.

'It appears that "bottom" was the common equivalent, in the secret language which I postulate, of the word "buttocks." Now, among primitive peoples *no man will utter common words which coincide with or merely resemble in sound tabooed names* and, though the twentieth century refused to admit itself primitive, we cannot now understand on what grounds this refusal could have been plausibly justified. The principle I have italicized is a quotation from Sir James Frazer's contemporary treatise on taboo. The author, a Cambridge professor, was able to substantiate this principle only in the case of the South African Zulus and other savage tribes; but there is little doubt in my mind that the point of the joke lay in the sensitivity of the Bottom families to the obscene connotations of their names. That the buttocks should have been tabooed is a surprising idea, but apparently a morbid extension of the lavatory taboo accounts for it: or so Mannheim holds. The Bottom names had no original connexion with the buttocks, as in Bottomwallop or Longbottom, which are geographical names, and were survivals of an unselfconscious age in which even the word "arse" (afterwards so stringently tabooed that it could be written only "a—e") was still in polite use. Yet the unfortunates of the nineteenth and twentieth centuries who inherited a name containing a tabooed syllable were in a quandary. If they changed their name by Deed Poll, the expense and embarrassment would be considerable; yet not to change it meant that they would continue to be aware of repressed snickering wherever they went beyond the circle of their immediate friends. Most of them were content to change the spelling from "Bottom" to "Botham," and thus thought to circumvent the taboo. Indeed, as Roberts tells the story, the Bottom-guests were all disguised as Bothams or Bottomes. One family, the Sidebottoms or Side Bothams, went so far as to pronounce their name "Siddybotaam"; and in Bigland's *Life and Times of Horatio Bottomley,* a famous practical joker, he is said to have protested against this excess of delicacy by introducing himself to a member of the Siddybotaam family as "H. Bumley, Esq." — "bum" being a common, but strongly tabooed, shortening of "bottom."

'Now, the secret language, popularly known as "smut," was so rich in its vocabulary, and drew so copiously on the legitimate language for obscene usages of common words, that great care was needed in legitimate speech to avoid the appearance of obscenity. Thus, so common a word as "bottom" (meaning a *base,* a *bed,* a low-lying meadow, a *fundament,* a *cause*) owing to its use in smut as an equivalent for "buttocks," could never be used in legitimate speech where a *double entendre* might be construed. Also the word "parts," having become a synonym in smut for the organs of generation, and "hole" and "passage," even, because of their use as synonyms for the vaginal and rectal orifices, were used most charily. These are merely isolated instances of a principle so strong that, when two persons who had been initiated into the third or fourth degree of smut entered into conversation, hardly a phrase lacked this *double entendre.* In the "Maud Allen Case," a *cause célèbre* of the early twentieth century, the plaintiff, Miss Maud Allen (a dancer and an intimate friend of the then prime minister, the Right Honourable H. H. Asquith), when challenged by counsel to explain the significance of a certain phrase she had used, retorted that it depended on the tone of voice in which it had been spoken. So simple a phrase as "Mary had a little lamb," she said, could be given an indecent significance by those who had dirty minds. Exactly what she meant is now beyond conjecture.

'And not merely the names themselves, but any words that sound like them are scrupulously avoided, and other words used in their place. A custom of this sort, it is plain, may easily be a potent agent of change in language, for, where it prevails to any considerable extent, many words must constantly become obsolete and new ones spring up.

'This is a quotation from the same ethnologist, who here discusses taboos in Melanesia and Australia on the mention of the names of certain relatives, whether dead or alive; but it also explains many linguistic changes in the vocabulary of the nineteenth, twentieth, and twenty-first centuries: for instance, the constant outmoding of popular equivalents to the words "whore" and "harlot" which, being Biblical, alone remained in daily use as pure descriptive terms; and the disappearance from common use of the phrase "a man of parts," meaning "a man of great attainments," and the phrase "He (or she) has no bottom," meaning that the person referred to has no stability of character. It will be seen that the furtive language of smut must have had a great influence on legitimate speech. Mannheim holds that the disappearance of the word *pansy,* in favour of *viola,* is to be explained by the connotation that "pansy" then had of "male harlot": he adduces in support an early twentieth-century libel case, Tharup *versus* Lilliput.

'The most curious observation on this subject is Dusmel's. He notes that jokes were permitted in Latin on tabooed subjects even in family papers, and he quotes in support of this a late nineteenth-century witticism in a well-known journal of clean fun called *The London Charivari.* The witticism concerns the death, at the early age of nineteen, of a young man named Longbottom: *Ars longa, vita brevis.* The legal theory, he says, was that those who could read Latin would have come across so many indecencies in that language that they were no longer "shockable."

'New words sprang up everywhere, like mushrooms in the night . . . The mint of words was in the hands of the old women of the tribe, and whatever term they stamped with their approval and put into circulation was immediately accepted without a murmur by high and low alike, and spread like wildfire through every camp and settlement of the tribe.

'Here is our ethnologist again on the Paraguay Indians: but he does not enlighten us as to who held the word-mint of smut in his own country. It seems probable, though, that the Stock Exchange was responsible for a great part of the new coinage, that from the Stock Exchange it spread to the big business houses and was distributed by commercial travellers to the provinces; and that the close connexion of the Stock Exchange with the Turf made the bookmakers also useful disseminators of new coinage. A smutty story or a new word seems to have been, with whiskey and soda, the customary ceremonial confirmation of a business deal or the laying of a bet. Other mints of greater or less importance were the major universities, the Inns of Court, and the military academies of Sandhurst and Woolwich.

'The composition of smutty rhymes, chiefly in a strict five-line verse form known as the "Limerick," with the conventional beginning: "There once was a . . .", became one of the chief occupations of these high priests of smut, and three, at least, of the legitimate poets famous at the turn of the twentieth century — Swinburne, Tennyson, and Henley — are known to have added considerably to the common stock.

'Even in our enlightened times, the sex and lavatory taboos linger to a certain extent, owing to the natural reserve that men and women feel about these functions. The lavatory taboo survives with us at mealtimes, but we find it difficult to understand the extraordinary customs to which the morbid enlargement of this natural reserve led. For instance, the playwright Hogg records that not only was it considered obscene for a man to show a woman the way to the lavatory, but that even man to man or woman to woman, evasive phrases had to be used: "Would you care to wash your hands?" "Have you been shown the geography of the house?" A drunk man is said to have asked his partner at a public dance: "Where is the lavatory?", to which she replied, disengaging herself: "On the right of the entrance hall you will find a door with the notice GENTLEMEN. Disregard the warning, go right in; and you will find what you want." This was held to be a very correct reply. Nor would even intimate friends consent to notice each other if one of them was emerging from the lavatory or entering it; and, if this was the first meeting of the day, they would greet each other half a minute later on untabooed ground with every pretence of novelty and surprise. If a woman had a contused breast it was considered obscene to mention it directly, but tender enquiries would be made after "your poor side" or "your injured shoulder." So our ethnologist, in a caustic account of the idea of virgin birth among primitive tribes, is forced to write: "Nana, the mother of Attis, was a virgin who conceived by putting a ripe almond in her bosom."

'The curious alternation of prudishness and prurience in the social life of the time makes strange reading. On one hand were to be found sexual extravagance so fantastic as to be unintelligible today even to advanced physiologists, on the other such delicacy of feeling that in some classes of society even the word "leg" was tabooed. Falk Johnson, a social historian of the early twentieth century, has written:

'When it was unrefined to call pants pants, it was unthinkable to call a leg a leg — even if it were only a chicken leg. Therefore it was sometimes called a *second wing*. And if the leg happened to be human and feminine? Well, a regulation in a fashionable female boarding academy read: "Young ladies are not allowed to cross their benders in school."

'A further illustration of the low state of *leg*: in 1839, when a visitor in this country [U.S.A.] used the word while talking to a young lady, she became violently indignant. She was not a prude, either. After accepting her companion's apologies, she explained: "I am not so particular as some people are, for I know those who always say limb of a table, or limb of a pianoforte." Indeed, piano-legs themselves were once considered so suggestive that they had to be draped to prevent a breakdown in parlour morals.

'In a middle-sized Iowa town as recently as thirty years ago, the word *leg* was still thought by some people to be indecent. Dr. Allen Walker Read recalls that "the wife of a prominent lawyer had broken her leg, and when my mother innocently asked the lawyer: 'How is your wife's leg?', he publicly reprimanded her before a large group: 'Limb, Mrs. Read! You mean limb!'"

'Until the decade following the "Great War for Civilization," the young women of the moneyed classes in England and the United States lived what was called "very sheltered lives": which meant that, in the name of modesty, they were left to find out for themselves the simplest facts about the sexual mechanism. These facts, probably owing to a morbidity induced by the lavatory taboo, they seem often to have been unable to grasp. Literature gave them little clue, because it was the custom to mention one part of the body when another was intended. And the use of words like "kiss," "embrace," and "hug" as synonyms for the sexual act confused them so completely that in most cases they were married without having the vaguest idea of the nature of sexual congress, or of how babies are born; the suddenness of the realization frequently causing severe nervous shock and even insanity. The young men, on the other hand, by the time they came to marry, usually had such a fantastic experience of sex life among the professional harlots of a lower social class that it was rare for a satisfactory sex adjustment to be made between them and their wives; and it is computed that at least nine marriages out of ten were wrecked before the "honeymoon" was over.

'As the century advanced, there was a marked relaxation of the sex taboos among the moneyed classes: in art exhibitions, though not in public galleries, paintings of female nudes in which the pubic hair was represented were admitted for the first time. There were also changes in the fashion of women's dresses. Skirts, which hitherto had hidden the ankles, revealed the knees; and "evening dresses" were worn, we are told, "without any backs," though it is difficult to understand how the front parts of these dresses were secured to the person — possibly with tapes around the neck, waist, and thighs. "Bathing dresses" worn by both sexes, even when actually swimming in the water, became

less voluminous (and finally skeletonized so as to expose as much
unfunctional skin as possible). There is record of an Irish tenor
with a flair for polyglot obscenity, named Joyce. His works,
though published in France, were smuggled into England, read
behind locked doors, and regarded as "modern classics" by a de-
bauched literary minority. Joyce seems to have defied all taboos
in his writing, even to the extent of making an obscene reference to the private life of Queen Victoria I, an ancestress of the
reigning Sovereign; and it is a thousand pities that the great
Cleanliness Crusade of 1989 destroyed every copy of *Ulysses,* his
most salacious work, which would have been a mine of information if available for our present enquiry.

'It is now quite impossible to suggest accurately what were the
different degrees of initiation of which Hogg speaks, nor how
the different dialects of smut — Club Smut, Mess Smut, Garage
Smut, School Smut — varied. But our knowledge of preceding
centuries is as scanty. We have no critical apparatus for filling
in the lacunae in Marcus Clarke's account of convict obscenity
in his Australian novel *For the Term of His Natural Life,* or in
Benjamin Disraeli's account of industrial obscenity in the 1830's
given in *Sybil;* nor can we supplement Alec Waugh's hints of
public school obscenity in his *Loom of Youth.* The poets were as
timorous as the novelists. James Stephens records a "shebeen"
curse of the 1920 period:

> 'The lanky hank of a she in the inn over there
> Nearly killed me for asking the loan of a glass of beer:
>
> May the Devil grip the whey-faced slut by the hair
> And beat bad manners out of her skin for a year.
>
> That parboiled imp with the hardest jaw you will see
> On virtue's path and a voice that would rasp the dead . . .
>
> . . . May she marry a ghost and bear him a kitten, and may
> The High King of Glory permit her to get the mange;

but it is most unlikely that this is a faithful example of the swearing of that day. It is known that swearing in the First World
War was of a very violent character . . . (Field records that in

1918 a party of deaf and dumb children were taken to see a silent film called *The Somme,* and had to be removed because of the "bad language" on the screen.) But not a trace of it, beyond an occasional *damn* or *bloody,* occurs in the "realistic" war poetry published between 1914 and 1918. Contemporary newspaper reports of divorce proceedings are also known to have been rigorously cut: such colourless phrases were employed as "a certain condition," "a certain posture," "a certain organ," "a certain unnatural vice," so that it is difficult to know why the readers of the newspapers found these reports worthy of perusal. Field suggests, plausibly, that a mouth-to-mouth understanding had been reached between the reporters and their readers as to what, say, a "certain posture" precisely meant, and how it differed physically from a "compromising position," an "immodest posture," and an "indecent position."

'Two cases are known of a whole edition (150,000 copies) of a daily newspaper having to be destroyed because a breach of the taboo had escaped the proofreader. Both are recorded by Brunel in his *Recent Press History,* 1968, but in neither case does he explain the matter in sufficient detail:

'The whole country edition of *The Times* had on one occasion to be suppressed because of a one-word change made in a leading article by a printer who was under notice of discharge: the alteration was made to the second, third and fourth letters of the word *farming* after the proofs had been passed. The offending passage originally read:

I saw in a Tory journal the other day (Jan. 23, 1882) a note of alarm in which they said: "Why, if a tenant farmer is elected for the North Riding, the farmers will be a political power to be reckoned with. The speaker then said *he* felt inclined for a bit of *farming.* I think that is very likely." (Laughter).

'The second occasion was this: an evening paper of the Harmsworth group injudiciously printed a letter on the disorganization of the London traffic without observing the signature: which was R. Supward. The edition had to be destroyed at the cost of several thousand pounds.

'It is a pity that Brunel left us in the dark about the obscene connotation of *Supward.* We do not even know what action would have been taken in this matter by the censor, an official charged with the protection of the public against obscenity, had the mistake not been noticed in time; but certainly it must have been a vigorous one — a heavy fine, or a temporary suppression of publication. A scandal was created, the historian Millard records, by the accidental phrasing of a review of Oscar Wilde's book *De Profundis,* which was written while he was serving a prison sentence for unnatural practices. The reference that Millard gives is *The Times Literary Supplement* of Feb. 24, 1905. The sentence to which objection was taken runs: "Not so, we find ourselves saying, are souls laid bare." Souls and soles seem for some strange reason to have fallen under the taboo. So innocent a remark as: "Ah, soles for breakfast!" at a country-house party made the guest liable to social ostracism. It seems possible, however, that it was not merely fear of the censorship which preserved the strength of these taboos: they were valued on their own account by men and women of otherwise considerable intellectual force. Thus, while our ethnologist writes of the primitive savage "so tightly bound" by taboos of another variety that he "scarcely knows which way to turn," he is careful to express "the enormous debts which we owe to the savage," and the context makes it plain that chief among these debts are the ideas of "decency" and "morals" in their more fantastic developments. Johnstone, an essayist of this period, provides a passage which it would not be out of place to quote here:

'But I cannot describe the awful look of horror which in the pre-War decade I remember in the eyes of married women of the great middle classes when they uttered the word *décolletée* ("with a low-necked dress cut almost to the bosom") or the embarrassment still shown by the young schoolmistress, or even the young schoolmaster, in the Divinity lesson, should the innocent question be piped: "Please, teacher, what does 'whoremonger' mean?"

'The ethnologist Frazer from whom we have been quoting gives us the most authoritative of all surviving late nineteenth-century accounts of the superstitions, taboos, and magic of earlier primitive peoples; but what impresses us most now, besides the lucidity of his argument, is the elaborate care with which, as we have seen, the author has consented to the sexual and religious taboos of his own society, and the great number also of literary and academic superstitions in which his accounts of savage superstitions are dressed. Though clearly a leader of the contemporary movement for the breaking of taboos that had outlasted their use, he never makes a direct attack upon them: he treats facetiously the beliefs and ceremonies of almost every religion except contemporary English Protestantism, but points out the resemblances and leaves the reader to make the inevitable conclusions.

'He is particularly careful not to sin against the sex taboo. While he writes with bantering condescension of the poor savage who uses the navel cord and severed genitals of his relatives for magical purposes, the language he chooses is perfectly academic. He claims, in fact, the priest's privilege of treating the holy mysteries plainly, but only in the sacred language. He is exquisitely circumlocutory in his accounts of primitive orgies:

'A striking feature of the worship of Osiris as a god of fertility was the coarse but expressive symbolism by which this aspect of his nature was presented to the eye, not merely of the initiated, but of the multitude . . . At Philae the dead god is portrayed lying on his bier in an attitude which indicates in the plainest way that even in death his generative virtue was not extinct, but only suspended . . . One may conjecture that in this paternal aspect . . .

'Klein, in a recent essay, has suggested that the whole book is satiric in intention.

'An interesting fragment of newsprint has recently come to light. It is undated, but may be confidently attributed to the middle 1930's and is housed at the great Dimitroff Library in Moscow. The heading is "Magistrate Consigns Obscene Book to Flames," and it refers to the destruction, at the orders of a London magistrate, of a book, the title of which does not appear. This fragment suggests the inevitable, that the decision as to what constituted indecency was not, as has previously been thought, the task of an official called the censor, but sometimes fell to the police magistrates. The magistrate remarks that not long ago a book of this kind would have been banned altogether (he does not say by whom) merely because it was written on a topic not considered fit to be discussed in decent society. But things have changed, he says. Books are now being written to satisfy the demand for information and education on sexual subjects. The magistrate adds:

'Whether from the medical and psychological aspect it is desirable that there should be such books on sale is a question which I raised before and which I raise again, having regard to the fact that any Tom, Dick, or Harry can write a book of this kind which is available for any person of either sex or any age who cares to purchase it. But that has nothing to do with me. It is now my task merely to decide whether this book comes under the heading of an obscene book. So long as a book of this kind is written sincerely, soberly, and straightforwardly I think it deserves its claim to be treated as a book of medical and educational value. Once a book on this subject is written in a style that is flippant, or a language that is coarse, or tends to the encouragement of practices that are indecent, immoral, or vicious, that book seems to me to fall into a very different category.

'The magistrate did not attempt to define coarseness or flippancy and the report contains no quotation from the book or any indication as to its main drift. He took exception to one chapter in particular that had been written "regardless of any sort of convention regarded as desirable in dealing with matters of this kind." (This paragraph is subtitled "Objection to Parts.") Apparently there had been a previous conviction against the same publishers in respect of a book entitled *Boys,* which was also held to be a suggestive title. Evidence had been brought by the publishers that the present book was a useful and serious work: well-known doctors and ministers of religion had spoken in its favour. The evidence of a doctor is found in full under the subtitle "Attention Called to a Passage":

'Dr. [name missing] proceeding, said that the manu- [script and proof] of the book were submitted by the defendant company for him to read. He advised the publishers that it was a very useful book, and that was still his opinion. He considered that it had scientific and educational value.

Defending counsel: Is it your opinion that we live in times when much greater attention is paid to sex matters? — I think so. I should say there has been a tremendous increase in the literature on the subject during the last ten years.

The prosecutor called attention to a passage in the book and asked what it meant.

Witness: It is an attempt to explode a lot of humbug which has been built up around chastity.

The magistrate: Is not the whole thing a sneer at pre-nuptial chastity as being a convention, and an empty convention at that? — I think it means that because a woman had not been chaste she was not a lost soul. I agree with pre-nuptial chastity, but I do not think it damns a woman if she has not been chaste.

Questioned by the prosecutor, the witness said, "I think it is very difficult to talk about sex at all without some people getting excited."

'Here the fragment is torn and it is greatly to be deplored that the sequel is unknown. Boucheroff, in his monograph on this fragment, discusses the legal question of what redress the witnesses were entitled to claim. The magistrate had branded them all as the possessors of obscene minds, since they had been united in praise of the inoffensive and instructive nature of the book; but Boucheroff holds that defamation of character was a magistrate's prerogative, granted him by the Crown in lieu of salary, and that the only possible redress would be to lodge an appeal with the Court of the Star Chamber, but Boucheroff is not always reliable in his dates. There is no evidence for the Court of the Star Chamber's continued existence beyond the year 1904, when it is mentioned disparagingly in a poem by the then poet laureate, Lord Alfred Austin.'

So much for the future, which means only an inaccurate view of the goddawfulness of the present. 'But what about the buccaneers of the Spanish Main?' someone will ask. Yes, those were the fellows for real oaths. Past and future holds nothing like them. '"Caramba," ejaculated Diego, swearing terribly.' I had always remembered that in a tale of G. A. Henty's and, as a child, used to wonder fearfully what *Caramba* meant. But the first Spaniard I ever heard using the word was a good old parish priest: he was expressing his polite surprise that a parishioner who had been seriously ill was now out of bed and had gone for a stroll in the sun. It had the precise force and intonation of 'Dear me!' Which is perhaps the most appropriate expletive with which to end this discussion.

[*Additional comment: 1949*]

The 'new shock to our national nervous system, such as war, pestilence, revolution, fire from Heaven, or whatever you please,' which I foretold in the first paragraph of this essay, did revive the habit of swearing some twenty years later. But the revival had no pleasurable new features; all that happened was that words that lay immediately behind the permitted line were pushed in front of it; by 1943, 'bloody bastard,' for instance, could appear without offence in the popular press. The Armed Forces discarded 'bloody' as a universal adjective in favour of 'f—ing,' which in the previous war had been reserved for emergencies. It soon ceased to have any sexual connotation.

The last appearance in a dictionary of this famous word, which has, however, been printed in its naked form by several famous modern writers, including D. H. and T. E. Lawrence and James Joyce, was in the Rev. John Ash's *New and Complete Dictionary of the English Language,* 1775. The nearest that the *Oxford English Dictionary,* which is some forty times larger, gets to the word is 'fuger — obsolete' for which the editors quote an enigmatic passage in Aphra Behn, 1681, but giving neither its meaning nor its etymology. Yet it is one of the oldest words in the language and appears in Anglo-Saxon as *fachan:* 'to take or seize.'

Mrs. Fisher, or the Future of Humour

(1928)

'*Vos estis, vos estis,* that is to saye, you be, you be. And what be you?' sayd Skelton. 'I saye that you bee a sorte of knaves, yea, and a man might say worse than knaves; and why I shall show you.'

Merrie Tales of Skelton
Tale vii

THERE are few even of the less obvious subjects in the encyclopaedia of revelation that have not been dealt with in the last few months by someone or other in one way or another. Yet the most important subject of all, the master subject conditioning all the rest, has so far been sedulously avoided. The futures of Xylography, of Yiddish, of the Zebra: these are interesting and even, to some readers, exciting titles. But the gap shows the more plainly with each new brilliant and provocative addition to the *Today and Tomorrow* series. It is like the hundred-yard gap that once opened menacingly in the Roman Forum. The soothsayers insisted that Rome's best must piously leap in and avert the

47

catastrophic omen, and one Mettus Curtius, a Roman knight, leaped in with horse and armour. The earth closed above him, nobody laughed, and he was never heard of again.

Why I am playing Mettus is that I really don't care any more than Mettus did whether I am heard of again. Other writers do. That is why they hold back and pretend that the gap is not there, and temporize with *Nutor,* or the Future of Nutting; *Nitor,* of Knitting; *Netora,* of Netting; *Notorius,* of Knotting; and *Nugae Bugae,* of Noughts and Crosses. The difficulty about writing a *Future of Humour* is, of course, that true examples of the humour of the future must necessarily be not-yet-funny and therefore dull and unplausible; so the writer will forfeit his claim to a sense of humour in the present. If, on the other hand, he remains a humorist of the present, his readers will justly complain that he has not conscientiously revealed the future. When Mettus Curtius leaped into the gap, he was not even given the alternative of trying to leap across it (though certainly, if one is in sufficient haste and desperation, it is possible to cross any chasm in safety simply by assuming, with all the humourlessness of faith, a bridge that is not there). The gap had to be filled, not bridged. He remains a type of tragic courage — and tragedy is too single-minded for humour — or of 'unconscious humour,' which is, if anything, less intrinsically humorous than faith. The joke is always on Mettus, but that does not matter to Mettus, since it is his own joke and he has disappeared with it.

Two paragraphs of swift and logical writing, and now I lay down my pen and scratch my right ear: wondering what to say next . . . Once in all seriousness I asked L. R. (to whom I dedicate this essay): 'How would one write a legend about an angel and a cuckoo?' She answered as seriously: 'One would have to build it up from the cuckoo.' But this cuckoo is still in the bush, and until it comes to hand and draws the angel after it, I must proceed slowly and contradict myself generously, and be altogether unsystematic, for humour's sake. I must also be dull, Reader, for your sake: because if at some point of the book you cannot pause and find it dull, you will think yourself dull. It is your sense of humour that is on trial, not mine; I have publicly thrown mine into the gap.

The happiest half-hour of my life was at Berkhamstead in 1918, when I was a young, temporary, and light-hearted infantry officer. I had been sent there on a command staff course along with thirty or forty rigidly regimental brother-officers who detested me because I was not one of them, and whom I detested because they were not one of me. I decided to entertain them from the Saturday-night stage. One of two things might happen: either I might highly amuse them, in which case our reciprocal detestation would make a beautiful and memorable moment of it for us all; or I might bore them as deeply — and the joy of boring people whom one detests under pretence of amusing them is more memorable and beautiful still because entirely one's own. I succeeded in deeply boring them, though honourably (for humour's sake) trying to amuse them. They concealed their boredom and detestation, as gentlemen, by a little perfunctory clapping. So I sang one more song, pretending to be flattered, and they rewarded me by not clapping that one at all; and next day the colonel in charge of the course failed me. The simpleton hoped, I suppose, to blight my military career.

The future of humour cannot be discussed as one discusses the future of medical research or mechanical invention. Humour, being a personal matter, loses virtue by diffusion. One cannot make predictions about personal matters; one can make them only about diffusion. Humour in diffusion concerns ideas in diffusion and people and things in diffusion. It is type humour; about Scotsmen, and Fishermen, and Marriage, and Widows, and Worms. It amuses only occasionally when all its comic ingredients are gathered up in a compact tansy cake as a missile against itself. As, for instance, in the story: 'There once was a Scottish fisherman who married a widow with worms.' Type humour will continue with this mad-merry civilization to confirm changes of fashion in dress and dancing and politics, and new discoveries and inventions. But jokes about steam engines in 1840, and telephones in 1870, and motor cars in 1900, and broadcasting in 1920, have been of exactly the same unfunny brightness as jokes about teledromy are going to be in 2040, and about pyrobatics in 2070, and about the alarming moechomechanistic series of 2090. These jokes of the future will be less crudely mechanical, but they will not be intrinsically more humorous. They will still be tagged on to Scotsmen, and Fishermen, and Marriage, and Widows, and Worms, and they will merely confirm the popular acceptance of scientific facts resembling in spurious novelty all previous scientific facts; which is not the future of humour except in a mere time sense.

Much of the future of humour is in the past: for instance, Blake's *Island in the Moon*. It is still personal, not diffused humour, and the out-of-dating of its topical references makes it still more of the future. Blake's biographers apologize for it on the ground that genius is irritable and the age was coarse. I doubt whether even in a hundred years' time its humour will be diffused. Imagine London a hundred years hence and ask yourself whether what Miss Gittipin sang will appear anything out of the ordinary. Can you dare to predict that in 2028 the time-defeating lodging houses and private hotels of Kensington and Bloomsbury will not still be furnished as they are today, and that there will not still be periodic revivals of roller skating at Holland Park, and Salvation Army meetings every Sunday at Hyde Park Corner, and ape tea-parties in the experimental house at the Zoo, and the D'Oyly Carte Opera Company still touring the suburbs, and the "Countryman's Diary" still running in the *Daily Mail,* and the centenaries of famous musicians coming round again for celebration, and the Roman emperors in a row to the left as you enter the British Museum, and hospital students still collecting tin foil, and Johnny Walker still going strong, and another twenty volumes being added to the *Today and Tomorrow* series? Set *that* against your teledromy and your pyrobatics and your most alluring moechomechanisms! There's future for you!

I am getting depressed already. Exactly how depressed, I shall show by predicting a few random and entirely unfunny cuttings from the daily press of a hundred years hence:

MYSTERIES OF THE BRAIN

Sir, — Referring to the letter, 'Mysteries of the Brain,' I had a remarkable and, I think, beautiful experience.

Some lines of Browning flitted through my mind, and I could not recollect which of his poems they were in. It was a Sunday afternoon and I lay down for a rest.

Then in a dream a scroll was unrolled and in gold letters — perpendicularly, not horizontally as would one expect — was spelt out letter by letter the word 'Paracilsus.' Twice I have had astronomical problems made clear to me in this way.

F.L.H. (Budleigh Salterton)

*　　*　　*

ABBEY ENLARGEMENTS

It is likely, I hear, that any proposed additions to existing structures at Westminster Abbey will be submitted for the public's opinion by contemporary canvas and plaster full-size erections *in situ,* with painted scenic effects, so that a precise view may be obtained of what the scheme implies.

The idea is good. Technical designs and plans convey very little to the uninitiated, and photographs are frequently misleading.

*　　*　　*

*　　*　　*

WHAT CONSTABLE FOUND

P. c. Double, in evidence, stated that at the scene of the accident he found a badly damaged Buick motorcar and also a motorcycle and a woman's bicycle. Later he went to Pampisford and interviewed prisoner's wife and rosinore, who made a voluntary statement. When charged at the police station he said, "It's absurd.'

The magistrates remanded prisoner on £200 bail.

*　　*　　*

FINANCIAL NOTE

The discerning investor will be aware that Victory Bonds have this outstanding advantage over other Government issues, that they are accepted at face value in payment of death duties.

BLACK WEDDING RINGS

To the Editor

Sir, — I should like to support the suggestion of your correspondent that black rings should be worn as a sign of widowhood.

Would it not be desirable, for many reasons, that some permanent and easily visible mark of status should be worn, and if necessary made compulsory, in the case of every man and woman?

(Mrs.) Harriet E. Trimble

* * *

PITH BATH DEATH MYTH

No further development reported today.

* * *

FROM THE PARLIAMENTARY CORRESPONDENT

House of Commons, Wednesday

The Solicitor-General moved the adoption of the new book in a speech which showed great industry of research and was prolific in detail, but lacked emotion.

Cheers and countercheers, pregnant with feeling, greeted his points. His appeal was to the intellect rather than to passion, but members listened with rapt attention. He said of Reservation that it had been technically illegal but not doctrinally wrong.

Padres who had never previously done so made Reservation during the recent War. The elements were consecrated in battery or battalion headquarters and carried under the padres' gas helmets and administered in the front line to men who were in greater peril than any in hospital.

Were those padres going to give up a practice which had such sacred associations for them?

* * *

MAN WITH 14 SONS

A man at Willesden Police Court today. — I have 14 children alive, all boys.

The magistrate. — You are a credit to your King and Country.

* * *

FASHION NOTE

Among next year's fashionable shades for women's silk stockings will be the following: Sombrero, Banana, Rose Nude, Blossom, Flesh, Nude, Peach, Evenglow, French Nude, Blush, Sunburn, Mirage, Champagne, Suntan, Woodland Rose, Irish Mauve, Pigeon Breast, Gazelle, Rose Mauve, Oak, Gun Metal. Also Black and White.

* * *

EX-LESBIAN PATRIARCH FINED

Fines amounting to £12 were inflicted by the Isle of Wight bench yesterday in the case of Johann Michelopoulos, 55, an enemy alien, described as a former Patriarch of the Island of Lesbos, who was convicted both of failing to notify the Police of his change of residence and of keeping a male servant, namely, a gardener, without a license. [Lesbos is a famous island in the Aegean Sea remembered as the home of the poetess Sappho. Its present population is 3,500.]

* * *

READER'S QUERY

'Poem Wanted' (6512) — Does any reader know a poem which describes life as a lump of clay which, with a bag of tools, man can fashion into a stumbling block or stepping stone?

* * *

SCARCITY OF SIXPENCES

Sir, — Your correspondent is right about the great scarcity of sixpences; has it occurred to him that this is due to sixpences being such useful coins that no one likes to part with them?

M.L. (Bournemouth)

* * *

Humour in that sort of future will be centrally organized and protected under the revived Safeguarding of Industries Act as a key industry employing many thousands of workers. There will be no more haphazard joke-making or joke-stealing. As soon as anyone thinks of a good one, he or she will at once apply to the Board of Humour for a copyright certificate. If not already recorded, the joke, however unpromising, will be registered and a stamped certificate issued, on payment of sevenpence. If the joke is then officially classed as 'popular jest, topical, subheads A, B, C, or D,' it will be claimable by the Board for circulation in the *National Humorous Gazette,* and for utterance on the national stage, on payment to the author of a sum of not less than one shilling but not exceeding five shillings. If classed in any other way, the joke will remain the property of the author, who will be authorized to circulate it verbally. Controversial jokes will not be subject to registration; neither will they be publishable.

'But are not all good jokes controversial?' Of course, I was just being dull. The Board will employ an enormous staff to sort and refine new material and file it for registration. They will catalogue the national output not by a subject index, but rather by 'grading.' 'Grades of humour,' not to be confused with the dangerously undemocratic concept 'degrees of humour,' will be determined by systematic use of the cinema laugh-recording apparatus: all jokes that come in will be tested on standing audiences consisting of Board officials graded according to the commercial value of their senses of humour. On the whole, the Board will be popular, though there will always be a certain dissatisfaction among the junior officials of the Board itself that the more highly paid grades are determined entirely by seniority and not by routine efficiency and general merit.

My tutor at Oxford used to say that there were forty-three recognizable degrees of humour. He began with (1) laughter at deformities, (2) the rapidly drawn-away chair, (3) cheese, (4) mothers-in-law, (5) people without a sense of humour; and so on, up to the rarified forty-third degree, which was 'God.' Here, I think, he erred: to laugh at God after passing the forty-second degree (which was 'Shakespeare') is to make a bad throw at the finish of the snakes-and-ladder game and to slide back to degree 5; for God has no sense of humour and that's all there is to the matter. The Greek gods could at least laugh at deformities: they shook with unquenchable laughter when they saw the crippled Hephaestus hobble across the floor of Olympus. But Jehovah did not even join with the naughty Canaanite children in laughing at the good bald prophet, and the one reasonable slapstick joke in the New Testament, 'the whole herd of swine ran violently down a steep place into the sea and was choked' (*Tableau!*) is, the Higher Critics agree, entirely unintentional. Perhaps by 'God' my tutor meant the philosophical Tory God preached from Cathedral pulpits and University Chairs of Ethics; that certainly is a joke in a higher degree than the rabbinical Jehovah. The newly discovered evolutionary Liberal God is a joke beyond that because he is not quite so gentlemanly.

There are, obviously, type jokes funnier than the most up-to-date sociological interpretation of God. For instance, 'The French' is a great deal funnier; honestly, I think so. It is at least far less diffused than 'Shakespeare.' For every ten wags who parody Shakespeare there is hardly one who does not take the French dead seriously. There is no question here of degree 5 (one must be careful not to reduce the joke to that). Put it in this way: suppose that the intelligence of the French can be denoted by the algebraic sign θ, then their humour can be denoted by the same algebraic sign θ and not by the sign $-\theta$; or $\theta+$. Nor, of course, because they eat frogs and snails and gesticulate, nor even because they do not really eat frogs and snails and gesticulate; nor even because after all they do in fact eat frogs and snails and gesticulate, but because, as Swift (I think) first discovered in surprise: 'Even the little children in France speak French!' And are French. If one has to stretch the argument any further than that, it snaps back on one's fingers like elastic; for the joke is simply 'The French.' People with uncomfortably symmetrical minds or people nervous of being accused of having only a limited sense of humour will suggest that there is a correspondingly rich joke 'Les anglais.' This is not so. Though we English do say Goddam and eat roast beef and have prominent teeth like the Montmartre stage Englishman, or though we don't really, or though after all we do, there is no high spiritual joke 'Les anglais.' 'Les anglais' is only a French mistranslation of a stale and pointless joke, 'The English,' made by the same wags who bat out a precarious livelihood by parodying Shakespeare; whose intelligence is $\theta - x$ and whose humour is $\theta - x$ and who therefore wish the aggregate national intelligence and the aggregate national humour to be θ, like the French. The joke is, in fact, on the French again.

Beyond 'The French' in the ideal academic scale (for, as I say, practical academic humour will stumble over 'The French') will be found further degrees. For instance, Absolute Nothing, People, the caterpillar on the leaf that reminded Blake of his mother's grief, Literature, Art, and such abstruse concepts as 'Degree,' 'Concept,' 'Value,' and 'Meaning.' Possibly (but here I am on difficult ground) the ultimate degree is Humour itself. I will say simply that I do not know and slide unsystematically back to the comfortable part of humour.

'Why can a tramp never starve in the desert?'

'Because of the sandwiches there.'

'How did the sandwiches get there?'

'Ham and his descendants bread and mustard there.'

'Is that all, grandfather? Is that all, grandfather?'

'No, no, my Peterkin: Lot's wife turned into a pillar of salt and all the family butter disappeared into the wilderness.'

'Pooh! And, can you tell me: Why the hypocrite's eye, can better descry, than you or I, upon how many toes the pussy cat goes?' 'Yes, I can, my Peterkin. The Man of Deceit, can best counterfeit, and so I suppose, can best count her toes.'

Arrange those under glass domes among the peacock's feathers, blue Bristol glass, early Picassos, the products of the Omega workshop, and other antiques. Or, at a gathering of first-class passengers only, enquire through a megaphone: 'How does a traveller who is going to the East, but who dreads the Bay of Biscay and *mal de mer,* yet does not know how to avoid them, resemble a first-class passenger going West with his wife on a Cunard liner, who cannot understand why his mother-in-law has insisted on accompanying them?' And then wait for the gigglingly lisped answer: 'Because he doesn't know via Marseilles.' Or again: 'Why is an old-fashioned chimney like a swallow?' 'Because it has a crooked flue.' Correct. Please understand that I am offering you a bright suggestion, free. Start the vogue, and for a season at least return the future of humour to the early Crinoline age and capitalize it in a Jest Book, *Beautiful Jokes by Beautiful People!* For *Vos estis, vos estis.* You be, you be. 'And what bee you?' sayd Skelton.

To show how little I care for you all and your jealously cultivated senses of humour, I will copy out the story of Toltoë from . . .

Toltoë was a Greek maiden, daughter of Cleombrotos of Samos and married to a king of the Royal Scythians, Bodonus by name. Now the Royal Scythians count it a disgrace to wash themselves with water. When therefore some of the maidens of the Scythians observed Toltoë how she washed herself in the Greek manner by the riverside, they reported the matter to the King. The King sent his honourable ladies to enquire of Toltoë why she washed with water and did not use Scythian plasters.

Toltoë replied: 'My mother and father were both trick-divers, and I was begotten six fathoms under the water.'

The honourable ladies took back this answer to King Bodonus, who listened with attention and sent them again to Toltoë to ask why her parents had done this thing.

Toltoë replied: 'In honour of Poseidon.'

This answer did not fully satisfy Bodonus, either, who sent to enquire why they honoured Poseidon thus.

Toltoë answered the third time that it was because they were Samians and islanders, thinking to end the questioning. But Bodonus was still unsatisfied . . .

As not one of you guessed, it is a satiric imitation of D. B. Wyndham Lewis writing a humorous satire on Herodotus on the middle page of the *Daily Mail* for the benefit of readers who have never read Herodotus but are insured against accidents in the home; but, for humour's sake, written too closely in the manner of Herodotus to be anything but dull. This is bucolic humour, meaning not-funny-to-the-power-of-not-funny: a regrettable aspect of the true future of undiffused humour. Had I been less strict I should have ended with:

'. . . Oh, but I misheard you,' said Bodonus, laughing heartily. 'I thought you said *truck*-drivers!'

Moral: 'What a job it is to be a near-Eastern politician,' pouted the little actress.

Then you would have recognized it, but it would not have been the future of humour.

I had an Irish Uncle Max who, once at Seaford in the year 1912, at the very end of the holiday season, bought up the balloon woman's entire stock and brought it, pole and all, back to our hotel. He took the balloons up to his room (it was rather a squeeze on the narrow back stairs) and shut the door carefully behind him. Of course, my sisters and I took turns watching at the keyhole. He produced a safety pin and slowly punctured the balloons with it one after another, laughing softly to himself as they shrivelled. He was very methodical, pricking them in order of the colours of the rainbow, starting with violet and ending with red. He cast suspicious glances at the door from time to time, and at last when all the balloons were gone he hid the pole up the chimney. Then he came rushing out in a great hurry with the soot still on his hands and stumbled over us. When we ran away, he pursued us down the passage and made us promise never to tell anyone what we had seen so long as he was alive.

We knew about the order of the colours of the rainbow from Uncle Max himself. He told us one day at dinner that they were always in the same order, and it was a curious thing that the first letters of the names of the colours made a word, and not only a word, but an important word. And after we had guessed all sorts of likely words such as 'Uncle Max,' 'Coronation,' 'Christmas,' and 'Seaford,' he told us solemnly that the word was VIB-GYOR, and then got up and said Grace.

Why the Scots offend as humorists is not that they fail as wits; they are a good deal wittier than the English and only less witty than the Irish. Nor is it that their humour never exceeds their intelligence, as in the case of the French. It is because they will make sure of their joke, hold it triumphantly up to the light, shake it to see whether it rattles. There was, for instance, Dr. Logan, author of the great Channel hoax. She made a typically Scotch joke: she emerged exhausted and dripping from the water at Deal, publicly accepted a thousand-pound cheque offered by a Sunday newspaper for the feat, and then went and owned up that she had spent most of the time in a rowing boat. She returned the cheque, explaining that she was calling attention to the ease with which people could not swim the Channel. Everyone said that was unfunny, and Dr. Logan was charged with perjury, condemned, and fined a lot of money. And everyone was right. Dr. Logan had spoilt what might easily have been a very good joke. She should never have owned up, should have had a good time with the thousand pounds or else dedicated it to medical research in the cause and cure of swimmer's cramp: in any case, she should have kept her joke religiously to herself. Then, if she had eventually been betrayed by one of her accomplices, she would at least have had her joke, and the warning to the public how easily it could be imposed upon would have had a real point.

My Aunt Jeannie, Uncle Max's relict, is a respectable Scottish widow — a class of women in whom the insurance company has built up a quite unjustified public confidence. (This is not a joke, but a plain libel.) When Uncle Max, who lectured in history at a Scottish university, died he left a fortune quite out of proportion to his income: this was easily accounted for by his accurate knowledge of the flaws in the pedigrees of four or five of the richest and most distinguished Scottish houses. Being Irish, he enjoyed his joke and kept it to himself: all his earnings from this source he left to an Irish university for the foundation of a Chair of Irish Genealogical History. What remained did not satisfy Jeannie, who supported her Scottish widowhood by a cruder blackmail and by simple theft. She once got possession of some silver spoons of mine by a confidence trick and nearly succeeded in taking them off to Edinburgh with her. I arrived indignantly at Euston Station just in time to make her take them out of her trunk on the platform. Later I got a postcard from Edinburgh saying that 'The trouble with you Englishmen (sic) is that you have no sense of humour.' If I had thought that this meant that she had intended to steal those spoons (as I knew she had already stolen some candlesticks of grandmother's, and a second edition of *Paradise Lost* from her brother-in-law's library), I should not have minded so much. A thief in the family can be a good joke. But I realized that what she really meant was that she had loganistically intended to send me back the spoons from Edinburgh to show how easily I could be hoaxed. That made me simply furious.

There is spade humour, and there is spillikin humour. Welsh humour is the simplest form of spade humour: the most restful and the most idiotic. It is folk humour, which means that it does not get less personal by diffusion, because the persons implicated do not vary personally: they are all equally nitwit.

A minister takes for his text: 'The high hills are a refuge for the wild goat and so are the stony rocks for the conies.'

'Brethren,' he says, 'Christian men! What wass *coniss?* What, I say to you, wass *coniss?* Wass it lions? No! Wass it TIGERS? No! Wass it ELEPHANTS? No! Brethren,' he says, 'Christian men! What wass coniss? . . . Coniss wass a little wee rabbit, you see!'

On the quay at Bardsey Island. Young Alfie Jones is coming home from a visit to the mainland. His father shouts to him from a window as the boat is drawing up: 'Alfie, Alfie, stupid lad! What in the name of fortune have you there in that shop-paper parcel under your arm, lad?'

'My trousseau, pa! For my marriage on Sunday, pa!'

'Your trousseau, stupid lad?'

'Ay, pa, my trousseau! A pair of new English boots with real porpoise-leather bootlaces!'

Dai Jones was a miner of Tonypandy and he had a dream of Paradise. He was in a mighty great amphitheatre, member of a mighty great angelic choir. They were singing hymns: they were indeed singing Welsh hymns. All were dressed in garments of snowy white, ranged in endless pews. There were millions of tenors, millions of contraltos, millions of sopranos, millions of trebles; and only one bass — Dai Jones himself. The Archangel Gabriel rapped with his baton on a celestial harmonium that stood beside him and cried in a loud voice: 'Brothers and Sisters, we will now sing Doctor Parry's world-famous melody "Aberystwyth."' The whole choir of Paradise crashed into the opening bars. Oh, boys, it was a glorious harmony indeed of all those millions of saints chanting together in unison. But hardly had they commenced when the Archangel Gabriel was seen to drop his baton and wave his hands, hush-hush, to stop the music. The music ceased, and there came a great calm and the Archangel was heard to say: 'Champion! Champion! my brothers and sisters!' But then he said: 'Dai Jones, too much bass!'

Chinese spillikin humour is the most nervous of all. A high-brow humorist once told me that after Chinese humour it was impossible to enjoy European humour at all and that the future of humour was inevitably Chinese. He told me the classical Chinese jests which are supposed to represent the two bottom spillikins of the whole delicate pile. The first was: 'An influential mandarin, by the machinations of certain of his enemies, was reduced from a position of affluence to one of infinite misery. He retired to a cell on the To mountain where he spent the remainder of his life inscribing with a burnt stick upon the walls of his apartment: "Oh, oh! strange business!"'

The second: 'The celebrated sage and ascetic Feng, after thirty years' withdrawal from the world, attained to such sanctity that he was able without suspicion to hold upon his knee and fondle Miss Ise, a famous beauty, daughter of the Mandarin Soin, his old schoolfellow.'

'But I suppose it loses a lot in translation?'

'I wouldn't know.'

Then do the Chinese play spillikins with spades? Do the Welsh shovel coal with spillikins? For the centuried refinement of Chinese humour results, in the first case, in a jest not to be distinguished in quality from that of Alfie Jones and his laces, and in the second in a joke rather more compact and dry than 'Strong in Prayer,' a Welsh story about the many unprintable sexual shortcomings of the famous Revivalist preacher, Rev. Crawshay Bailey, whose sole virtue was that he could lift the sinful soul out of the f—ing body by the chastening eloquence of his tongue, man!

'Ay' (said Dr. Johnson), 'that is the state of the world. Water is the same everywhere.'

This road leads nowhere. If the humour of tomorrow is really to be a sort of Sino-Welsh classicism, then the reaction of the day after tomorrow will be the so-called 'pure humour' of the day before yesterday — the irresponsible after-dinner-fable-without-moral of the Edwardian era. Let me recall one or two of these fables, whose claim to purity is that they are neither topical nor directed towards any classical point.

A man went into Buzzard's and ordered a cake. He explained diffidently that it was rather an unusual order. He wanted the cake shaped like a letter *S*. The manager said, certainly, it was somewhat difficult; a special mould would have to be made, but he could promise to make a satisfactory job of it. When it was ready the man arrived and said: 'I am delighted with the cake, but it was very stupid of me; I did not make my order clear. I wanted a small *s,* not a capital *S.*' The manager apologized and promised to have a new cake made by the following week. When this was ready, the man came again. 'Yes, that is exactly right.' 'Where shall we send it?' asked the manager. 'Send it?' asked the man in surprise. 'Oh, please don't trouble to send it. I'll eat it at once.'

To which may be added the 'Fable of the Young Serpent' which, as nearly as I can recall, goes like this: A young serpent was one day surprised by her mother in the act of trying on a new bonnet in front of the pier glass. 'Where are you going?' asked the fond parent. 'Nowhere at all,' replied the startled daughter, 'not even into the garden.'

And then there was the mathematician at a dinner party who, on being passed a bowl of salad (while engaged in animated conversation with a lady on his left), absent-mindedly emptied it on her head. When his attention was called to what he had just done, he replied in some confusion: 'And I had thought it was the spinach!'

This salad joke (originally Jewish, told of a rabbi), with one or two others of the same sort that I have forgotten, was quoted about fifteen years ago in a correspondence in the *Morning Post* as to whether women had a sense of humour. The late W. H. R. Rivers, the psychologist, explained: 'The reason that no woman laughs at it is that the symbolism of crowning the head with salad or spinach is one that would have active appeal to the male sexual fancy in suppression and none to the female. And much as one dislikes accepting Freud's theory of sexual symbols, the trouble is that he is so often right.' As a matter of fact, many women do think the story funny, though, like the others, too delicate to be laughed at aloud. It is a very gentle joke and having no more to do with sex than with mathematicians. If a Scot picks it up and shakes it he will not make it rattle. But it is not pure humour because it relies too much on style. It differs from Chinese classicism only by not ending, so to speak, with a comfortable full stop, but with an uneasy comma.

As for the Freudian, it is a very low, Central European sort of humour. If you accept an arbitrary group of symbols — serpents, salads, umbrellas, tunnels — as having a latent sexual significance, all you have to do, whatever your sex, is to laugh cynically whenever you lose your umbrella in a tunnel or find a serpent in the salad bowl.

The dictionary definition of humour is the faculty of recognizing the incongruous or illogical elements in normal ideas or situations. That is just about what one *would* expect from a dictionary. Humour (though this is not intended for definition) is rather the faculty of recognizing the congruous elements in supranormal or supralogical situations, ruled by necessity alone. 'Thank God for my sense of humour!' my Aunt Jeannie used to say. But humour is not of the gods, who have only the most rudimentary sense of the ridiculous, or of God, who has none at all, but of the Fates and their mother Necessity who, according to the Greek theologians at least, ranked above the gods. Humour is pitiless; metaphysically pitiless. It is no suppressed anti-Negro bias that makes me laugh at the story of the two coloured women — who were walking behind a Chicago slaughterhouse over a piece of waste ground littered with the offal of cattle, horses, and donkeys — when one of them, looking at something lying at her feet, exclaimed: 'O Mercy, de Ku Klux done got our beloved Pastor.' Nor is it antiecclesiastical bias that makes me laugh at today's newspaper poster: RECTOR'S FIGHT FOR HIS HONOUR: PICTURES. I am almost as sorry for the rector as for the rumpled heroine of yesterday's headline: LOVE TUSSLE IN WOOD.

Humour is reasonable, in measure. Hysteria is unreasonable,

beyond measure. Laughter in humour is voluntary and propor-
tioned; in hysteria it is involuntary and out of proportion. Humour was never enough by itself to reduce anyone to a state of
uncontrolled laughter; the confusion between humour and hysteria
has been made by professional humorists who sadistically flog
the ass always on the same raw spot. Budd and Judd stage a misunderstanding, say, about the town of Ware, the river Wye, or
Wych House in Watt Street, until the suspense becomes insup-
portable, a girl in the gallery screams hysterically, and the rest of
the audience follows in sympathy. This is how Budd and Judd
became famous comedians. Chaplin himself is a Budd-Judd, his
sadism disguised as masochism. The first comedy in which he
ever appeared, *Kids' Auto Races,* consists of nothing but Charlie
as the dude continually posing in front of the cameraman who is
trying to film the races, continually being flung out of the way,
continually returning.

The Board of Humour will no doubt improve on the Budd-
Judd technique. Its phototonic gagsmen will know exactly how
many panes of the cucumber frame the stage gardener must
break; and how often he must stand on the points of the rake and
get rapped on the nose by the handle; and how often he must
nearly fall into the goldfish pond and how often he must actually
fall in, before general hysteria supervenes.

There's something wrong with me. I cannot laugh at jokes
about childbirth, or jokes about mothers-in-law. They belong to
the same tradition of male humour that includes jokes about
drunks coming home late at night after committing adultery with
chorus girls. Here I blame myself as being too symmetrically
minded; I think drunken husbands unfunny only because they
have as yet no popular counterpart in drunken wives coming
home late at night after committing adultery with chorus boys.
I think mothers-in-law unfunny because they have as yet no popular counterpart in fathers-in-law and because in the words of the
mournful little Spanish song: 'What is a mother-in-law after all,
but a mother?' *Y madres tuvimos todos* — and we all know what
mothers are. As for childbirth jokes, I would appreciate their
brutality if they were invented by married women for the disport

of mothers' meetings, and not by commercial travellers as a means of breaking down the sales resistance of ham-faced provincial shopkeepers who have never asked themselves how or why they came into this world.

Male humour must be directed against itself to make me laugh. Driving once near Amiens with an old colonel, I asked him to tell me about the various places of interest we passed. He knew a lot about the churches and castles and public institutions. He pointed out a fantastically decorated villa on a hill surrounded by beautiful gardens. 'That's a house you should visit, young man.'

'What's so remarkable about it, colonel?'

'Listen! You go up that path among the roses and you ring at the side door — not the front door, remember! After a few minutes it will be opened by an enormous Negro, really enormous. He's nearly seven foot tall and dressed entirely in scarlet. He'll blindfold you and lead you to a room where twenty exquisitely beautiful girls are seated at little tables, dressed in the height of fashion. They're all different in type; tall, small, medium, blonde, brunette, brown, or red. You can choose the one you fancy and sit at her table. She'll invite you to drink with her, and you can choose what drink you like — they keep a marvellous cellar — and you needn't pay a sou. Then she'll ask you to play a game with her. You can choose the game: draughts or chess, backgammon or cribbage, whatever you like. If you win, you can take the girl to a private room close by and do what you like with her. But I warn you, young man, that you must be very, very clever to beat any of these girls. They are colossal players.'

'Naturally,' I said, 'but what is the penalty if I lose?'

'Oh, then,' replied the colonel, in a tempest of laughter, 'then you yourself are aristotled by the enormous Negro!'

Apart from this sort of joke, I don't, as I say, appreciate male humour. And I don't appreciate jokes about tramps at the back door and their dislike of work, because I know too much about workhouses and the low diet of the casual ward. I don't mind cruel jokes about war so long as they are made by soldiers during the war in which I am myself engaged; but jokes about corpses and lice and the red lamp, and Lieutenant Scrimshank's right buttock carried off by a whizz-bang, and the drunken storeman whom we trod face downwards into the mud as we went into action at Loos, I find perfectly unfunny now that we are again, temporarily at least, in the epoch of rolling pins and wasp nests. But when the next war comes . . .

I have often been accused of sentimentality because I am loyal to the cheese joke which, it will be remembered, was placed only in the third degree of academic humour. It is classed by my Marxist friends with my devotion to folk song, Hanoverian royalty, and nature. I do not choose to argue about the cheese joke. I am not ashamed of it even though I share it with *Punch*. I may say at once that I am too symmetrically minded to laugh at almost any other *Punch* jokes. I can't, for instance, bear the ones about correct society and vulgar parvenues, about weary mistresses and impudent servants, about ingenuous mothers and precocious children, about the workingman on the dole, about dear old clergymen and village reprobates, about patient doctors and ignorant patients. They are never balanced by jokes about correct parvenues and vulgar society, or about impudent mistresses and weary servants; ingenuous children and precocious mothers; about the employer not on the dole; about dear old villagers and reprobate clergymen; about patient patients and ignorant doctors. I should have been happier if *Punch* had been content to remain where he began, with hump and nutcracker face as his whole stock-in-trade, in the first degree of academic humour. It would at least have saved him from the indignity of being the subject of degree 5.

Pamela: Daddy works at the Stocking Change.
Visitor: Indeed, darling? What sort of work does he do there?
Pamela: He buys pennies for Mummy.

One day perhaps I shall meet Sir Owen Seaman, the editor of *Punch*. I rather like the idea of him. I am told that he has a charming practice of returning all jokes sent to him with detailed explanations of why they are not funny. The rest he prints. I

heard a story about Sir Owen which also involves a story about
Pavlova. Two old Scottish ladies were sitting in the gallery of
a Glasgow theatre watching Pavlova dance the *Mort du Cygne,*
and one said to the other: 'She's awfu' like oor Mrs. Wishart.'
When this comment was reported to Sir Owen by my Aunt
Jeannie, he asked briskly: 'And, pray, who is Mrs. Fisher?'

Well, who *is* Mrs. Fisher? Sir Owen didn't know. My Aunt
Jeannie didn't know. I don't know. But she sounds so plausible
that I suspect her of being the future of humour itself and intend to give her the benefit of the doubt.

I would not, of course, deny with any great assurance the possibility of advanced humour in *Punch*. Some of the best jokes of
all are pleased to lustre by a careful choice of setting — the school-
room, the asylum, the prison cell, the deathbed; some have even
been witty enough to conceal themselves in the joke corners of
daily newspapers. And if ever, hundreds of years hence, a Phoenix
of a joke comes flying with purple wings and barred tail feathers
across the Western world in search of an altar on which to con-
sume itself, there can be little doubt where that altar will be
found: Phoenix will blaze up in glory among the 'Charivaria'
of *Punch* and all subscriptions will cease and there will be no
more humorous national weekly, and Mrs. Fisher in her crown
of stars and top boots will descend and reign her Sothic year.

If while considering the future of humour we find ourselves
consumed by morbid jealousy of the occasions that posterity will
have for laughing at us, what prevents us from forestalling posterity? The laughs are all here. We do not laugh only because to
laugh would mean seeing goddawful things as they are; and if
we did this, we should do something about them before we
laughed. Perhaps even then we should not laugh, and perhaps
even posterity will not laugh — either because it will see how
goddawful things really were or, more likely, because they will
still be equally goddawful and posterity will have inherited our
capacity for looking absent-mindedly away from them.

Let us at this point, Reader, have a private laugh of our own,
for when may it ever come to this again? At the adventures of
meat from the stockyards to the docks and from the dockyards to

the gas stove; at pedestrians who are encouraged to dodge across main roads between trams, buses, and private cars but are strictly forbidden to trespass on railway embankments even of branch lines; at correct evening wear for men; at the enforced prudery of the revues; at dust carts; at street musicians; at representative government; at the amateur status in first-class cricket; at visiting cards; at district visitors; at the ethics of advertising; at the shapes of sofas and the choice of lampshades; at the millions of victims (but let us lower our voices at this point, for we are about to commit a misdemeanour) of the economic system who unaccountably refrain from bashing in the skulls of the few thousand victors with paving stones, brass-bound ledgers, coal picks, empty beer bottles, or monkey wrenches whenever they come across them; at contemporary flowered cretonnes; at the book-reviewing system; at medical etiquette; at the price of old masters; at the contents of china shops.

Speaking of china shops, the following is clipped from an official list of military stores published for the current year:

Vessels, CHBR: Porcelain, with rims and handles, officers, for
　　　　　　　　the use of.
　　Do.　　　　China, rimless, with handles, warrant-officers, for
　　　　　　　　the use of.
　　Do.　　　　Earthenware, rimless, without handles, other
　　　　　　　　ranks, for the use of.
　　Do.　　　　India-rubber, collapsible, mental cases, for the
　　　　　　　　use of.

When things are really as goddawful as this, it is no use trying to reform them by earnest means — reviving the Liberal Party, spreading Communist leaflets among the armed forces of the Crown, committing suicide and leaving an explanatory manifesto behind; or writing them up in the Jack London or Sinclair Lewis style. Either one gracefully absents oneself from civilization, or else one must seek ingenious means for making things a little more goddawful than before, until they overreach themselves. In this case, for example, one might threaten a question in the House and blackmail the Army Council into providing a new type of Vessel, CHBR — cut glass, with two handles, and a rim emblazoned with battle honours, field-officers, for the use of. Swift wrote his *Modest Proposal for preventing the children of poor people from being a burden to their parents or the country,* and Defoe his *Shortest Way with Dissenters,* in this spirit; unfortunately both were unable to put their schemes into active operation.

Realistic humour has great capabilities in the hands of those with energy enough to add more wheels and cranks and cylinders to the insensate machinery of civilization, to make it function still more crankily. Perhaps Mrs. Fisher is the woman to organize the task; certainly no man would ever have the deadly thoroughness needed to carry it through. She will, I believe, first reveal herself in a series of embarrassing gifts to civilization: cheap and unsafe family aeroplanes, synthetic food at a nominal cost, minute but powerful pocket wireless sets that can be pinned on a coat lapel, a perfectly simple, fool-proof contraceptive that is at the same time an effective oestrific, a new humanitarian religion based on the left-handed Sakta cult, an undetectible poison (of which she alone has the antidote) with an unrestricted sale at all grocers' shops, and an infallible system of prognosticating the winners of horse and dog races. After that she will proclaim herself Dictator and take control of the entire State, which will also be the much-heralded World State, and ride in a coach drawn by six white asses and an ostrich, and set up a nude statue of herself two miles high at Braintree, Essex, and marry M. Judy, the French President, in a little synagogue in Marrakesh, compelling him to take her name and sign the register as Mr. Fisher — after which she will sacramentally eat him.

In the concluding years of Mrs. Fisher's reign no half-and-half jokes will be made anywhere, even on the stage. When the comedian slips on the banana skin he will inevitably break his silly neck; in the stage duel the combatants will use real rapiers and simultaneously run each other through; the prima ballerina, instead of roguishly throwing souvenir dolls among the audience, will roguishly throw little bombs of poison gas; nor will the curtain be dropped on the sexual crisis of the bedroom farce.

There will be strict control of the publishing trade: no fiction will be permitted to appear unless plainly libellous and no historical work unless containing at least twenty per cent of mischievous and entirely plausible misstatements. Mrs. Fisher will then experiment in organic chemistry and repeople the world with dragons, pterodactyls, sabre-toothed tigers, and the earlier varieties of man. She will make all single flowers double and all double flowers treble and standardize the rose as thornless, scentless, blue, and perpetually flowering. She will condemn all existing sewage systems and standardize one of her own invention with a marked tendency to retroactivity. She will make the use of sandpaper toilet rolls and silver-paper handkerchiefs compulsory and order that everyone of fifty years of age and over or, alternatively, with an income exceeding three hundred pounds a year, shall run about naked, except for black kid gloves and football boots. She will institute compulsory grand opera with community singing of the tenor parts. Her standardized designs for lampshades, tea services, cruets, cretonnes, and sofas will make the present goddawful look goddlovely by contrast. In her edicts and dispensation of justice she will make the Emperor Claudius Caesar himself, who alone of the ancients seems to have had a Sino-Welsh sense of humour, look like a mere Joe Miller, yet will insist on the continued use of the phrase 'The progress of Civilization.' When her powers of invention flag and she sees the whole perfectly and utterly goddawful raving world prostrate and paralysed before her, she will quite simply and sordidly commit suicide by putting her head in the gas oven.

I began by saying that the gap cannot be filled. On reconsideration, I add: 'Except by Mrs. Fisher.'

'And, pray, who is Mrs. Fisher?' asks Sir Owen Seaman.

The Shout

(1926)

WHEN we arrived with our bags at the Asylum cricket ground, the chief medical officer, whom I had met at the house where I was staying, came up to shake hands. I told him that I was only scoring for the Lampton team today (I had broken a finger the week before, keeping wicket on a bumpy pitch). He said: 'Oh, then you'll have an interesting companion.'

'The other scoresman?' I asked.

'Crossley is the most intelligent man in the asylum,' answered the doctor, 'a wide reader, a first-class chess-player, and so on. He seems to have travelled all over the word. He's been sent here for delusions. His most serious delusion is that he's a murderer, and his story is that he killed two men and a woman at Sydney, Australia. The other delusion, which is more humorous, is that his soul is split in pieces — whatever that means. He edits our monthly magazine, he stage manages our Christmas theatricals, and he gave a most original conjuring performance the other day. You'll like him.'

He introduced me. Crossley, a big man of forty or fifty, had a queer, not unpleasant, face. But I felt a little uncomfortable, sitting next to him in the scoring box, his black-whiskered hands so close to mine. I had no fear of physical violence, only the sense

71

of being in the presence of a man of unusual force, even perhaps, it somehow came to me, of occult powers.

It was hot in the scoring box in spite of the wide window. 'Thunderstorm weather,' said Crossley, who spoke in what country people call a 'college voice,' though I could not identify the college. 'Thunderstorm weather makes us patients behave even more irregularly than usual.'

I asked whether any patients were playing.

'Two of them, this first wicket partnership. The tall one, B. C. Brown, played for Hants three years ago, and the other is a good club player. Pat Slingsby usually turns out for us too — the Australian fast bowler, you know — but we are dropping him to-day. In weather like this he is apt to bowl at the batsman's head. He is not insane in the usual sense, merely magnificently ill-tempered. The doctors can do nothing with him. He wants shooting, really.' Crossley began talking about the doctor. 'A good-hearted fellow and, for a mental-hospital physician, technically well advanced. He actually studies morbid psychology and is fairly well-read, up to about the day before yesterday. I have a good deal of fun with him. He reads neither German nor French, so I keep a stage or two ahead in psychological fashions; he has to wait for the English translations. I invent significant dreams for him to interpret; I find he likes me to put in snakes and apple pies, so I usually do. He is convinced that my mental trouble is due to the good old "antipaternal fixation" — I wish it were as simple as that.'

Then Crossley asked me whether I could score and listen to a story at the same time. I said that I could. It was slow cricket.

'My story is true,' he said, 'every word of it. Or, when I say that my story is "true," I mean at least that I am telling it in a new way. It is always the same story, but I sometimes vary the climax and even recast the characters. Variation keeps it fresh and therefore true. If I were always to use the same formula, it would soon drag and become false. I am interested in keeping it alive, and it is a true story, every word of it. I know the people in it personally. They are Lampton people.'

We decided that I should keep score of the runs and extras

and that he should keep the bowling analysis, and at the fall of every wicket we should copy from each other. This made story-telling possible.

Richard awoke one morning saying to Rachel: 'But what an unusual dream.'

'Tell me, my dear,' she said, 'and hurry, because I want to tell you mine.'

'I was having a conversation,' he said, 'with a person (or persons, because he changed his appearance so often) of great intelligence, and I can clearly remember the argument. Yet this is the first time I have ever been able to remember any argument that came to me in sleep. Usually my dreams are so different from waking that I can only describe them if I say: "It is as though I were living and thinking as a tree, or a bell, or middle C, or a five-pound note; as though I had never been human." Life there is sometimes rich for me and sometimes poor, but I repeat, in every case so different, that if I were to say: "I had a conversation," or "I was in love," or "I heard music," or "I was angry," it would be as far from the fact as if I tried to explain a problem of philosophy, as Rabelais's Panurge did to Thaumast, merely by grimacing with my eyes and lips.'

'It is much the same with me,' she said. 'I think that when I am asleep I become, perhaps, a stone with all the natural appetites and convictions of a stone. "Senseless as a stone" is a proverb, but there may be more sense in a stone, more sensibility, more sensitivity, more sentiment, more sensibleness, than in many men and women. And no less sensuality,' she added thoughtfully.

It was Sunday morning, so that they could lie in bed, their arms about each other, without troubling about the time; and they were childless, so breakfast could wait. He told her that in his dream he was walking in the sand hills with this person or persons, who said to him: 'These sand hills are a part neither of the sea before us nor of the grass links behind us, and are not related to the mountains beyond the links. They are of themselves. A man walking on the sand hills soon knows this by the tang in the air, and if he were to refrain from eating and drinking, from sleeping and speaking, from thinking and desiring, he could continue among them for ever without change. There is no life and no death in the sand hills. Anything might happen in the sand hills.'

Rachel said that this was nonsense, and asked: 'But what was the argument? Hurry up!'

He said it was about the whereabouts of the soul, but that now she had put it out of his head by hurrying him. All that he remembered was that the man was first a Japanese, then an Italian, and finally a kangaroo.

In return she eagerly told her dream, gabbling over the words. 'I was walking in the sand hills; there were rabbits there, too; how does that tally with what he said of life and death? I saw the man and you walking arm in arm towards me, and I ran from you both and I noticed that he had a black silk handkerchief; he ran after me and my shoe buckle came off and I could not wait to pick it up. I left it lying, and he stooped and put it into his pocket.'

'How do you know that it was the same man?' he asked.

'Because,' she said, laughing, 'he had a black face and wore a blue coat like that picture of Captain Cook. And because it was in the sand hills.'

He said, kissing her neck: 'We not only live together and talk together and sleep together, but it seems we now even dream together.'

So they laughed.

Then he got up and brought her breakfast.

At about half past eleven, she said: 'Go out now for a walk, my dear, and bring home something for me to think about: and be back in time for dinner at one o'clock.'

It was a hot morning in the middle of May, and he went out through the wood and struck the coast road, which after half a mile led into Lampton.

('Do you know Lampton well?' asked Crossley. 'No,' I said, 'I am only here for the holidays, staying with friends.')

He went a hundred yards along the coast road, but then turned off and went across the links: thinking of Rachel and watching the blue butterflies and looking at the heath roses and thyme, and thinking of her again, and how strange it was that they could be so near to each other; and then taking a pinch of gorse flower and smelling it, and considering the smell and thinking, 'If she should die, what would become of me?' and taking a slate from the low wall and skimming it across the pond and thinking, 'I am a clumsy fellow to be her husband'; and walking towards the sand hills, and then edging away again, perhaps half in fear of meeting the person of their dream, and at last making a half circle towards the old church beyond Lampton, at the foot of the mountain.

The morning service was over and the people were out by the cromlechs behind the church, walking in twos and threes, as the custom was, on the smooth turf. The squire was talking in a loud voice about King Charles, the Martyr: 'A great man, a very great man, but betrayed by those he loved best,' and the doctor was arguing about organ music with the rector. There was a group of children playing ball. 'Throw it here, Elsie. No, to me, Elsie, Elsie, Elsie.' Then the rector appeared and pocketed the ball and said that it was Sunday; they should have remembered. When he was gone they made faces after him.

Presently a stranger came up and asked permission to sit down beside Richard; they began to talk. The stranger had been to the church service and wished to discuss the sermon. The text had been the immortality of the soul: the last of a series of sermons that had begun at Easter. He said that he could not grant the preacher's premiss that *the soul is continually resident in the body*. Why should this be so? What duty did the soul perform in the daily routine task of the body? The soul was neither the brain, nor the lungs, nor the stomach, nor the heart, nor the mind, nor the imagination. Surely it was a thing apart? Was it not indeed less likely to be resident in the body than outside the body? He had no proof one way or the other, but he would say: Birth and death are so odd a mystery that the principle of life may well lie outside the body which is the visible evidence of living. 'We cannot,' he said, 'even tell to a nicety what are the moments of birth and death. Why, in Japan, where I have travelled, they reckon a man to be already one year old when he is born; and lately in Italy a dead man — but come and walk on the sand hills and let me tell you my conclusions. I find it easier to talk when I am walking.'

Richard was frightened to hear this, and to see the man wipe his forehead with a black silk handkerchief. He stuttered out something. At this moment the children, who had crept up behind the cromlech, suddenly, at an agreed signal, shouted loud in the ears of the two men; and stood laughing. The stranger was startled into anger; he opened his mouth as if he were about to curse them, and bared his teeth to the gums. Three of the children screamed and ran off. But the one whom they called Elsie fell down in her fright and lay sobbing. The doctor, who was near, tried to comfort her. 'He has a face like a devil,' they heard the child say.

The stranger smiled good-naturedly: 'And a devil I was not so very long ago. That was in Northern Australia, where I lived with the black fellows for twenty years. "Devil" is the nearest English word for the position that they gave me in their tribe; and they also gave me an eighteenth-century British naval uniform to wear as my ceremonial dress. Come and walk with me in the sand hills and let me tell you the whole story. I have a passion for walking in the sand hills: that is why I came to this town . . . My name is Charles.'

Richard said: 'Thank you, but I must hurry home to my dinner.'

'Nonsense,' said Charles, 'dinner can wait. Or, if you wish, I can come to dinner with you. By the way, I have had nothing to eat since Friday. I am without money.'

Richard felt uneasy. He was afraid of Charles, and did not wish to bring him home to dinner because of the dream and the sand hills and the handkerchief: yet on the other hand the man was intelligent and quiet and decently dressed and had eaten nothing since Friday; if Rachel knew that he had refused him a meal, she would renew her taunts. When Rachel was out of sorts, her favourite complaint was that he was overcareful about money;

though when she was at peace with him, she owned that he was the most generous man she knew, and that she did not mean what she said; when she was angry with him again, out came the taunt of stinginess: 'Tenpence-halfpenny,' she would say, 'tenpence-halfpenny and threepence of that in stamps'; his ears would burn and he would want to hit her. So he said now: 'By all means come along to dinner, but that little girl is still sobbing for fear of you. You ought to do something about it.'

Charles beckoned her to him and said a single soft word; it was an Australian magic word, he afterwards told Richard, meaning *Milk:* immediately Elsie was comforted and came to sit on Charles' knee and played with the buttons of his waistcoat for awhile until Charles sent her away.

'You have strange powers, Mr. Charles,' Richard said.

Charles answered: 'I am fond of children, but the shout startled me; I am pleased that I did not do what, for a moment, I was tempted to do.'

'What was that?' asked Richard.

'I might have shouted myself,' said Charles.

'Why,' said Richard, 'they would have liked that better. It would have been a great game for them. They probably expected it of you.'

'If I had shouted,' said Charles, 'my shout would have either killed them outright or sent them mad. Probably it would have killed them, for they were standing close.'

Richard smiled a little foolishly. He did not know whether or not he was expected to laugh, for Charles spoke so gravely and carefully. So he said: 'Indeed, what sort of shout would that be? Let me hear you shout.'

'It is not only children who would be hurt by my shout,' Charles said. 'Men can be sent raving mad by it; the strongest, even, would be flung to the ground. It is a magic shout that I learned from the chief devil of the Northern Territory. I took eighteen years to perfect it, and yet I have used it, in all, no more than five times.'

Richard was so confused in his mind with the dream and the

handkerchief and the word spoken to Elsie that he did not know what to say, so he muttered: 'I'll give you fifty pounds now to clear the cromlechs with a shout.'

'I see that you do not believe me,' Charles said. 'Perhaps you have never before heard of the terror shout?'

Richard considered and said: 'Well, I have read of the hero shout which the ancient Irish warriors used, that would drive armies backwards; and did not Hector, the Trojan, have a terrible shout? And there were sudden shouts in the woods of Greece. They were ascribed to the god Pan and would infect men with a madness of fear; from this legend indeed the word "panic" has come into the English language. And I remember another shout in the *Mabinogion,* in the story of Lludd and Llevelys. It was a shriek that was heard on every May Eve and went through all hearts and so scared them that the men lost their hue and their strength and the women their children, and the youths and maidens their senses, and the animals and trees, the earth and the waters were left barren. But it was caused by a dragon.'

'It must have been a British magician of the dragon clan,' said Charles. 'I belonged to the Kangaroos. Yes, that tallies. The effect is not exactly given, but near enough.'

They reached the house at one o'clock, and Rachel was at the door, the dinner ready. 'Rachel,' said Richard, 'here is Mr. Charles to dinner; Mr. Charles is a great traveller.'

Rachel passed her hand over her eyes as if to dispel a cloud, but it may have been the sudden sunlight. Charles took her hand and kissed it, which surprised her. Rachel was graceful, small, with eyes unusually blue for the blackness of her hair, delicate in her movements, and with a voice rather low-pitched; she had a freakish sense of humour.

('You would like Rachel,' said Crossley, 'she visits me here sometimes.')

Of Charles it would be difficult to say one thing or another: he was of middle age, and tall; his hair grey; his face never still for a moment; his eyes large and bright, sometimes yellow, sometimes brown, sometimes grey; his voice changed its tone and accent with the subject; his hands were brown and hairy at the back, his nails well cared for. Of Richard it is enough to say that he was a musician, not a strong man but a lucky one. Luck was his strength.

After dinner Charles and Richard washed the dishes together, and Richard suddenly asked Charles if he would let him hear the shout: for he thought that he could not have peace of mind until he had heard it. So horrible a thing was, surely, worse to think about than to hear: for now he believed in the shout.

Charles stopped washing up; mop in hand. 'As you wish,' said he, 'but I have warned you what a shout it is. And if I shout it must be in a lonely place where nobody else can hear; and I shall not shout in the second degree, the degree which kills certainly, but in the first, which terrifies only, and when you want me to stop put your hands to your ears.'

'Agreed,' said Richard.

'I have never yet shouted to satisfy an idle curiosity,' said Charles, 'but only when in danger of my life from enemies, black or white, and once when I was alone in the desert without food or drink. Then I was forced to shout, for food.'

Richard thought: 'Well, at least I am a lucky man, and my luck will be good enough even for this.'

'I am not afraid,' he told Charles.

'We will walk out on the sand hills tomorrow early,' Charles said, 'when nobody is stirring; and I will shout. You say you are not afraid.'

But Richard was very much afraid, and what made his fear worse was that somehow he could not talk to Rachel and tell her of it: he knew that if he told her she would either forbid him to go or she would come with him. If she forbade him to go, the fear of the shout and the sense of cowardice would hang over him ever afterwards; but if she came with him, either the shout would be nothing and she would have a new taunt for his credulity and Charles would laugh with her, or if it were something, she might well be driven mad. So he said nothing.

Charles was invited to sleep at the cottage for the night, and they stayed up late talking.

Rachel told Richard when they were in bed that she liked

Charles and that he certainly was a man who had seen many things, though a fool and a big baby. Then Rachel talked a great deal of nonsense, for she had had two glasses of wine, which she seldom drank, and she said: 'Oh, my dearest, I forgot to tell you. When I put on my buckled shoes this morning while you were away I found a buckle missing. I must have noticed that it was lost before I went to sleep last night and yet not fixed the loss firmly in my mind, so that it came out as a discovery in my dream; but I have a feeling, in fact I am certain, that Mr. Charles has that buckle in his pocket; and I am sure that he is the man whom we met in our dream. But I don't care, not I.'

Richard grew more and more afraid, and he dared not tell of the black silk handkerchief, or of Charles' invitations to him to walk in the sand hills. And what was worse, Charles had used only a white handkerchief while he was in the house, so that he could not be sure whether he had seen it after all. Turning his head away, he said lamely: 'Well, Charles knows a lot of things. I am going for a walk with him early tomorrow if you don't mind; an early walk is what I need.'

'Oh, I'll come too,' she said.

Richard could not think how to refuse her; he knew that he had made a mistake in telling her of the walk. But he said: 'Charles will be very glad. At six o'clock then.'

At six o'clock he got up, but Rachel after the wine was too sleepy to come with them. She kissed him goodbye and off he went with Charles.

Richard had had a bad night. In his dreams nothing was in human terms, but confused and fearful, and he had felt himself more distant from Rachel than he had ever felt since their marriage, and the fear of the shout was gnawing at him. He was also hungry and cold. There was a stiff wind blowing towards the sea from the mountains and a few splashes of rain. Charles spoke hardly a word, but chewed a stalk of grass and walked fast.

Richard felt giddy, and said to Charles: 'Wait a moment, I have a stitch in my side.' So they stopped, and Richard asked, gasping: 'What sort of shout is it? Is it loud, or shrill? How is it produced? How can it madden a man?'

Charles was silent, so Richard went on with a foolish smile: 'Sound, though, is a curious thing. I remember once, when I was at Cambridge, that a King's College man had his turn of reading the evening lesson. He had not spoken ten words before there was a groaning and ringing and creaking, and pieces of wood and dust fell from the roof; for his voice was exactly attuned to that of the building, so that he had to stop, else the roof might have fallen; as you can break a wine glass by playing its note on a violin.'

Charles consented to answer: 'My shout is not a matter of tone or vibration but something not to be explained. It is a shout of pure evil, and there is no fixed place for it on the scale. It may take any note. It is pure terror, and if it were not for a certain intention of mine, which I need not tell you, I would not shout for you.'

Richard had a great gift of fear, and this new account of the shout disturbed him more and more; he wished himself at home in bed, and Charles two continents away. But he was fascinated. They were crossing the links now and going through the bent grass that pricked through his stockings and soaked them.

Now they were on the bare sand hills. From the highest of them Charles looked about him; he could see the beach stretched out for two miles and more. There was no one in sight. Then Richard saw Charles take something out of his pocket and begin carelessly to juggle with it as he stood, tossing it from finger tip to finger tip and spinning it up with finger and thumb to catch it on the back of his hand. It was Rachel's buckle.

Richard's breath came in gasps, his heart beat violently and he nearly vomited. He was shivering with cold, and yet sweating. Soon they came to an open place among the sand hills near the sea. There was a raised bank with sea holly growing on it and a little sickly grass; stones were strewn all around, brought there, it seemed, by the sea years before. Though the place was behind the first rampart of sand hills, there was a gap in the line through which a high tide might have broken, and the winds that continually swept through the gap kept them uncovered of sand. Richard had his hands in his trouser pockets for warmth and

was nervously twisting a soft piece of wax around his right forefinger — a candle end that was in his pocket from the night
before when he had gone downstairs to lock the door.

'Are you ready?' asked Charles.

Richard nodded.

A gull dipped over the crest of the hand hills and rose again
screaming when it saw them. 'Stand by the sea holly,' said
Richard, with a dry mouth, 'and I'll be here among the stones, not
too near. When I raise my hand, shout! When I put my fingers
to my ears, stop at once.'

So Charles walked twenty steps towards the holly. Richard
saw his broad back and the black silk handkerchief sticking from
his pocket. He remembered the dream, and the shoe buckle and
Elsie's fear. His resolution broke: he hurriedly pulled the piece of
wax in two, and sealed his ears. Charles did not see him.

He turned, and Richard gave the signal with his hand.

Charles leaned forward oddly, his chin thrust out, his teeth
bared, and never before had Richard seen such a look of fear on a
man's face. He had not been prepared for that. Charles' face,
that was usually soft and changing, uncertain as a cloud, now
hardened to a rough stone mask, dead white at first, and then
flushing outwards from the cheek bones red and redder, and at
last as black, as if he were about to choke. His mouth then slowly
opened to the full, and Richard fell on his face, his hands to his
ears, in a faint.

When he came to himself he was lying alone among the stones.
He sat up, wondering numbly whether he had been there long.
He felt very weak and sick, with a chill on his heart that was
worse than the chill of his body. He could not think. He put
his hand down to lift himself up and it rested on a stone, a larger
one than most of the others. He picked it up and felt its surface,
absently. His mind wandered. He began to think about shoemaking, a trade of which he had known nothing, but now every trick
was familiar to him. 'I must be a shoemaker,' he said aloud.

Then he corrected himself: 'No, I am a musician. Am I going
mad?' He threw the stone from him; it struck against another
and bounced off.

He asked himself: 'Now why did I say that I was a shoemaker? It seemed a moment ago that I knew all there was to be known about shoemaking and now I know nothing at all about it. I must get home to Rachel. Why did I ever come out?'

Then he saw Charles on a sand hill a hundred yards away, gazing out to sea. He remembered his fear and made sure that the wax was in his ears: he stumbled to his feet. He saw a flurry on the sand and there was a rabbit lying on its side, twitching in a convulsion. As Richard moved towards it, the flurry ended: the rabbit was dead. Richard crept behind a sand hill out of Charles' sight and then struck homeward, running awkwardly in the soft sand. He had not gone twenty paces before he came upon the gull. It was standing stupidly on the sand and did not rise at his approach, but fell over dead.

How Richard reached home he did not know, but there he was opening the back door and crawling upstairs on his hands and knees. He unsealed his ears.

Rachel was sitting up in bed, pale and trembling. 'Thank God you're back,' she said; 'I have had a nightmare, the worst of all my life. It was frightful. I was in my dream, in the deepest dream of all, like the one of which I told you. I was like a stone, and I was aware of you near me; you were you, quite plain, though I was a stone, and you were in great fear and I could do nothing to help you, and you were waiting for something and the terrible thing did not happen to you, but it happened to me. I can't tell you what it was, but it was as though all my nerves cried out in pain at once, and I was pierced through and through with a beam of some intense evil light and twisted inside out. I woke up and my heart was beating so fast that I had to gasp for breath. Do you think I had a heart attack and my heart missed a beat? They say it feels like that. Where have you been, dearest? Where is Mr. Charles?'

Richard sat on the bed and held her hand. 'I have had a bad experience too,' he said. 'I was out with Charles by the sea and as he went ahead to climb on the highest sand hill I felt very faint and fell down among a patch of stones, and when I came to myself I was in a desperate sweat of fear and had to hurry home. So I came back running alone. It happened perhaps half an hour ago,' he said.

He did not tell her more. He asked, could he come back to bed and would she get breakfast? That was a thing she had not done all the years they were married.

'I am as ill as you,' said she. It was understood between them always that when Rachel was ill, Richard must be well.

'You are not,' said he, and fainted again.

She helped him to bed ungraciously and dressed herself and went slowly downstairs. A smell of coffee and bacon rose to meet her and there was Charles, who had lit the fire, putting two breakfasts on a tray. She was so relieved at not having to get breakfast and so confused by her experience that she thanked him and called him a darling, and he kissed her hand gravely and pressed it. He had made the breakfast exactly to her liking: the coffee was strong and the eggs fried on both sides.

Rachel fell in love with Charles. She had often fallen in love with men before and since her marriage, but it was her habit to tell Richard when this happened, as he agreed to tell her when it happened to him: so that the suffocation of passion was given a vent and there was no jealousy, for she used to say (and he had the liberty of saying): 'Yes, I am in *love* with so-and-so, but I only *love* you.'

That was as far as it had ever gone. But this was different. Somehow, she did not know why, she could not own to being in love with Charles: for she no longer loved Richard. She hated him for being ill, and said that he was lazy, and a sham. So about noon he got up, but went groaning around the bedroom until she sent him back to bed to groan.

Charles helped her with the housework, doing all the cooking, but he did not go up to see Richard, since he had not been asked to do so. Rachel was ashamed, and apologized to Charles for Richard's rudeness in running away from him. But Charles said mildly that he took it as no insult; he had felt queer himself that morning; it was as though something evil was astir in the air as they reached the sand hills. She told him that she too had had the same queer feeling.

Later she found all Lampton talking of it. The doctor maintained that it was an earth tremor, but the country people said that it had been the Devil passing by. He had come to fetch the black soul of Solomon Jones, the gamekeeper, found dead that morning in his cottage by the sand hills.

When Richard could go downstairs and walk about a little without groaning, Rachel sent him to the cobbler's to get a new buckle for her shoe. She came with him to the bottom of the garden. The path ran beside a steep bank. Richard looked ill and groaned slightly as he walked, so Rachel, half in anger, half in fun, pushed him down the bank, where he fell sprawling among the nettles and old iron. Then she ran back into the house laughing loudly.

Richard sighed, tried to share the joke against himself with Rachel — but she had gone — heaved himself up, picked the shoes from among the nettles, and after awhile walked slowly up the bank, out of the gate, and down the lane in the unaccustomed glare of the sun.

When he reached the cobbler's he sat down heavily. The cobbler was glad to talk to him. 'You are looking bad,' said the cobbler.

Richard said: 'Yes, on Friday morning I had a bit of a turn; I am only now recovering from it.'

'Good God,' burst out the cobbler, 'if you had a bit of a turn, what did I not have? It was as if someone handled me raw, without my skin. It was as if someone seized my very soul and juggled with it, as you might juggle with a stone, and hurled me away. I shall never forget last Friday morning.'

A strange notion came to Richard that it was the cobbler's soul which he had handled in the form of a stone. 'It may be,' he thought, 'that the souls of every man and woman and child in Lampton are lying there.' But he said nothing about this, asked for a buckle, and went home.

Rachel was ready with a kiss and a joke; he might have kept silent, for his silence always made Rachel ashamed. 'But,' he thought, 'why make her ashamed? From shame she goes to self-justification and picks a quarrel over something else and it's ten times worse. I'll be cheerful and accept the joke.'

He was unhappy. And Charles was established in the house: gentle-voiced, hard-working, and continually taking Richard's part against Rachel's scoffing. This was galling, because Rachel did not resent it.

('The next part of the story,' said Crossley, 'is the comic relief, an account of how Richard went again to the sand hills, to the heap of stones, and identified the souls of the doctor and rector — the doctor's because it was shaped like a whiskey bottle and the rector's because it was as black as original sin — and how he proved to himself that the notion was not fanciful. But I will skip that and come to the point where Rachel two days later suddenly became affectionate and loved Richard she said, more than ever before.')

The reason was that Charles had gone away, nobody knows where, and had relaxed the buckle magic for the time, because he was confident that he could renew it on his return. So in a day or two Richard was well again and everything was as it had been, until one afternoon the door opened, and there stood Charles.

He entered without a word of greeting and hung his hat upon a peg. He sat down by the fire and asked: 'When is supper ready?'

Richard looked at Rachel, his eyebrows raised, but Rachel seemed fascinated by the man.

She answered: 'Eight o'clock,' in her low voice, and stooping down, drew off Charles' muddy boots and found him a pair of Richard's slippers.

Charles said: 'Good. It is now seven o'clock. In another hour, supper. At nine o'clock the boy will bring the evening paper. At ten o'clock, Rachel, you and I sleep together.'

Richard thought that Charles must have gone suddenly mad. But Rachel answered quietly: 'Why, of course, my dear.' Then she turned viciously to Richard: 'And you run away, little man!' she said, and slapped his cheek with all her strength.

Richard stood puzzled, nursing his cheek. Since he could not believe that Rachel and Charles had both gone mad together, he must be mad himself. At all events, Rachel knew her mind, and they had a secret compact that if either of them ever wished to break the marriage promise, the other should not stand in the way. They had made this compact because they wished to feel themselves bound by love rather than by ceremony. So he said as calmly as he could: 'Very well, Rachel. I shall leave you two together.'

Charles flung a boot at him, saying: 'If you put your nose inside the door between now and breakfast time, I'll shout the ears off your head.'

Richard went out this time not afraid, but cold inside and quite clear-headed. He went through the gate, down the lane, and across the links. It wanted three hours yet until sunset. He joked with the boys playing stump cricket on the school field. He skipped stones. He thought of Rachel and tears started to his eyes. Then he sang to comfort himself. 'Oh, I'm certainly mad,' he said, 'and what in the world has happened to my luck?'

At last he came to the stones. 'Now,' he said, 'I shall find my soul in this heap and I shall crack it into a hundred pieces with this hammer' — he had picked up the hammer in the coal shed as he came out.

Then he began looking for his soul. Now, one may recognize the soul of another man or woman, but one can never recognize one's own. Richard could not find his. But by chance he came upon Rachel's soul and recognized it (a slim green stone with glints of quartz in it) because she was estranged from him at the time. Against it lay another stone, an ugly misshapen flint of a mottled brown. He swore: 'I'll destroy this. It must be the soul of Charles.'

He kissed the soul of Rachel; it was like kissing her lips. Then he took the soul of Charles and poised his hammer. 'I'll knock you into fifty fragments!'

He paused. Richard had scruples. He knew that Rachel loved Charles better than himself, and he was bound to respect the compact. A third stone (his own, it must be) was lying the other side of Charles' stone; it was of smooth grey granite, about the size of a cricket ball. He said to himself: 'I will break my own

soul in pieces and that will be the end of me.' The world grew
black, his eyes ceased to focus, and he all but fainted. But he
recovered himself, and with a great cry brought down the coal
hammer crack, and crack again, on the grey stone.

It split in four pieces, exuding a smell like gunpowder: and
when Richard found that he was still alive and whole, he began
to laugh and laugh. Oh, he was mad, quite mad! He flung the
hammer away, lay down exhausted, and fell asleep.

He awoke as the sun was just setting. He went home in confusion, thinking: 'This is a very bad dream and Rachel will help
me out of it.'

When he came to the edge of the town he found a group of
men talking excitedly under a lamppost. One said: 'About eight
o'clock it happened, didn't it?' The other said: 'Yes.' A third
said: 'Ay, mad as a hatter. "Touch me," he says, "and I'll shout.
I'll shout you into a fit, the whole blasted police force of you.
I'll shout you mad." And the inspector says: "Now, Crossley, put
your hands up, we've got you cornered at last." "One last chance,"
says he. "Go and leave me or I'll shout you stiff and dead." '

Richard had stopped to listen. 'And what happened to Crossley
then?' he said. 'And what did the woman say?'

' "For Christ's sake," she said to the inspector, "go away or he'll
kill you." '

'And did he shout?'

'He didn't shout. He screwed up his face for a moment and
drew in his breath. A'mighty, I've never seen such a ghastly
looking face in my life. I had to take three or four brandies afterwards. And the inspector he drops the revolver and it goes off;
but nobody hit. Then suddenly a change comes over this man
Crossley. He claps his hands to his side and again to his heart, and
his face goes smooth and dead again. Then he begins to laugh
and dance and cut capers. And the woman stares and can't believe
her eyes and the police lead him off. If he was mad before, he
was just harmless dotty now; and they had no trouble with him.
He's been taken off in the ambulance to the Royal West County
Asylum.'

So Richard went home to Rachel and told her everything and

she told him everything, though there was not much to tell. She had not fallen in love with Charles, she said; she was only teasing Richard and she had never said anything or heard Charles say anything in the least like what he told her; it was part of his dream. She loved him always and only him, for all his faults; which she went through — his stinginess, his talkativeness, his untidiness. Charles and she had eaten a quiet supper, and she did think it had been bad of Richard to rush off without a word of explanation and stay away for three hours like that. Charles might have murdered her. He did start pulling her about a bit, in fun, wanting her to dance with him, and then the knock came on the door, and the inspector shouted: 'Walter Charles Crossley, in the name of the King, I arrest you for the murder of George Grant, Harry Grant, and Ada Coleman at Sydney, Australia.' Then Charles had gone absolutely mad. He had pulled out a shoe buckle and said to it: 'Hold her for me.' And then he had told the police to go away or he'd shout them dead. After that he made a dreadful face at them and went to pieces altogether. 'He was rather a nice man; I liked his face so much and feel so sorry for him.'

'Did you like that story?' asked Crossley.

'Yes,' said I, busy scoring, 'a Milesian tale of the best. Lucius Apuleius, I congratulate you.'

Crossley turned to me with a troubled face and hands clenched trembling. 'Every word of it is true,' he said. 'Crossley's soul was cracked in four pieces and I'm a madman. Oh, I don't blame Richard and Rachel. They are a pleasant, loving pair of fools and I've never wished them harm; they often visit me here. In any case, now that my soul lies broken in pieces, my powers are gone. Only one thing remains to me,' he said, 'and that is the shout.'

I had been so busy scoring and listening to the story at the same time that I had not noticed the immense bank of black cloud that swam up until it spread across the sun and darkened the whole sky. Warm drops of rain fell: a flash of lightning dazzled us and with it came a smashing clap of thunder.

In a moment all was confusion. Down came a drenching rain, the cricketers dashed for cover, the lunatics began to scream, bellow, and fight. One tall young man, the same B. C. Brown who had once played for Hants, pulled all his clothes off and ran about stark naked. Outside the scoring box an old man with a beard began to pray to the thunder: 'Bah! Bah! Bah!'

Crossley's eyes twitched proudly. 'Yes,' said he, pointing to the sky, 'that's the sort of shout it is; that's the effect it has; but I can do better than that.' Then his face fell suddenly and became childishly unhappy and anxious. 'Oh dear God,' he said, 'he'll shout at me again, Crossley will. He'll freeze my marrow.'

The rain was rattling on the tin roof so that I could hardly hear him. Another flash, another clap of thunder even louder than the first. 'But that's only the second degree,' he shouted in my ear; 'it's the first that kills.'

'Oh,' he said. 'Don't you understand?' He smiled foolishly. 'I'm Richard now, and Crossley will kill me.'

The naked man was running about brandishing a cricket stump in either hand and screaming: an ugly sight. 'Bah! Bah! Bah!' prayed the old man, the rain spouting down his back from his uptilted hat.

'Nonsense,' said I, 'be a man, remember you're Crossley. You're a match for a dozen Richards. You played a game and lost, because Richard had the luck; but you still have the shout.'

I was feeling rather mad myself. Then the Asylum doctor rushed into the scoring box, his flannels streaming wet, still wearing pads and batting gloves, his glasses gone; he had heard our voices raised, and tore Crossley's hands from mine. 'To your dormitory at once, Crossley!' he ordered.

'I'll not go,' said Crossley, proud again, 'you miserable Snake and Apple Pie Man!'

The doctor seized him by his coat and tried to hustle him out.

Crossley flung him off, his eyes blazing with madness. 'Get out,' he said, 'and leave me alone here or I'll shout. Do you hear? I'll shout. I'll kill the whole damn lot of you. I'll shout the Asylum down. I'll wither the grass. I'll shout.' His face was distorted in terror. A red spot appeared on either cheek bone and spread over his face.

I put my fingers to my ears and ran out of the scoring box. I had run perhaps twenty yards, when an indescribable pang of fire spun me about and left me dazed and numbed. I escaped death somehow; I suppose that I am lucky, like the Richard of the story. But the lightning struck Crossley and the doctor dead.

Crossley's body was found rigid, the doctor's was crouched in a corner, his hands to his ears. Nobody could understand this because death had been instantaneous, and the doctor was not a man to stop his ears against thunder.

It makes a rather unsatisfactory end to the story to say that Rachel and Richard were the friends with whom I was staying — Crossley had described them most accurately — but that when I told them that a man called Charles Crossley had been struck at the same time as their friend the doctor, they seemed to take Crossley's death casually by comparison with his. Richard looked blank; Rachel said: 'Crossley? I think that was the man who called himself the Australian Illusionist and gave that wonderful conjuring show the other day. He had practically no apparatus but a black silk handkerchief. I liked his face so much. Oh, and Richard didn't like it at all.'

'No, I couldn't stand the way he looked at you all the time,' Richard said.

Avocado Pears

(1929)

Tom's father was a respectable chemist in Birmingham, an old-style Christian Socialist, and Tom, who went as day boy to a local grammar school and did brilliantly and came up to Oxford with a scholarship and had no friends there except among the serious Labour crowd at Ruskin College, was surprisingly ignorant of certain perverse but familiar facts of life. One day he came to borrow my French dictionary. I asked him what he wanted to look up. 'Just the name of a fruit,' he said carelessly. But someone else had borrowed the dictionary. 'It doesn't matter,' he said. Then he told me the story.

'A month ago I was in Paris for a week end, and I was wandering about vaguely looking at things the evening I arrived — I had never been in Paris before. I walked steadily in one direction until I came to a very poor quarter — I don't know where, but it was somewhere in the northern part. The streets were narrow and full of garbage. After a time I came on two policemen: they were busy kicking a man who was lying in the gutter. He had a pretty long wound in his scalp and looked bad; certainly he hadn't any fight left in him. I ran up and took a flying kick at the bigger of the policemen, from behind, and sent him sprawling, and then I took a standing kick at the other

92

and sent him sprawling, too. They were lovely kicks; modelled on those long shots at goal by Dorrell of "The Villa." The policemen saw I was angry so they ran away.

'I wasn't wearing a hat — I never do — and wore a muffler round my neck, so the man's friends came up from where they had been hiding in a doorway — they were Communists — and began embracing me and slapping me on the back. When I answered in English they were surprised at first, but said: *"Vous êtes bon camarade, tout de même."* They explained that they hadn't attacked the policemen, because they carried revolvers and generally weren't afraid to use them. This was all right for me. So we went to a pub and they gave me coffee — I don't drink, as you know. The brother of the man whom I had rescued came up later. He was a printer's foreman, he told me, and could talk a little English. He said how grateful he was and offered to show me the sights of Paris. First he took me round the slum parts — my God! it *was* a filthy place. It even beat what I saw while I was helping with that survey of housing conditions in Glasgow for the Labour Research Bureau. "Well, now let's look at the prettier part," I said. "I'll find the money." The printer laughed and said that we must disguise ourselves first as good bourgeois. So I went back to my hotel and changed and met him later over at Montmartre. He was a big hefty fellow and looked magnificent; he had borrowed a dinner jacket from another brother who was a waiter; and for a joke he had put a ribbon of the Legion of Honour in his buttonhole to make it look more realistic.

'We went to a show called *La Revue Ultra-Nue,* and it was; I don't care for that sort of thing, so we didn't stay there long. Then he took me to see a fashionable brothel. His sister was the concierge there, so there was no gate money to pay and we had some champagne with the women who happened to be disengaged; the printer explained that I was not a customer but a serious young man studying social conditions. The women were all Communists, so we got on well together; they were quite simple about their profession: *"il faut vivre,"* they said, shrugging, and one of them who was an Italian — I talk a little Italian, you know — told me what their ambitions were. They would save up for five or six years until they had put by quite a decent sum and could retire. It was a house frequented by Americans, and Madame la Propriétaire, though a Royalist, was a decent sort, and didn't take too high a percentage of their earnings. So when they had put by so-and-so many francs — it came to about £500, I reckoned — they would advertise for a husband in the matrimonial papers: *"Jeune Fille Avec Tâche Désire Mari Affectueux,"* and be sure to find a good one. *"Avec Tâche"* means "slightly soiled." "And after all," said the Italian girl, "this is the best possible school to learn *'comment se plaire á son mari.'* Men are all the same."

'Then we went to a wrestling match, and there were two enormously fat practically naked men rolling about on the floor. They were carefully greased, so that they couldn't get a decent hold on each other, but at last one did and began slowly breaking the other fellow's arm. I couldn't bear to wait for the crack, so we went out. The filthy look on the faces of the young bloods who were watching!

'After that we watched the crowd coming out of the Opera, and the printer spat and muttered *Assassins!* There was one absolute caricature group of four men with opera hats, monocles, and canes and I said: "Let's follow them." So we followed them to a swell restaurant; it was a dreadful place, all plush and mirrors and salon pictures of nymphs and satyrs. We sat in a corner and the printer ordered oysters and said something to the waiter: it was a Communist password or something because when I paid for the oysters with a twenty-franc note, I got twenty francs change.

'Well, we sat there and I watched the four comics out of the corner of my eye while the printer told me all the ins and outs of Communism. Apparently he was an important official of the Party; I had noticed that his friends, though they called him Comrade, made it a sort of title. I wish I could have understood it all. He got excited and talked too fast. He told me he had been foreman of a munitions works during the war and sabotaged output for two or three years until he had been caught; then he had to disappear quickly into one of the Apache quarters of Paris where army deserters lived in a sort of fortress, and the police didn't dare round them up because they knew that they had bombs and rifles and even machine guns. At least, that's what I made out of the story.

'While we were talking I saw a chap about my own age — no, he was a bit younger, say about nineteen — staring in at the food in the window. He was a good-looking kid, but he seemed hungry. I was listening to the printer, who had his back to the window, and waiting for him to finish the story: then I thought I'd invite the kid in to give him a meal. Well, I was surprised. The eldest-looking of the four comics, a fattish fellow with a falsetto voice, saw the kid, dashed out of the door, and came back, pulling him in. He made him sit down at their table and called to the waiter to lay a place for him. The waiter laid a place, trying not to look furious, but I could see that he was: he was digging the fingers of his disengaged hand into the palm. The kid looked embarrassed but happy at the idea of something to eat. So this fattish fellow put him at his ease by introducing him. It was about an hour after the opera and these comics were half tight. As he called their names in turn, they pulled themselves up unsteadily, and said in a nasty sneering sort of voice: *"A votre service, monsieur."* One was the count of something and another the marquis of something else, and the third was the nephew of the minister of war. The fat fellow was the editor of one of the chief Royalist papers.

'He ordered oysters for the kid, and the kid obviously didn't want oysters: he wanted a big lump of meat and potatoes and cabbage and things. He ate the oysters in an awkward sort of way, trying not to look hungry: but first he ate the little bits of brown bread and butter that they serve with them. Then he wiped his mouth and thanked them. The fat fellow and the nephew of the war minister were talking in Italian about the kid; I couldn't make it out at all. It seemed quite mad to me. They got all soppy and talked about his beautiful eyes, and how strong his body was; they might have been a couple of grandmothers discussing their soldier grandson just going off with the draft for his military service. The marquis and the count were not interested in the kid. They were talking about women's breasts, very seriously and intensely, as though they were in the corset business. They were making drawings on the tablecloth with the count's gold pencil; they had tried the marquis's fountain pen first, but the ink ran too much.

'The waiter passed and slipped a piece of paper into the printer's hand. He read it, crumpled it up, and stuffed it into his shoe. Then he stopped his story about that morning's fight — I didn't tell you that this was the first of May — in which he had half killed one Royalist by hitting him on the head with another Royalist, because the Royalists had tried to spoil their parade, and began to pay attention to the other table.

'The kid, having had his oysters, wanted to excuse himself, say good night, and go off — probably to sleep in the Bois. He looked as though he needed sleep. But the fat fellow, whom they called "Mon cher Grégoire," wouldn't let him. He said that the little angel, meaning the kid, must have some dessert. I ought to have mentioned that they had already given him two or three glasses of old brandy and the kid was feeling a bit dizzy, by the look of him. The way he had eaten the brown bread and butter, he couldn't have had much in his stomach to begin with. Mon cher Grégoire and the nephew of the war minister had now changed places with the other two and were sitting next to the kid and gently detaining him, holding his arms in a sickly, affectionate sort of way.

'Grégoire called the waiter; the waiter looked angrier than ever, but obviously didn't want to lose his job by refusing to do what he was told. Grégoire asked him what fruit he had, and he said: "Every sort, sir." "Good," said Grégoire, "and now what angel's food would my little Cupid like to eat?" (The printer translated this for me; I didn't recognize the word *cupidon.*) Would he have guava or persimmon or pampelmousse? The kid shook his head.

'"*Alors une pêche?*"

'"*Merci, monsieur!*"

'"*Alors, ananas?*"

' "*Merci, merci, monsieur!*"
' "*Alors, une poire d'avocado?*"
' "*Merci, merci, monsieur.*"

'The kid was almost in tears with embarrassment, gratitude mixed with a rising shame, even fear. The nephew of the war minister had laid his sleek yellow head on the kid's shoulder, and was quoting a bit of Racine or something. Grégoire filled the kid's glass again, and said with some impatience that Monsieur Pierre — Pierre was the kid's name — was remarkably fastidious about his dessert. He went on with the list of fruits — mandarins and medlars and mangoes and God knows what. Then the nephew got hold of Pierre's hand and began admiring it, what strong, firm fingers, what a slender wrist, and actually picked it up and began kissing it. It was the funniest thing you ever saw. He was probably the drunkest of the four. The count and the marquis were still discussing breasts, but in a very inconsequential way. Grégoire wasn't so drunk, though.

'Well, at last the kid shouted out in a hysterical but somehow proud way: "*JE SUIS OUVRIER! AU DIABLE AVEC VOS POIRES D'AVOCADO!*" He tried to get up, but couldn't, because the nephew was clawing on to him and kissing his neck. But Grégoire did not seem in the least put out; he turned to the waiter and said: "*Alors, garçon. De la merde pour ce monsieur.*" Well, at that the printer picked up a carafe of water and, walking over to Grégoire, broke it over his head. Then he detached the nephew, and jerked him backward on the floor, and grabbing the kid, pulled him out. He got him into a taxi that happened to pass, and off they went at full speed. The waiter had pretended to stop us, but had allowed me to push him over with a bang against a door. As soon as he saw the kid and the printer safe in the taxi, he began to blow a police whistle. But, of course, the taxi got away. I had thrown a loaf of bread at the marquis, which hit him on the cheek, and that made me feel good. As it happened, I had only a few hundred yards to walk to my hotel, so I escaped all right.

'I never saw the printer again, or the kid. I was thinking of them just now and wondering what sort of a fruit *merde* was.'

Old Papa Johnson

(1929)

IN July 1916 I was in hospital with one Captain H. H. Johnson of the Army Service Corps, who had a habit of referring to himself in the third person as 'Old Papa Johnson.' I was in with a lung wound, and he with a badly fractured pelvis. 'Of all the inappropriate happenings!' he said. 'Imagine, Old Papa Johnson, of all people, being laid out by the kick of an Army mule in the middle of a European war!' He added, to remove any misunderstanding: 'No, the A.S.C. isn't my corps, except just now for convenience. I'm cavalry, really — did fifteen years off and on in the Lancers. I was with them at Le Cateau and got wounded. And then rejoined them at Ypres and got it again. This time it was shell, not bullet, and the medical board gave me "Permanently unfit for Combatant Service." So I transferred to the A.S.C. — yes, I know you fire-eating young infantry officers look down on that worthy corps — and I hadn't any great passion for acting as baker's boy and butcher's delivery man myself. Still, it was better than being in England. But now that ridiculous mule . . .'

Papa Johnson was about forty-five years old; very broad shoulders, medium height, I judged (but it is difficult to judge the vertical height of a man whom one sees only in a horizontal position), and a comedian's face. I only once saw it as anything but a comedian's face, and that was when a hospital orderly was impertinent. Then it set hard as stone, and his voice, which was ordinarily a comedian's voice, too, rasped like a drill instructor's; the orderly was terrified. Papa Johnson talked the most idiotic patter half the time and kept the nurses in hysterics. I had to ask him once to stop it, because it was bad for my wound to laugh like that; it might start a haemorrhage again. He had a small make-up box with a mirror and grease paints, and an assortment of beards and moustaches. While Sister Morgan was taking his temperature he would get under the blankets with a pocket torch — the thermometer in his mouth — and when the two minutes were up he would emerge in some new, startling character. A handkerchief and a towel were his only other stage properties. Sister Morgan would take the thermometer from him gravely, and he would say: 'Hello, boys and girls, I'm Queen Victoria as a young wife and mother!' or 'Beware, you wicked old men, I'm the Widow Twankey,' or 'Give ear, O Benjamin, I am Saul the son of Kish in search of his father's asses,' and she couldn't help laughing. And he would insist on talking in character until breakfast came up. Biblical parts were his specialty.

One day I was watching him at work on a complicated paper-cutting trick. He folded a sheet of newspaper this way and that, snipping it carefully here and there with a pair of nail scissors; he had told me that when it opened out it was going to be what he called 'Bogey-Bogey Ceremony in Sumatra.' He was full of tricks of this sort. I quoted a verse of the Psalms at him about it — I forget which it was — and he said, shaking his head at me sorrowfully: 'No, no, little Gravey-spoons, you've got that all awry. Never misquote the Psalms of David to Old Papa Johnson, because he knows them all off by heart.' And so he did, as I found when I challenged him, and Proverbs, too, and St. Mark's Gospel ('it's the one that reads truest to me,' he said, 'the others seem to me to have been played about with by someone who wanted to prove something'), and most of Isaiah and the whole of Job. Also Shakespeare's *Sonnets*. I was astonished. 'Where on earth did you come to learn all that?' I asked. 'At a Jesuit College as a punishment for independence of character?'

'No, no, no; bethink yourself, child. Do Jesuits use the *Sonnets* as a textbook? I learned most of my stuff in the Antarctic — I was on two expeditions there — while we were snowed up. Some of it in the Arctic. But I learned most when I was Crown Agent on Desolation Island.'

'Where's that? Is that one of the Fiji group?'

'No, no, no, child. That's in the Antarctic, too. It's the most southerly land under the British flag. The appointment is made yearly — it's well paid, you would say — but others wouldn't agree — £1,000 a year and everything found. Usually a Scot takes it on. The Scots don't mind living entirely alone in a howling wilderness as much as we English do; they are a very, very sane people. But my Scottish predecessor stuck it only for nine months, and I stuck it for two years: you see Old Papa Johnson is just a little bit insane. Always was so from a child. So he didn't come to any harm there. Besides, he had company for the last ten months.'

'If the island's a wilderness, what's the sense of keeping an agent there and wasting all that money on him? Is it just to keep the British claim from lapsing? Mineral deposits waiting for development?'

Johnson carefully laid down his 'Bogey-Bogey' business before answering. It was, by the way, a birthday present for Sister Morgan. Johnson went out of his way to be friendly with Sister Morgan, though I couldn't understand why. She was a V.A.D. nurse, middle-aged, incompetent, and always trying to play the great lady among the other nurses; they detested her. But with Johnson she behaved very well after a time and I came to like her, though when I was in another ward I had thought her impossible.

'As Crown Agent, I would have you understand, Captain Graves, I had to supervise His Majesty's customs, and keep a record of imports and exports, and act as Postmaster-General and Clerk of Works, and be solely responsible for maintaining the Pax Britannica in Antarctic regions — if necessary with a rope or a revolver.'

I never knew when Papa Johnson was joking, so I said: 'Yes,

your Excellency, and I suppose the penguins and reindeer needed a lot of looking after; and what with their sending each other so many picture postcards and all, you must have had your hands full at the office.'

'Hignorance!' snapped Papa Johnson, in the idiotic tones that he used for the Widow Twankey, 'Reindeers hindeed! Hain't no sich hanimals hin hall Hant-harctica. Them dratted reindeers honly hinhabitates *Harctic* hareas. Which there wasn't no penguins neither, not a penguin hon hall that hisland. There was prions, and seahawks, and sea helephants come a-visiting; but they wasn't no trouble, not they.' Then he continued in his usual voice: 'The gross value of imports and exports in the two years I was there amounted to . . . guess, child!' I refused to guess, so he told me that the correct answer was something over one million seven hundred thousand pounds sterling.

'For I should have told you, little Gravey-spoons, that Desolation Island has a harbour which is more or less ice-free for a month or two round Christmas every year. The whalers put in there then. It isn't every ship that can deal, like the *Larssen* can, with an unlimited quantity of whale; so when the smaller ships have more oil than they can manage comfortably and don't want to go back to Norway yet — half the world away — they dump it in barrels on Desolation Island, in the care of the Crown Agent, and get a chit from him for it. There are big store caves blasted out of the rock. The oil tankers come to collect the stuff. Also, a Norwegian company had put a blubber-boiling plant on the island for the convenience of its smaller boats — three great metal cauldrons, each about twice the size of this room, and weighing I don't know how many hundred tons. They must have been landed in sections and welded together on the spot; but that was before my time.

'When those fellows came ashore to boil down their blubber, I always had a busy time. I had to watch that they didn't pinch Government property or the oil belonging to other ships that I had in bond, or raid my house when my back was turned. I carried my revolver loose and loaded and hardly had time to sleep. But I was the sole representative of His Majesty, and he had given me unlimited power to make laws for the entire period of my stay, and to see that they were kept. After my first experience with a blubber party, which ended in a death and a fire, I issued an edict that henceforth Desolation Island was to be the driest as well as the coldest of His Majesty's possessions. I couldn't stop the brutes from boozing themselves silly aboard their own vessels in the harbour, but I saw to it that not a drop was landed on British soil. (Tough! you wouldn't believe how tough these Norwegian whalingmen were. But their ships' officers were tougher still and kept them under.)

'One day a tanker put in and two unexpected vistors came off her. One of them, a tall fellow with a Guards' Brigade moustache (here Papa Johnson made one up to show me, from his make-up box) and a quarrelsome sort of face (here Papa Johnson made up the sort of face he meant) came up to me and said in superior tones (here Papa Johnson imitated them) : "Mr. Henry Johnson, the British Crown Agent, I believe? My name's Morgan, Major Anthony Morgan of the Indian Army. I have come to live here with you. This is Professor Durnsford, who is on the staff of the New York Museum of Natural History," and he pulled forward a harmless-looking little fellow with a snubnose and the expression of a Pekinese. "We intend to do research work here." He handed me an introductory letter from the Government of New Zealand. I was too busy with customs business to read it, so I put it into my pocket — you see I disliked the man at first sight and didn't like having his company forced on me without a please or thank you — and I said: "Well, I can't refuse you, I suppose, if you have decided to dwell among me. There's my house; it's the only one on the island. Make yourselves at home while I attend to these papers. I'll send your stuff ashore when I've examined it."

'Morgan flared up. "You will certainly do no such thing as to tamper with my personal luggage."

'I shrugged my shoulders and said: "It's my job; I'm Customs here. Give me your keys."

'He saw that I was serious, and realized that the tanker was still in the harbour and able to take him off; I could refuse to put him up at my house and so he would have to go back in her. He threw me the keys with very bad grace, and Durnsford politely handed me his. They were numbered keys, so I had no trouble finding the right boxes for them.

'That evening I cooked the supper and Morgan got a mess kit out of his tin trunk to eat it in. The man Morgan actually tried to old-soldier Papa Johnson with his row of ribbons. And do you know what they were? Child, one was the Coronation ribbon and one was the Durbar ribbon and one was the Osmanieh, which one gets almost as a matter of routine if one is seconded to the Egyptian Army, and the fourth and last was the M.V.O. of the Third Class. So, pretending to be dazzled, I went off with the frying pan in my hand and changed into my old campaigning tunic, which sported Ashanti, Egypt, China, King's and Queen's medals South Africa, and North-West Frontier. Not a routine ribbon among them; they made his display look pretty sick. But I had only two stars up, so he tried to high-hat me with his crown.

'Believe me, child, there was the devil to pay about my embargo on wines and spirits; he had brought out twenty cases of Scotch. At first he didn't realize that Scotch was not drunk on Desolation Island. He said that in his opinion it would have been courteous of me, perhaps, to have put a bottle of my own stuff on the table, since I had not taken off any of his with the first boatload. But when I explained how it was, he went up in the air and bellowed at me as though he was in his Orderly Room and I was a poor devil of a Sudanese recruit. I won't repeat what he said, child, because a nurse might come in and catch a word or two and misunderstand. I was pleasant but firm; reminding him that I was Lord Chief Justice and Lord High Executioner and everything else on the island and that what I said went. Professor Durnsford had been a witness to his threats, I said, and I would subpoena him, if necessary, for the trial. And I quoted *Alice in Wonderland:* "I'll be judge, I'll be jury," said cunning old Fury, "I'll try the whole cause and condemn you to death."

' "You can't prevent me bringing it ashore," he said at last.

' "Can't I?" I said, in nasty tones, showing him my Colt.

'He broke into worse language than ever and the only true things he said about me were that I must be a little insane and that I had a face like Dan Leno on one of his off-nights. He ended: "Remember these words, for they are the last I shall address to you while I remain on this island." I answered, improving on poor Dan Leno: "Ha, Comma, Ha, among the trumpets. I'm Job's war horse, and I scent the battle from afar."

'Morgan kept it up throughout the meal. If he wanted the salt or beans or mustard when they happened to be right close to my plate, he would ask Durnsford, who sat between us, to pass them to him. I had decided to ship Morgan back home with his whiskey the very next day, but when he started this baby game of sending me to Coventry, I was so pleased that I decided to keep him with me. As you know, child, I love baby games. It was a nice game, because Morgan and I held the cards and Durnsford was pool for the winner to take. Not that I cared much about Durnsford then, but he seemed a decent little Pekinese of a man, too good to go coupled with an ill-tempered great mastiff like Morgan. They had arranged to come on this expedition together, by letter, before actually meeting. Morgan had written that he could get permission from the New Zealand Government for them both to put up at my house; and Pekey Durnsford was glad of a companion. Neither of them had been in the Antarctic before.

'Durnsford was the best possible "kitty" for our game of nap; he tried to be so neutral. Of course, I didn't go out of my way to make myself pleasant to him; that would have been no sort of game — an auction with the bidding in sugar plums and the prize to go to the men who bid highest. No, no, no! I answered his questions civilly, though not always pertinently, I supplied him with necessaries, and saw that he didn't run into danger: but I allowed him no loose conversation. Little Pekey Durnsford felt ever so uncomfortable (and even, I believe, went so far as to ask Morgan to apologize to me), but I felt perfectly happy. You see, child, having got accustomed to the deathly silence of Desolation Island when I was by myself for months at a time, I thoroughly enjoyed the very lively silence of the man Morgan. Often he was on the point of asking me something important about the island which only I could tell him, but then his haughty pride choked back the question. And so next day the question would come innocently enough through Durnsford. I would put on my "Schoolgirls we" voice and say: "Darling, that's a *great* secret. But if you promise *on your honour* never to tell anyone else in the world about it, I'll whisper it to you." Durnsford would smile unhappily, and Morgan would scowl.

'There were several rooms in my shack, but mostly storerooms, and only one big stove. Morgan made a show of moving his belongings into another room; but he got too cold and had to sneak back. It was a log-built shack, by the way, with steel doors and steel window shutters. It had an airtight lining and it was anchored to the rock with four great steel cables that went right across the roof. Understand, child, that in the Antarctic we keep a special and unique sort of blizzard, so these were necessary precautions.

'Well! The oil tanker had steamed off and the whalers had come and dumped their barrels and had their blubber parties and said goodbye; so unless there came a chance call from a vessel that was built pretty sturdy against the ice, like the one my predecessor went away in — he was killing himself with Scotch and couldn't lay off it because nobody was at hand to tell him not to make a beast of himself — unless a chance vessel called, you see, there we were together for another nine or ten solid months. I had a wireless apparatus, but it hadn't much of a range, and it was rarely I picked up a passing ship except in the season.

'For five solid months the man Morgan kept it up' (here Papa Johnson resumed the moustache, which had fallen off). ' "Durnsford, old fellow, do you think that you could prevail on that comedian friend of yours to disencumber the case he's sitting on? It happens to contain the photographic plates. He has apparently taken a three-year lease on it, with the option of renewal. Haw! Haw! Haw!" ' Durnsford looked at me apologetically. 'I didn't get off the packing case, of course . . . I never asked Durnsford to relay a message to Morgan. I pretended he didn't exist, and if he had been sitting on the packing case and I had wanted anything inside it, I should simply have opened it with him on it. He was afraid of me and careful not to start a roughhouse.

'They didn't get on too well with their natural-history studies, because they didn't know where to look. I knew my island well and there's a surprising amount of life on it, if you look in the right places, besides the prions and the other creatures I mentioned before, which don't take much finding, and a few ratlike animals that spend most of their life hibernating, and even a few honest-to-God birds. In the interior are fresh-water pools with all sorts of little bugs living in the ice. Heaven knows how they keep alive, but when you thaw them out they wriggle nicely. Durnsford didn't know that I knew and I didn't let on; his big friend took him round to see the sights, but he wasn't by any means so good a guide as Old Papa Johnson would have been.

'One day, it was twelve noon on Midsummer Eve with the thermometer forty-five below and the stars shining very prettily — you have heard of our beautiful long Polar night, I expect, that goes on month after month without a spot of daylight to help it out? Well, one day — or one night, if you prefer — after break-fast — or after supper if you like — the man Morgan puts on his snowshoes and says to Durnsford: "Coming out for a shuffle, professor?" "All right, major," Durnsford answers, putting down his book and reaching for his snowshoes.

' "Durnsford," I said, "don't go out!" He asked: "Why?" in a surprised voice, so I said: "Look at the barometer!" Morgan interrupted, saying to Durnsford: "Your imbecile acquaintance has no understanding of barometers. This one has been rock-steady for the last twenty-four hours."

' "Durnsford," I said again, "don't go out!"

'Morgan haw-hawed: "Oh, don't listen to it; come along for a bit of exercise. Leave old Red Nose with his string of sausages and his red-hot poker; he's not in his best vein these days."

'Durnsford hesitated, with one snowshoe already on. He hesitated quite a long time. Finally he took it off again. "Thank you, Mr. Johnson," he said. "I'll take your advice. I don't know what you mean about the barometer, but you must certainly understand conditions here better than Major Morgan,"

'That was good to hear; I had won my game of nap with the man Morgan at last and scooped the kitty. And it wasn't bluff: the unnatural steadiness of the barometer meant trouble. I had made sure that the shutters were fast some hours before.

'So Morgan went alone, whistling "Oh, it's my delight on a starry night in the season of the year," and two minutes later a creaking and groaning and humming began. Durnsford looked puzzled and thought I was playing a trick. "No," I said, "it's only the house moving about a little and the cables taking the strain. A capful of wind. But have a look at that rock-steady barometer."

'He went over to it, and behold! the creature had gone quite off its chump and was hopping about like a pea in a saucepan. Durnsford was silent for a minute or two and then he said: "Johnson, I know that the major has behaved abominably to you. But don't you think — ?"

' "No, dearie," I said, "your poor old granny is very, very sleepy at the moment, and simply hasn't got it in her to think thoughts about troublesome majors and the likes of them."

' "Oh, stop your jokes, for once!" he shouted, "I'm going out to look for him."

'He grabbed his shoes again. So I spoke to him severely and showed him my gun. I said that I didn't mind his slaying himself if he felt so inclined, but that I drew the line at his killing Old Papa Johnson too. They were double doors; the outer one was steel and the inner one solid two-inch oak planking, with an air-lock between them. The moment he unbolted the outer door the wind would get into the air-lock and blow the inner one in and then tear the shack to pieces in three seconds.

' "But the major?" he gasped. "Won't he get frozen to death?"

' "Your intelligent friend was killed by the first gust of wind a few seconds after leaving the shack," I said.

'That blizzard blew without stopping for seventy-two hours; any moment I expected the cables to go. I set myself to learn the Book of Ruth to keep my mind from dwelling on our imminent fate. Then it stopped as suddenly as it began. We found the body only fifty yards from the shack, wedged between two rocks. And you wouldn't believe it, but that blizzard had got inside one of those big metal cauldrons — twice the size of this room, I'm tell-ing you — and blown it clean into the harbour! As local registrar of births, deaths, and marriages I reported all these occurrences to a distant whaler, a month or two later, and when the tanker eventually turned up, it came with a letter from the man Mor-gan's sister, asking me to put her brother's remains in the lead coffin which she enclosed. So I had to dig them up again, though I had said the burial service over them and left nothing out.

"As for Pekey Durnsford, he was so full of gratitude to me for saving his life that he slobbered all over me. And soon I found that he liked silly games, just like I did. It was he who first taught Old Papa Johnson how to do this paper-folding business, though Papa's improved on Pekey's methods a lot since. And in return Papa showed him where to scare up all the living creatures in our kingdom. Pekey found one quite new species of fresh-water cheese mite which he called Something-or-other Papa-johnsonensis. And you should have seen the letter of thanks that I got from the New York Museum of Natural History!

'Morgan's sister — now child, for goodness' sake don't remind her who H. H. Johnson is — I recognized her handwriting when she put my name on the fever chart — is not a bad woman in spite of her airs, though it's taken me three weeks and a lot of patience to coax her to be my playmate. And do you know, little Gravey-spoons? if it hadn't been for that whiskey business I verily believe that Old Papa Johnson could even in time have made a playmate of her ill-tempered brother.'

Interview with a Dead Man

(1929)

AFTER awhile the dead man, recognizing my voice, began to whistle and imitate the masters of his old school, many of whom, bicentenarians, survived him. 'Though perhaps no longer, ahem, in the active pursuit of pedagogy,' he intoned in a mock-clerical voice.

'What's the news?' I asked.

'News?' he said. 'Well, for a start here's a letter that came last night from my executors informing me that I am expected to write a posthumous Anthem for the League of Nations suitable for translation into at least twenty-seven languages.'

He went on to say that he had indeed already executed the commission: early that morning he had written a marching song of hope, to rhythms heavily stressed for percussion purposes, and poked it up through the letter slit of the stout Welsh-quarried slabs of slate, inscribed 'HE BEING DEAD YET LIVETH,' which formed the roof of his quasi-eternal resting place. He had, however, recollected the nearness of the church, where the song would undoubtedly be sung at Christmas and Easter, on Empire Day, the King's Birthday, and all similar semireligious, semipolitical feasts; and had slowly pulled the composition back and torn it up before the sexton had caught a glint of it.

'It was an ironic production,' he said, 'but the living can never believe that the dead have a sense of humour, so whenever any reference had been made to the song in my hearing or whenever it was sung or whistled, I should have been forced to chuckle audibly to disprove this popular fallacy.'

'I am beautifully embalmed,' he continued. 'They were obliged, of course, to remove my digestive and sexual organs, which are corruptible, but I still have my fingers free to pick my nose in the old absent fashion, to scratch my head when it itches and to use a pencil thoughtfully when the itch is eased. This is a lidless coffin allowing me plenty of elbowroom. My eyes are shut with coins, but that is no handicap in the decent darkness of the vault; even when alive, I always had the knack of writing with my eyes shut. I lay the left hand flat as a margin to the paper and, pricking the skin with my pencil each time, know by sensory indication just where to begin the new line.'

Thus he rattled on, remarking among other things that at least he had no more financial worries. He had benefited handsomely under his own will and paid the lease of the vault and of a small plot of land around it for ninety-nine years in advance. Unfortunately the freehold, the property of the Ecclesiastical Commissioners, was not for sale; he had, however, secured the option for renewal at the same terms when the ninety-nine years should have expired. He asked for news of his wife and children and of their stepfather.

In short, he was perfectly dead, and his daily postbag, because of the recency of his death, was enormous; he used the blank pages of letters and the back of envelopes for his replies. He was in no position to buy stationery, even if his signature to cheques or letters had been valid, which it was not. However, he calculated that the serviceability of his large gold propelling pencil (which held, screwed in its base, a copious supply of refills) could even at the present extravagant rate of daily use be prolonged for fully another three hundred years.

'With care, for as long as three thousand years,' he cried, 'and by that time who will care for my work except antiquarians?'

His mood was now so hilarious that I had no compunction in

leaving him without another word of commiseration or encouragement. His parting joke was one about the legal impossibility of the dead libelling the living.

'But,' he said, 'I am careful not to trade on my immunity. I flatter myself that I died a sportsman and lie buried as such.'

Thames-side Reverie

(1929)

(Written while I was living in a converted Thames barge moored at
Hammersmith.)

A SUDDEN hoarse shouting woke me. I looked out of the
window beside my bed. Nearly full tide on the river and no wind;
a tug was neatly casting off one of its train of barges at the wharf
next door. A consignment of glassware in crates. The early morning greetings of tugmaster and wharfman were of their usual
mock-abusive friendliness. After all this hubbub there followed
half an hour of calm, in which I half slept and half watched a
pair of dabchicks bobbing about only a few yards from the window. The water was pink and grey in the dawn, the towpath on
the opposite bank was deserted and there was no river traffic.
The stage was well set for the five swans that floated up with the
tide and swam about under my window for some time. They
expected bread; they should have known that it was too early. I
could distinguish the plebeian swans, with their nicked beaks, the
property of the Vintners' and Dyers' Companies, from the royal
swans with unnicked beaks which owe immediate allegiance
to the Crown. But I could distinguish them only by their nicks,
not by their carriage. They went off sulkily after a while.

The next event was the drifting past of a brown-paper parcel,
accompanied by a flock of about twenty gulls. They screamed

and wheeled and dived and tore at it; and fluttered and squab-
bled and grew very excited. Though it passed slowly, I could not
make out what it contained. I was glad when it had gone, because I was still sleepy. The amount of things that drift by!
Especially at high tide, when there has been heavy rain two days
previously up the Thames Valley. Baskets, cabbages, chairs, fruit,
hats, vegetables, bottles, tins, heaps of rushes or straw, dead things.
Not so many dead things now as in the summer. Far fewer dogs.
That is because in the winter they don't go in so much after
sticks and get carried away by the current or murderously held
under water by the swans, who are jealous of their river.

Twelve lemons have just gone past. Now there are several
more. They look sound enough. An accident to a barrow? One
learns to distinguish accidental flotsam from intentional flotsam.
That hat over there, for instance, was accidental, blown off at
Westminster or Kew, by the look of it; the one that went by a
few minutes ago was surely intentional — a discard from Brent-
ford or Rotherhithe?

The amount of drift-wood is extraordinary. I wonder that
someone does not farm it for profit. But perhaps someone does.
I do not count the old woman who walks along the narrow fore-
shore at low tide and puts a few pieces into a muddy sack; I
mean somebody who collects it by the ton, dries it in front of
huge furnaces, and sells it in bundles for firewood. Perhaps the
supply would give out sooner than I suppose. A lot of the variety
is repetitious. After all, certain pieces that I recognize when I
see them again (for instance, that bit of 'Diving Girl' apple box)
go up and down with the tide for a week or more before I lose
sight of them.

Human corpses are rare. If one can catch a corpse and pull it
out, one is paid seven shillings and sixpence. I wouldn't do it for
that. And I suppose one also would have to give evidence at the
inquest. No, I would leave the corpse for someone else to earn
money with. There go the river police in their motor launch.
They are watching suspiciously in case I throw my apple core
out of the window. It is a prosecutable offence. I will wait until
they have gone. Here comes the *Mary Blake.* I am getting to

know the tugs well. I can distinguish the *Mary Blake,* the *Vixen* or the *Elsa* at half a mile. But every day something new of one sort or another goes by. One early morning last year was sensational. There went by an opera hat, a submarine, and a seal. Today I am content with the dabchicks and the lemons. At low tide I expect the old woman with the sack and the old man who pokes about under the stones and puts what he finds into jam jars. He would puzzle you, but I have been at this window long enough to find out what he is after. He is an anthology poem by William Wordsworth, *The Leech Gatherer.* Plenty of leeches on these beaches. The demand, I hear, is steady. Whether from extremely old-fashioned doctors or from extremely modern ones I do not know. Or care much at the moment. I am busy being pleased with the river, which is now as still as a lake, at the exact balance of the tide. A child's ball floats motionless under the window. I am tempted to get up and rescue it. But it looks as though it mightn't bounce. I'll stay in bed a little longer.

-Ess

(1929)

THE feminine word-ending -*ess*.

English was once a language in which a noun might capriciously decide to be masculine, feminine, or neuter. One sort of war weapon or drinking vessel might take the feminine gender, another the masculine, a third the neuter, yet nobody could have guessed which was boy, which was girl, or which neither. Gender was dropped as a general system some time after the Norman Conquest, and little trace of it remained. Instead there was a sex variation in all nouns expressing what grammar books call 'agency'; so the mediaeval English spoke of 'teacheress,' 'servantess,' 'neighbouress,' 'danceress,' even 'charmeress' and 'friendess.'

This was grammatical and without prejudice. The point to be observed is that we now say 'teacher,' 'servant,' 'neighbor,' 'dancer,' whether a man or woman is concerned, and that the gradual extension of this usage to other nouns tends to throw a great deal of suspicion on words that retain a distinctive -ess ending. Of course, some -ess words will always remain beyond suspicion: 'prophet' and 'prophetess,' 'giant' and 'giantess,' 'host' and 'hostess,' 'god' and 'goddess' (though 'goddess' has an objectionable use in metaphor) are evenly matched pairs. But such pairs are few.

115

If a general rule must be laid down, it is this: that wherever a noun is to be used to denote an occupation (say for example that of writing), and there is an available form, 'writer,' which has not varied with the sex since mediaeval times, then a word that does vary like 'author, authoress' should be avoided, or else the form 'author' used interchangeably for man and woman. For 'authoress' will have a ring of male prejudice in it.

This rule might be extended to words denoting race. 'Jewess,' for instance, is prejudiced. 'Jewess' means lascivious, blowzy, softspoken, sly, heavily perfumed. Women who happen to be Jews should be referred to simply as Jews unless they happen by a peculiar and unlikely chance to be Jewesses, like Keats':

> . . . Curled Jewesses with ankles neat
> Who as they walk abroad make tinklings with their feet.

'Negress,' too, is prejudiced. It hides a false gallantry, as of someone saying behind his hand: 'She is black as my hat, strong as a horse, and ugly as sin, but do not let us forget that she is a *Woman.'*

If I were a woman and a Negro, I should insist on being called a 'Negro,' not a 'Negress.'

'Shepherd' and 'shepherdess.' If I were a woman and a shepherd, I should not permit myself, for business reasons, to be described as a 'shepherdess.' Market days would be embarrassing.

'Murderer' and 'murderess.' A 'murderer' is usually an angry or brutal person, but 'murderess' has treachery and immorality in it too. Clytemnaestra, who, for adulterous reasons, killed her husband in a bath after his return from the wars, was a typical 'murderess'; Miss Frankie of the American folk song, who shot her Johnny with a forty-five while he was 'loving-up Nellie Bly' was as plainly a 'murderer.' 'Murderess' is a term that should be abolished in the interests of justice. And 'adulteress' is another: now that liability for divorce proceedings is evened up between husband and wife, it must give way to the interchangeable form 'adulterer.'

'Actress' is an unusual case. It is a word of less prejudice than 'actor,' because acting is a somewhat despised profession for men and an honoured one for women. The social proof is to compare the number of peers or their sons who marry actresses with the number of peeresses or their daughters who marry actors. Still, if I were a woman and an actor I should prefer on the whole to be called an actor, not an actress.

'Poet' and 'poetess.' Of all feminine forms 'poetess' is the most suspect. It is used almost invariably in a quarter-gallant, three-quarter-contemptuous sense to denote a woman who longingly aspires to rival man in his most sublime and peculiar province. Of course, many women do accept the word with all its connotations of assured failure. Felicia Hemans was a 'poetess,' as Sappho and others have been 'poets.' But, on the other hand, there are men who write poetry of a dull male quality that corresponds with the insipid female quality of the work of poetesses, but there is no male word of offence to correspond. Perhaps we should make one and say that if Felicia Hemans was a poetess, then Southey, Rogers, Leigh Hunt and Company were 'buck poets.' But poetry should not be an affair of sex any more than, for example, surgery. One says: 'Mary Smith is a surgeon,' not 'Mary Smith is a surgeoness,' or even 'Mary Smith is a lady surgeon.' Sex has no place in the operating theatre. Poetry is a sort of operating theatre.

Charity Appeals

(1929)

I ALWAYS destroy charity appeals. They are too well written, too cunningly pathetic, too heavily ornamented with lists of titled patrons to do anything but repel my sympathies. In any case, I don't believe in charitable institutions supported by voluntary subscriptions. They should be financed by the State. I know nothing more undignified in a rich country like this than that the big hospitals should have to send out their students in fancy dress collecting money in the streets, and organize bazaars and benefit matinées and ballots. One ought to give money out of one's private purse to private people who need it from time to time, but be regularly taxed for public service — hospitals, orphanages, institutions for the blind, and so on — which should not be regarded as charities. I always give to nuns because they have quiet, melancholy voices; I never give to the Salvation Army because they have loud, happy ones. I never give anything to anyone who tries to bully me into charity by singing hymns, playing the barrel organ, cornet, harmonium, fiddle, bagpipes, or gramophone, showing certificates of good character, exhibiting scars, handing me printed cards of poetry, asking for railway fares to Manchester, or by any similar means. But if, when I am in the country, a man comes to my door and says that he's on the

118

road and would like a cup of tea and can refrain from pitching a hard-luck tale, or from wasting my time in any other way, he'll get his cup of tea and his bread and cheese and a few coppers and an old shirt if there's one put by for him. And he'll call again in six months' time when he's working that part of the country again.

Beggars in London are a different problem. Sometimes I give money to a pavement artist if he can refrain from annotating his drawings with irrelevant remarks about the number of his children or the years he spent in the navy or the wounds he acquired while fighting for King and country, and if his drawings have that good-bad quality which excuses his calling himself an artist and yet accounts for his remaining on the pavement. The old-fashioned themes please me best — fish on dish, cat on mat, house on fire, and Noah's Ark with dove returning. I never, as I say, give money to ordinary street musicians — there is far less excuse for bad music in the street than for bad music in the concert room; but I have a tenderness for one-man bands, players of the Welsh triple harp, and men who perform with French chalk on the rims of wine glasses. They are sufficiently uncommon not to be public nuisances, and I like ingenuity. That is why I always give money to the man who folds and cuts paper into unexpected shapes, and to the lightning make-up artist. I give money to little girls who dance when their fathers whistle a tune to them. I give money to little boys who turn cartwheels, a thing I could never do myself when a boy. On flag and flower days I do not buy flags or flowers. I never give money to blind beggars; blindness is so heavily endowed in this country that a blind man who stands at a crowded corner and makes an additional pound or two a day in coppers is a mere financier. And he seldom has the good feeling to conceal his painful loss with a shade. And if he does conceal it the chances are that he is not blind at all, even though, or especially when, he reads the Bible aloud, in Braille. I never give money to Punch-and-Judy shows; I give to other marionettes, but I dislike Punch personally as a bullying humpbacked dago making capital out of his deformity. I never give money to contortionists. I always give money to old women who sell groundsel, because one must be in a very low state indeed to sell groundsel. I always 'remember the Old Guy,' but no more than once every Fifth of November; I always send the waits away penniless, unless it happens to be snowing or the carol is sung in Latin. I always give money to beggarwomen with babies, because babies are very troublesome things to carry, even if they are borrowed.

'But It Still Goes On': A Play in Three Acts

(1930)

DRAMATIS PERSONAE

CECIL TOMPION:	*well-known novelist and poet.*
DOROTHY TOMPION:	*his daughter, a doctor.*
DICK TOMPION:	*his son.*
DAVID CASSELIS:	*friend to Dick, an architect.*
CHARLOTTE ARDEN:	*friend to Dick and Dorothy.*
JANE ARDEN:	*her sister.*
RICHARD PRITCHARD:	*a poet from Wales.*
ELIZABETTA BEHRENS.	
A BUTLER.	
A WAITER.	
ANOTHER: A YOUTH.	

TIME: THE PRESENT

ACT I

SCENE I. The library of the Tompions' house at Hampstead; late August.

II. The same; eight days later.

III. In the rough at a neighbouring links; the following day.

ACT II

ACT III

ACT I

Scene I

(Dick Tompion *and* David Casselis *in the library of the Tompions' house at Hampstead; late August. David in an armchair, facing the audience, smoking a pipe (right). Behind him is an open window with a view of garden and a garden wall with fruit trees (right). There is a road beyond the wall: occasional traffic sounds are heard and once or twice the top of a lorry is seen over the wall. When the lorries go by, the speakers stop because of the rumbling noise. David's age is thirty-eight. He is well-built, good-looking, nervous, tall, fastidious, ironic, never looks at anyone he speaks to, has a small apologetic cough, gives the impression of feeling himself under restraint. He takes great care of his clothes. Dick is walking about the room (left). He is thirty, small but strong-looking, pale face, black hair. He speaks evenly, without emphasis. Nothing surprises him, as a rule, or shakes him out of his composure; the strength of his feelings is deduced from the circumstances rather than indicated by his manner. He dresses neatly but unconventionally with an open-necked shirt. His attitude to David is casual but friendly. David's attitude to him is repressedly romantic. The room has bookcases all round and a table covered with magazines (left); also a large old-fashioned globe, plaster casts of Shakespeare and Milton, and the usual encumbrances of the library of a successful literary man. Back (left) is another window overlooking the garden; under it a table spread with papers, obviously the writing table of* CECIL TOM-PION.)

DICK. I like the library, David. It's such a perfect giveaway of my father. Imagine being able to work in a room like this — plaster casts above, Persian rugs below, books all round, the current literary magazines behind, and all that litter on the table beside you — look, even photographs in silver frames, and a view of rose trees when you happen to look up from your work. Two hours before breakfast. Two hours after lunch. Three after dinner. That's his schedule. Three thousand five hundred words a day regularly. Besides poems. And letters — all carefully, carefully written for an eventual *Life and Letters of.* (*A knock.*) Come in.

(*Enter* BUTLER.)

BUTLER. This morning's papers, sir.

DICK. All right, Denman, put 'em out. (*Goes over to table.*) Saturday, is it? The five leading literary weeklies. No, David, look! here's another new one. Six. *Saturday Morning,* 'a new journal devoted to Art, Literature, Politics, Music, Science, etc.' Sixpence. Volume I, number 1. August 26. And all the usual deadheads in it.

(*Exit* BUTLER.)

'This week in Parliament.' 'Around the galleries.' 'Cinema notes.' Hullo! '*Shame:* A short story by Cecil Tompion.' (*Reads for a moment, throws it down. Walks about the room again.*)

DAVID. Is it any good, Dick?

DICK. Is what any good?

DAVID. Your father's story.

DICK. It was written in this room with the usual infiltration of plaster casts, silver photograph frames, rose pergolas, art, literature, politics, and music — not to mention motor lorries. Of course it's good. What do you expect?

DAVID. Some of his stuff isn't as bad as the rest.

(DICK *does not answer. Walks about the room, stops at the globe, which he revolves faster and faster: then suddenly stops it with the flat of both hands.*)

DICK. The extraordinary thing to me, David, is: that it's finished and ended and over, but it still goes on.

(*Comes forward to where* DAVID *can see him.*)

DAVID. What still goes on?

DICK (*makes a rotary movement with his hand*). *It* still goes on, like — like the watch in the pocket of a dead man.

DAVID. Do you mean literature?

DICK. No, not just that. The whole sixpennyworth, with every possible etcetera. The whole doings.

DAVID. This human world, you mean?

DICK. Well, if you like. Have you ever considered how ridiculous a live person would feel in a world that was finished, and over, but still went on?

DAVID. Isn't this just another lament for 'The Manner of the World Nowadays'? Wait a moment. *So many . . .* oh, I know:

> *So many pointed caps*
> *Laced with double flaps*
> *And so gay felted hats*
> *   Saw I never.*

> *So many good lessons*
> *So many good sermons*
> *And so few devotions*
> *   Saw I never.*

DICK. What's that?

DAVID. Sunday journalism of the reign of Henry VIII.

> *The streets so sweeping*
> *With women's clothing*
> *And so much swearing*
> *   Saw I never.*

> *So many sluttish cooks*
> *So new-fashioned tucking-hooks*

(what's a tucking-hook?)

And so few buyers of books
Saw I never.

So few buyers of books. That's *your* complaint, isn't it, Dick?

DICK. Nonsense. They buy my father's by the hundred thousand.

DAVID. But not yours?

DICK. No, not mine. And why should they? I wonder sometimes that I ever sell enough to cover the cost of printing; that usually happens, though. I suppose I'm mistaken for a poet of tomorrow, and because I publish in limited editions and because nobody can make me out, I'm regarded as a good buy. The knowing ones buy my hundred and fifty signed copies and put them down in pickle. They don't read them, of course; 'fine uncut condition' is their pride. The joke's on them, of course: the whole edition's in a fine uncut condition.

DAVID. You don't think that in 1960, say, they'll be rewarded for their foresight?

DICK. No! There's no reason to expect posterity to be any less turnipheaded. It'll still be reading my father's stuff probably. Or someone equivalently god-awful. You asked me if it were my *complaint*. David, sometimes I wonder what I'm doing talking to you as though you were a friend. *I* complain that the sort of people who buy my father's books don't buy mine?

DAVID. You could do with a bit more money, couldn't you?

DICK. Not really. He allows me three hundred a year out of his winnings. He loves making money — he's never so happy as when he's writing a best seller — and he loves giving it to me because he loathes me and wants me to feel dependent on him and jealous of his literary successes. And he expects me to have feelings of shame about taking the money. (*Chuckles.*) Three hundred is all I'll ever want. By the way, that poem. How does it end?

DAVID. On the usual note of optimism:

God is neither dead nor sick —
He may amend all yet.

For better I hope ever —
Worse was it never.

DICK. It *would,* of course. That's just the difference.

DAVID. Between?

DICK. Between then and now. I mean, it's too late for amending the world now; the bottom has fallen out of it. The Sunday journalists and the politicians and the Church, of course, all pretend that it hasn't, and everyone else plays up to them. But it's no good. It's finished; except that it still goes on.

DAVID. Bad as all that? What's wrong with you today, Dick? *(Grabs his arm in a sentimental way.)*

DICK *(detaching himself and pretending not to notice).* David, you're eight years older than me. You went to Cambridge in 1912, wasn't it? When tucking-hooks were still in fashion and the streets were still unaffectedly sweeping with women's clothing.

DAVID. Yes, I'm a good old prewar vintage.

DICK. So you'll never be able to forget that the world had a bottom once. You'll go on for the rest of your life pretending it's still there.

DAVID. You're crazy, Dick. What are these 'Lost Bottom Blues' about? Begin at the beginning. What *was* the bottom?

DICK. You can't understand if you think that I'm making a blues of it. I'm stating quite simply — just making a dry historical pronouncement — that the bottom of things, after working looser and looser for centuries, has at last dropped out: and that no public recognition has been made of what is, after all, the most important human catastrophe that's ever happened. I don't mean catastrophe in any tragic sense. Tragedy and comedy both fell through the hole. So did optimism and pessimism. And rebellion and reaction.

DAVID. I like you when you declaim, Dick. It's so seldom you open your mouth at all.

DICK *(ironically).* My musical voice! Shut your eyes and listen, but don't trouble about the sense.

DAVID. No, I'm listening, I swear. Tell me more about the bottom of things. (*Grins.*)

DICK. I can't put it more clearly. If I try to define it in religious terms or social terms or philosophical terms or aesthetic terms or any other terms, it's not the truth.

DAVID. When did it drop out, then? In the War?

DICK. No, the War came later. The War was a diversion, to distract public attention from the all-important loss. The War is always made to account for every remarkable change in human affairs that has happened since the true catastrophe. The pretence is that the War was only a temporary morbidity, and that these changes are morbid hangovers from war and so only temporary too. Well — reckoning back I should say that the bottom dropped out of things suddenly, early one Sunday morning, towards the end of . . . (*Reckons to himself, but does not end the sentence.*) The crash was so terrific that nobody heard it — but it sent everyone mad all the same.

DAVID. And the War was part of the madness, I suppose?

DICK. Yes. First there was a shocked pause — two years; then . . . Wait a second, I'll show you.

(*Exit (right); returns with a revolver.* DAVID *does not look round; he is lighting his pipe.* DICK *standing close behind his chair looks out of the window, smiles ironically, takes careful aim and fires at something in the garden. Then quickly moves away out of view. A lorry goes by.*)

DAVID (*jumps up, pauses a moment speechless with shock, then picks up a heavy agate paperweight from the table, and is about to throw it, shouting*): Damn and blast your soul!

DICK (*stands with his revolver pointed*). Quiet, David. Put that down. Sorry, and all that. I was only showing you.

(DAVID *sullenly puts back the paperweight.*)

There was this sudden, unexpected, terrific crash . . . And what did people do? What you've just done. Paused for a moment and then went mad. (*He watches something out of the window and smiles.*) Made as loud a noise as they could to relieve their feelings. That's what the War was — the loudest noise humanly possible, a counternoise to the noise the bottom made dropping out of things.

DAVID. Damn and blast you, Dick, for your fancies. You know what my nerves are like since then. By the way, that wasn't a live cartridge, was it?

DICK. Yes, it was. I always keep a loaded revolver in the drawer of my worktable upstairs.

DAVID. My God, you gave me a fright. Dick dear, you really are absolutely wanton sometimes. (*Seizes him by the shoulders and looks at him, but does not meet his eye.*)

DICK. That's all right. Have a whiskey and soda. I'll get you one.

(*Goes away and gets it. Returns without revolver.*)

DAVID. What's the idea of the loaded revolver? (*Drinks.*)

DICK. It's like the human skull, or the coffin, that holy men in the middle ages used to keep about the place to remind them of death. I had that Webley in France — do you remember coming with me when I bought it at the Havre Ordnance Depôt in 1917?

DAVID. Yes, that's right. By the way (excuse me talking about those days), how often did you use it in the trenches — apart from rat-shooting?

DICK. Four times. Once to kill a pack mule, wounded in the belly — guts hanging out — once in that raid near Bouchavesnes to plug a German — it took the top of his head off — once at Bullecourt — you weren't with us then — on a man of my own company — 91 Evans his name was — when he wouldn't get out of the trench to attack. And once on myself the same night when I came back alone and found 91 Evans' corpse grinning at me with a bloody mouth, the only other man in the trench. A shell burst just as I pulled the trigger and it spoilt my aim. The bullet glanced off. Here's the scar. It gave me the devil of a headache — knocked me out for a couple of hours.

DAVID. You never told me that before, Dick. (*Laughs nervously.*) I'd never have forgiven you if you'd killed yourself. Dick, dear, I don't like your *memento mori* Webley. I wish it were a nice harmless skull; wouldn't that do as well? I'll buy you one.

DICK. No, not nearly as well. This thing reminds me not only that death must eventually come, but that I can fix whatever date suits me.

DAVID. What did you aim at just now? A tree?

DICK. No, I've no spite against trees.

DAVID. Just at nothing? Dick, you're mad.

DICK. Well, whatever I am, don't blame it on the War.

(*Enter* CECIL TOMPION, *from left. A young-looking man of fifty-two, dressed like a country gentleman, unpleasant voice, decisive gestures, florid complexion. He is breathing heavily.*)

TOMPION. Here, you fellows. Let's have a whiskey too. (*Helps himself.*) Do you know what's just happened? Someone's tried to kill me.

DAVID. You don't mean it! (*Steals a look at* DICK, *who is quite impassive.*)

TOMPION. Didn't you hear the shot? It must have come from the garden wall. It must have been fired quite close to this window.

DICK. We thought it was a tyre-burst. A lorry was passing.

TOMPION (*sniffs*). I can smell the smoke here: it must have drifted in . . . I was out there among the roses, and whoever it was fired two shots. The first whistled past my cheek —

DICK. Sure it was meant for you, father?

TOMPION. Meant for me? The next one took these gardening-scissors clean out of my hand. (*Shows them.*) Lucky I was holding them loosely. Then he yelled out something like 'Blast you!' and disappeared. I rushed round to the garden gate and into the road to collar him. But he was gone.

DICK. Let's see the scissors. Pretty bit of shooting, David, wasn't it, even with the top of the wall for a rest? Yes. (*Meditatively.*) You *did* say Pritchard had been practising, and I wouldn't believe you. I apologize.

TOMPION. Who? What? Not Richard Pritchard?

DICK. Didn't the voice sound familiar?

DAVID. Yes, I was telling Dick about it only this morning. It appears that ever since you were made a Companion of Honour, Pritchard has been eating his heart out in jealousy.

DICK. The poor fellow isn't even a Fellow of the Royal Society of Literature yet.

TOMPION. Well, after all, he can hardly expect that sort of thing. He never had more than an elementary-school education.

DAVID. Someone told me that he'd bought a service revolver and a few cartridges and that he'd pinned up your photograph from the *Sketch* on the top landing of the place where he's living and was using it as a target. But, of course, we thought it was only symbolic.

DICK. I must say, I didn't believe it. The idea of anyone being jealous of . . .

DAVID. I didn't want to worry you, unnecessarily. Did it sound like Pritchard's voice?

TOMPION. I couldn't swear to it; it was distorted with anger.

DAVID. Pritchard's a simple fellow, as you know. He's got the delusion that he's the only poet living who's really good: he can't bear to hear you praised everywhere. But I don't think he tried to kill you. He reads *Wild West* stories. There's a hero called Ace Bradley, a gunman, who always shoots the revolver out of the sheriff's hand instead of killing him. Pritchard's playing Ace Bradley. Now he's shot the scissors out of your hands he'll be satisfied. By Jove, Mr. Tompion, you had guts to run after him!

TOMPION. A fellow who is coward enough to shoot at me, an unarmed man, from cover, would never have had the courage to face me if I came after him in the open. He'd have tossed the gun away and legged it. How like a Welshman!

DICK. What are you going to do about it? Shall I ring the police?

TOMPION (*who has been drinking and is feeling better*). No, no! I don't want Pritchard locked up. I wouldn't bring a charge against a brother poet. He's quite good in his simple way. Heaven knows there are few enough of us good poets writing today. We ought to stick together. No, I'm going straight to his place — where is it? — West Streatham, isn't it? — and make him give me his gun for safe keeping.

DAVID. Well, Mr. Tompion, I wouldn't do that, quite.

TOMPION. And why on earth not? Do you think I'm frightened of *that* little Welsh rabbit?

DAVID. It occurred to me that you'd be taking away his self-respect if you tried to take his gun and then he'd really try to kill you.

DICK. At present he's feeling all warm and golden inside. He's saying to himself (*imitates Welsh accent*). 'Duw! Duw! By Christian Damn I gave that bloody swine a proper fright, what-effer. Companion of Honour Tompion! Companion of the bloody Back House!' And then he'll laugh: 'Oh dear me, to goodness. I'll never forget that look of absolute bloody terror on his great face, when I shotted those scissors from his hand. Oh, Deoul, it was a dramatic situation, indeed!' Seriously, father, I think David's right. Leave the poor nitwit to enjoy his triumph.

TOMPION. Well . . . Perhaps you fellows are right. . . . So you advise me to do nothing?

DAVID. If you don't mind me making the suggestion, the best thing that you can do is to be a good Christian. Heap coals of fire on his head. You think he's a good poet. Write and tell him so. Or congratulate him on his new book. It's being published today.

TOMPION. Well, perhaps there's something in that. If he's suffered from jealousy of my success, I suppose I'm responsible in a sense. That new review *Saturday Morning* — by the way I've a short story in it, might amuse you boys — has asked me to do reviews for it — of any book that interests me. Yes, I'll ring them up now and get them to send it. Pritchard's not a bad poet, though a bit overingenuous. You know, he started as an errand boy in a Carnarvon drapery shop; that's really greatly to his credit.

(*Exit, saying as he goes:*)

Don't tell anyone about this business, you fellows. Nobody seems to have heard the shots but ourselves.

DAVID. Dick, tell me. Did you fire at your father on purpose?

DICK. No, at the scissors. Why did he say *two* shots? Just to make it more exciting, I suppose.

DAVID. Good Lord! You didn't really! But you're no Ace Bradley yourself. I remember in 1917 when you were passing your young-officer's revolver test at the Depôt — I came down to laugh at you — the R.S.M. yelled: 'Oh, Mr. Tompion, Mr. Tompion, cease fire, Mr. Tompion. It's too dangerous. I'll give you a possible, if you'll only cease fire, Mr. Tompion.'

DICK. Yes, I was nervous then. It was a Test. And with you sniggering behind me and the sergeant-major confusing me with his instructions; plus a borrowed revolver. Of *course* my wrist wobbled and I sprayed the countryside in general. This was different. A snapshot — my own choice of target — my own gun — no one watching — not a moment to consider whether it was possible to miss. Instinctive shots never do miss, anyhow, if you know the weapon. It's one of the laws of Nature.

DAVID. I give you up, Dick. Suppose your father had suddenly moved or something had distracted your aim? Suppose you'd killed him?

DICK. Oh, cut out the supposes. Or else put in a few more. Suppose that I loved him so dearly that I'd have been afraid of killing him. Or suppose I detested him so utterly that I'd have been afraid of missing him (but as you know I don't allow myself to have any feelings for him one way or the other). Or suppose even that the bottom had never dropped out of things — suppose it were still possible to have moral scruples about letting off firearms in a gentleman's residence.

DAVID. Damn that! Now you've got me mixed up in the Pritchard story, what's the next move? Are you going to let him believe in it?

DICK. You helped it along nicely, thank you, David. Yes, why not? It's a dramatic story. My father loves to find himself in dramatic situations. I'm going to improve on it, as a matter of fact. This is going to be an interesting and instructive round-game for any number of players.

DAVID. I'm not playing.

DICK. We'll see about that.

DAVID. Well, anyhow, I might as well know what the rules are.

DICK. They'll be improvised as the games goes on. It's a sort of musical chairs without the music or the chairs — a romping elimination of the unfit.

DAVID. What will you use for chairs, then?

DICK. My Webley, chiefly.

DAVID. If you fire that damned thing again, I'll ring Scotland Yard and have you removed to Broadmoor.

DICK. *I'm* not going to use it. On the contrary, I'm resigning my title to it and passing it round.

DAVID. I don't understand you.

DICK. Passing it round, putting it in circulation as everyone's *memento mori;* then watch how soon things will start happening.

DAVID. Why do you want things to happen?

DICK. I believe in signs. That shot — I fired it off without malice aforethought —

DAVID. In sheer wantonness —

DICK. By sudden inspiration — it was certainly a sign. There's a staleness in the air around here. Can't you feel it? There's nothing like a revolver to clear the air.

DAVID. Which is it to be: farce or tragedy?

DICK. That distinction isn't relevant any longer: as I explained. If you *must* have a label, call it a Post-Catastrophic Comedy.

DAVID. I have a good mind to tell your father the whole story.

DICK. He'd never allow you in the house again if he knew you'd been laughing at him.

DAVID. Dick, you're about the most dangerous person I know. You're a constant misery to me.

DICK. And you're a constant pain in my belly.

CURTAIN

Scene II

(The same, eight days later. DOROTHY TOMPION *and* CHARLOTTE ARDEN. DOROTHY *is twenty-seven, a woman doctor just beginning to practise. She is small and dark-haired like her brother* DICK, *with a dark, tailor-made dress. Her feelings are much more to the surface than* DICK's. *She is slim, conventional, and good-look-*

ing. CHARLOTTE, *the same sort of age, is fair but not blonde.
Dressed in a summer frock. Has a particularly attractive voice,
and is a much more sophisticated person than* DOROTHY, *whom
she treats with great affection.*

CHARLOTTE *is reading* Saturday Morning, *standing, at the magazine table.* DOROTHY *is sitting in the chair where* DAVID *sat in
Scene I.*)

CHARLOTTE (*to herself*). Dick's right. He's getting really worse
than ever.

DOROTHY. What did you say?

CHARLOTTE. Nothing. Only that this new paper's a dud.
(*Throws it away.*)

DOROTHY. Come and sit down, Charlotte . . . I want to tell
you something, and I don't know just where to begin.

CHARLOTTE (*in a stage whisper*). 'Let me guess!' Oh, Dorothy,
I must tell you about 'Let me guess!' It's Dick's joke: about a
dreadful old don at Oxford who's ninety-something years old,
and a professor of geology. He has a delusion that he's an em-
bodiment of perpetual youth; so he's always mad keen on pro-
tecting the undergraduates against being bored by the other dons.
'Old fossils' he calls them, even when they happen to be fifty
years younger than himself. A horrible aged playfulness: his
chief joy is outliving his contemporaries. When someone dies and
they come to him with solemn faces and say: 'Tertiary Granite,
old fellow, we have bad news for you,' his face always lights up.
He says in a fiendish whisper . . . 'Let me guess!'

DOROTHY. Well?

CHARLOTTE. 'Let me guess!' Who's the man? Why do you
hesitate? Aren't you sure he's in love with you? (*Sits down.*)

DOROTHY. Well it *is* about a man I'm in love with. You've
guessed that far. Guess again.

CHARLOTTE. Anyhow, it's David Casselis.

DOROTHY. Charlotte, how on earth did you guess that? How
could you have known? I didn't myself till this morning.

CHARLOTTE. Easy. You see, I was nearly in love with him too,
last year. He's very easy to be in love with. Everyone *is,* almost.
That's the trouble with men of David's er — temperament —

psychology — whatever the polite word is. Women get interested in the sort of men who give them absolutely no encouragement; it's such a relief from the usual sex bears.

DOROTHY. But aren't you in love with him now?

CHARLOTTE (*draws her finger across her throat*). Drop dead!

DOROTHY. Why, bother you? What was wrong?

CHARLOTTE. Nothing. I thought it would be a good plan to fall in love with him, but . . . Look here, I'll tell you why you're in love with him. That's much more interesting.

DOROTHY. No, I'll tell *you*. First of all —

CHARLOTTE. First of all he's so charmingly dishonest and he never looks at you when he speaks. Shy as a little boy.

DOROTHY. Yes, that's right. I met him first at Lady Anstruther's dance — Dick made him come — and you know how well he dances — not brilliantly or showily, but so considerately. He was very nervous afterwards sitting out with me. Both of us had coffee, and he was gently, gently, very gently breaking an Apostle spoon in his fingers, to see if it wouldn't. But it did; and he blushed all over his ears and head; and then he jumped up, spilling his coffee, and muttered something about apologizing to Lady Anstruther. He went off with the pieces; and I followed a little way behind to hear what excuses he'd make. And guess what he did!

CHARLOTTE. Of course the poor creature funked it. What did he do with the pieces?

DOROTHY. He looked carefully round to make sure no one was watching and then hid them in a hyacinth pot. Bless his naughty little ways.

CHARLOTTE. Do you know why he was nervous with you?

DOROTHY. I couldn't imagine. After all, I'm the sister of his best friend.

CHARLOTTE. Well, I'll tell you. He's nervous of all women except the ones he doesn't suspect of being in love with him — the comfortable old women with black satin fronts and good-looking grown-up sons. He warms up to *them,* all right — spends hours with them at the tea table, actually writes them long newsy letters. All men of David's — what *is* the word? — of David's persuasion, are like that. I hadn't known at first that he was one of them — he's the athletic type and usually they're either slobby or dainty — but as soon as I saw him with old Bugle, our house-keeper — I suddenly understood. That was when I tried to fall in love with him. You see, I'm of the complimentary persuasion. (Well, you know *that* at least.) It seemed a good idea. David is always at his ease with me; he feels that I'm not a danger to him.

DOROTHY. Really, Charlotte, I can't understand a word of all this. What persuasion?

CHARLOTTE. Don't you know, really?

DOROTHY. Stop teasing me.

CHARLOTTE. A woman doctor, too? Didn't they tell you about all that at the Hospital?

DOROTHY. Maybe I'm awfully stupid, but it sounds absolute nonsense to me. You tried to fall in love with him because he was sympathetic with Mrs. Bugle about her son being killed. (That's as far as I can get.) But then you couldn't keep it up?

CHARLOTTE. Well, if you want it plainly: he's the sort of man who can never be in love with any girl.

DOROTHY. That's exactly where you're wrong. He's just asked me to marry him.

CHARLOTTE (*utterly surprised*). Well, I go to Chicago! Protestations of love and all that? Honest?

DOROTHY. In writing. In his neat, regular, pretty, slightly back-ward-sloping, dear handwriting.

CHARLOTTE. Too shy to ask you by word of mouth . . . or kiss of mouth?

DOROTHY. Charlotte, you're jealous, you poor darling.

CHARLOTTE (*laughs*). No, dear. I admit I'm confused, though. I can't make it out. But you're in love with him; and he's ap-parently in love with you. It seems good enough. All the same, it's a shock. I didn't think he had it in him to fall in love with a girl.

DOROTHY. Well, what else do you think he could possibly fall in love with? Old ladies with black satin fronts? Really, Char-lotte, you're insane. Is this your fantastic Freudian stuff about maternal fixations? No, thank goodness, we didn't have any

nonsense of that sort taught us in our psychology course . . .
It's this, Charlotte. Do you think that it's right for me to marry
when I'm a doctor? Suppose I have children: is it fair to them?
Bringing children up properly is a whole-time job; so is the
practice that I'm building up. It looks as though I'll have to
choose between them.

CHARLOTTE. Do you mean you're worrying about *that?* Well,
why *have* children?

DOROTHY. What do you mean?

CHARLOTTE. Well, what do *you* mean? They're damned little
nuisances anyhow.

DOROTHY. I mean: one can't help it usually when one's married,
can one?

CHARLOTTE. Dick *was* right. My goodness! My supreme and
ineffable goodness!

DOROTHY. Right about what?

CHARLOTTE. I told him it was impossible for anyone to go
through a seven-year medical course — gynaecology and all —
and remain ignorant of any of the more important bad jokes of
nature.

DOROTHY. Well?

CHARLOTTE. All right: I'll tell you what he told me. About a
month ago you told him a story about a woman who'd had an
operation when you were house surgeon. Her husband . . .
(*Pauses, slightly embarrassed.*)

DOROTHY. Yes, go on.

CHARLOTTE. Her husband asked you whether it would be all
right for him to sleep with her now, and you said, 'yes, if you're
careful not to bump against her in the dark.' And then he looked
embarrassed and puzzled. And you asked him whether he
snored. And he said *Snore?* in a withering tone.

DOROTHY. It didn't wither me. Yes, it *was* funny, wasn't it?

CHARLOTTE. Well, *I* go to . . . to — the ancient University of
Upsala. What a triumph of dissociation! (*Laughs.*)

DOROTHY. What's dissociation?

CHARLOTTE. Not being able to understand connexion. Or put
this and that together.

DOROTHY (*angry*). This is like a nightmare (*Shakes* CHARLOTTE, *who is convulsed with laughter.*) Charlotte, dear, you've not spoken two words of sense this afternoon. Tell me seriously. What ought I to do?

CHARLOTTE (*laughing still*). Honestly, Dorothy, I haven't . . . the . . . very . . . slightest idea. I'm like you at the beginning of the conversation. 'I don't know just where to begin.'

(*Enter* TOMPION, *left.*)

TOMPION. Hullo, Dorothy. (*Kisses her.*) Hullo, Charlotte; where's your little sister Jane? (DOROTHY *is polite to her father, but no more.* CHARLOTTE *plainly dislikes him.*)

CHARLOTTE. In the garden with Dick and David.

TOMPION (*opens the window and shouts*). Jane, David, Dick! Something to show you!

(*Enter* JANE, DICK, DAVID (*left*). JANE *is twenty-two or so, dresses rather wildly but not sluttishly; fair, determined-looking without* CHARLOTTE's *unhappiness. Looks like a girl who has just left Oxford without troubling much about a degree.*)

JANE. Hullo, Mr. Tompion.

TOMPION. Too old to kiss me, Jane?

JANE. Yes, no offence, please.

TOMPION. None at all. Look here, boys and girls: look at this treasure. A messenger has just brought it. Sorry that I can't give you the thrill of opening the seals. Note: postmark, West Streatham. No other clue to the sender except that the brown paper has been used for wrapping books. Publisher's name: Glenway and Good. Guess! Now, Dorothy, my dear, you guess first.

DOROTHY. I don't know, father. How should I? An infernal machine sent you by a group of your admirers?

TOMPION. Pretty good, Dorothy. Really, that's pretty good. Nobody'll get nearer than that.

DICK. I bet I will. Glenway and Good are Pritchard's publishers. West Streatham is where he lives. I guess a revolver.

TOMPION. Absolutely right, Dick. But you had a clue. (*Opens the parcel.*)

JANE. What a funny present. Is it loaded?

TOMPION. Of course not — yes, by Jove, it is! Here, hands off!

. . . However, the safety catch seems to be on.

JANE. I've never handled a loaded revolver before. Do let me! *Please,* Mr. Tompion.

TOMPION. Well, youth and beauty will be served. All right. Be very careful not to point it at anyone.

JANE (*takes it and examines it curiously*). Which is the safety catch? (*She is standing (left) away from the others, with her back to them.* TOMPION *is at her side.*)

TOMPION. Here at the side. You press it. Now it's ready to fire.

JANE. Is it *really?* Oh, what a perfect feeling. I could kill anyone I liked now. Couldn't I, Charlotte? And there are so many people who ought to be killed. (*She has slowly turned round with the revolver raised and pointed.*) Is the trigger easy to pull?

(CHARLOTTE *throws her hands above her head. So does* DAVID. TOMPION *drops flat.* DOROTHY *springs in front of David. A pause.*)

Oh, isn't everyone terrified of me? Dorothy heroic but terrified. The others just plain terrified. Oh, no, all except Dick. What are you doing, Dick?

DICK. Half a moment. I'm winding the clock. (*Compares it with his watch.*) It's just this moment stopped. Fright, I suppose.

JANE (*repentant*). Oh, Dick, was it awful of me?

DICK. Awful? Hell no! Absolutely the right spirit. Let's have a feel of it myself. (*Comes and looks at it.*) It looks a nice weapon. I wonder how many people it's shot? It's an army revolver.

JANE (*holding the revolver pointed at* DICK). I wonder how many more it's going to shoot?

DICK. People oughtn't to be so frightened, ought they? There are so many other simple ways of getting killed in a house. Falling downstairs, for instance. Thank you. (*Takes it.*) The old-fashioned convention was to handle a revolver butt first. But that way's just as good these days.

(*Everyone recovers and begins to scold* JANE *all at once.*)

CHARLOTTE. Stupid little idiot!

DOROTHY. Jane, *really!*

TOMPION. 'Pon my soul, Jane, I must say!

DAVID. Jane, you ought to be spanked.

JANE. Sorry, everyone. It seemed alive, eager to go off. It twisted round like that by itself. Funny feeling.

TOMPION. That's the second time I've been near death from that gun.

DOROTHY. Once is enough for me. Put the hateful thing away, Dick. At once! At once! (*Stamps.*)

DICK. It's safe enough with me. Safety catch up. There. Or look, I'll unload it. This is how you unload it, girls. Press here and bend. (*Breaks it open.*) Here are the cartridges. (*Ejects them.*) They go in again quite easily. (*Reloads.*) And then you click it back. (*Shuts the revolver.*) Simple, isn't it? (*Puts it away on a top shelf behind the bust of Milton.*) Now everyone knows how to use it. It's quite safe there. Nobody ever dusts the top of bookcases.

JANE. Oh, Mr. Tompion, I really *am* sorry. Don't be too angry with me. It was only a joke. Of course, I wouldn't *really* have pulled the trigger. Do tell me: who sent it?

TOMPION. Ought I to tell the story, you fellows?

DICK. Now that Pritchard's name's been mentioned, you might as well.

TOMPION. Well, gather round. Eight days ago, the Saturday before last, I was in the garden over there (*leans out of the window and points*) cutting off the dead roseheads. David and Dick were in here. Suddenly I heard a well-known voice shout at me over the wall. 'Blast you, Tompion!' Then he let fly with this revolver. The first shots came pretty near. You fellows say that you only heard two? That was because he fired so fast. The third took the gardening scissors clean out of my hand. (*Opens the table drawer and shows them.*) Look! That's true, you fellows, isn't it?

DOROTHY. Oh, father, what did you do?

TOMPION. I ran out at once to collar him.

> (DAVID *makes a pantomime caricature for* DICK, *indicating that* TOMPION *was very frightened and ran for cover.* DICK *does the same.* JANE *notices this and smiles.*)

But the street was empty. I am . . . informed — that he'd been having target practice with a portrait of mine for weeks past. The fact is, he's insanely jealous of my work.

DAVID (*to* DOROTHY). Dick and I advised your father to take no notice. But he improved on our advice. He magnanimously put that review of Pritchard's new poems — what are they called? *The Gardener's Lad* — into *Saturday Morning*.

CHARLOTTE. Yes, I read it. It was very affable.

DICK. And now apparently Pritchard has repented and done the decent thing by sending back the gun.

DAVID. You really should hand it over to the police, Mr. Tompion.

JANE. No, no. Don't do that. It's such a useful thing to have about the house. Burglars. Give it to me, if you don't want it. I'll take it home with pleasure.

DICK. I agree with Jane. Don't give it up. The police would probably ask awkward questions.

JANE. And anyhow, why should they have it? Imagine giving them a valuable present like that.

TOMPION. Well . . . I think I'll keep it as a trophy. I'll hang it here by my table.

DICK. Yes, good! And you can fire it off at the end of every ten thousand words.

CHARLOTTE. Are you going to send any message of acknowledgment to Pritchard?

TOMPION. I hadn't thought of it. A neatly worded telegram of thanks?

CHARLOTTE. No, he'd not appreciate it. Send him just those gardening scissors. He'd like them as a trophy.

JANE. Clever Charlotte. Yes, Mr. Tompion, do send them! Look, I'll wrap them for you. You needn't write anything at all. Here's paper and string all ready.

DICK. Just enclose your card.

TOMPION. Very well; it's an amusing exchange. (*Produces his card. They all help to tie the parcel, laughing.*)

CURTAIN

Scene III

(In the rough at a neighbouring links, the following day. David *and* Charlotte *looking for a ball. They are carrying their own clubs.* Charlotte *kicks the ball up from a tussock.* David's *back is turned. She picks it up furtively, drops it into her bag and goes on looking.)*

David *(testily)*. What possessed you to slice your drive into a wilderness like this, Charlotte?

Charlotte. Just dishonesty, learned from watching you. I always get fed up after about six holes. I want to talk. *(Signals to golfers behind to pass through.)*

David. This is no place to talk. You can't sit out at golf.

Charlotte *(sits down)*. Cigarette?

David. Thanks. I can't escape, I see.

Charlotte. Anyhow, I've found the ball and picked it up. And you didn't drive at all. So why shouldn't we stop for a bit?

David. There's nothing to talk about. You know there's nothing.

Charlotte. Oh, *isn't* there? Look here, I'll say it out at once. Why did you write and ask Dorothy to marry you?

David *(gets up, takes a ball and club, and answers her in a defiant schoolboy way, between putts, without looking at her)*. What do you mean, *why?* Anybody else want to marry me? You, for instance?

Charlotte. You can't play it that way, Dishonest David. I know all about you from Dick. I guessed and asked him wasn't it so; and he said yes, you *were* that way.

David. I don't know what you're getting at. Let's play some more golf. I'll allow you to drop your ball without forfeit.

Charlotte. You're a pretty poor liar, David. I mean, well, that you have no romantic feelings for people of the opposite sex. That's right, isn't it?

(He does not answer: takes out a driver and practices a swing.)

Good Heavens, it's nothing to be ashamed of.

David *(mutters)*. No . . . it's the way one's born.

CHARLOTTE. Then why are you going to marry Dorothy?

DAVID. What business is it of yours?

CHARLOTTE. David, do behave. I'm not bullying you. Really. I'm just asking for information. You see, I'm that way myself. I'm sort of involved.

DAVID (*puts down his club*). By Jove, are you, Charlotte? I rather suspected you were.

CHARLOTTE. You said just now 'it's the way one's born.' Do you believe that?

DAVID. I meant that it's no crime — just a misfortune. You do agree, Charlotte?

CHARLOTTE. What *I* mean is, do you think that it's something one's born with or something that happens to one, say, at school? Something that can be got over?

DAVID. Well, of course, *that's* the important question. Probably there are two types. The congenital and the acquired. That's what's usually said. But I don't know.

CHARLOTTE. We neither of us look congenitals, do we? (*They laugh.*)

DAVID. I've always wanted to talk with a woman who was like that.

CHARLOTTE. Well, I'll talk. I'll tell you my story if you like.

DAVID. Yes, please do.

CHARLOTTE. You know that at all girls' schools there's that sort of thing always going on. Everyone has crushes on the elder girls or the younger mistresses — you know — giving flowers and being jealous and keeping diaries about how often one saw the adored one and writing sentimental poetry. But it ends as soon as one leaves school and begins to meet men; or even before. Only the mistresses — you'd laugh if you knew the common-room life of a big girls' school — they keep it up. There's a sort of competition as to which mistress can have the most girls romantic about her — a jealous counting of bouquets. It grows on them and becomes an obsession; they see no men, and don't want to marry and lose their jobs. Of course it's all *silly,* with a semireligious side to it.

DAVID. You mean nothing — er — serious ever happens?

CHARLOTTE. Practically never. Girls aren't pigs like little boys;

they're just kittenish little beasts. And no mistress would think of . . . I mean if you read the police court news you find scores of cases of boys' schoolmasters behaving like swine. Little pigs end up as swine. Kittenish little beasts just end up as old cats. Anyhow, in girls' schools everyone sneaks, so it couldn't be kept a secret if it did.

DAVID. I've always wondered about girls' schools.

CHARLOTTE. Well, I'll tell you what happened at mine. Mine was just the exception. It was a big expensive one and supposed to be faithfully run on the Eton system. That's a good joke to play on girls, isn't it?

DAVID. Yes, I should have thought one Eton was enough glory for England.

CHARLOTTE. I had a hopeless crush on an elder girl. She was a member of our imitation 'Pop.' She was Captain of the Boats, too. (Yes, we even had that.) I was sixteen and she was eighteen. Oh, she was lovely. She was Irish. We used to exchange notes whenever we got a chance. I was in another house from hers, but I saw her a lot — I coxed the school boat. Well, the notes got more and more — of course, absolutely what's called *innocent* — but more and more extravagant. She used to begin hers 'My darling little wife,' and I began mine, 'My darling husband.' Silly! Are you bored?

DAVID (*who has his putter out again*). No, indeed not.

CHARLOTTE. She only kissed me once, almost by mistake. Well, one day — I got expelled.

DAVID. You! What on earth for?

CHARLOTTE. Because *she* got expelled. For something else. I mean she was *really* like that. I didn't know she was. They found my letters to her, so naturally they suspected 'the worst' (*makes a face*).

DAVID. Wouldn't they take your denials?

CHARLOTTE. I didn't know what all the fuss was about. I admitted that she'd kissed me and said that I liked it, and that it was none of their business anyway and that I didn't give a damn for them and their carpet-slipper spies and that I was glad to be expelled with Bridget. They didn't like that.

DAVID. So that's the story. And I suppose since that shock you've stayed temperamentally where it hit you. Arrested emotional development?

CHARLOTTE. Maybe it's that. Maybe it isn't. That's what I'm anxious to know. What was your story?

DAVID. There wasn't any shock. The thing was more progressive with me. I was at — well, a rotten public school where the fees were £100 a term and nearly everyone was a pig. Except me. I was pious, not to say priggish, my time at school. I was very good-looking as a kid and the bloods were buzzing round all the time. I was frightened by the business at first: after a while I liked the sense of power it gave me. I . . . are you bored?

CHARLOTTE. No, go on.

DAVID. Well, I got sort of minxish and flirtatious like a society belle. I kept my innocence — but only technically. Do you despise me, Charlotte?

CHARLOTTE. I do rather, but go on.

DAVID. Well, nothing happened except that I eventually became a blood myself and had romantic feelings for the smaller boys; but somehow I never became a pig.

CHARLOTTE. And you went to Cambridge. Why didn't you recover there?

DAVID. I got in with a set of aesthetes. We were all very handsome fellows. Amateur theatricals, music, poetry. They called us the Swans. I was up for two years and then . . .

CHARLOTTE. Well, then the War. Surely in the War . . . ?

DAVID. That's another part of life that isn't generally known. Do you know how a platoon of men will absolutely worship a good-looking, gallant young officer? If he's a bit shy of them and decent to them, they get a crush on him. He's a being apart; an officer's uniform is most attractive compared with the rough, shapeless private's uniform. He becomes a sort of military queen bee.

CHARLOTTE. And his drilling them encourages the feeling?

DAVID (nods). Of course, they don't realize exactly what's happening, neither does he; but it's a very, very strong romantic link. That's why I had the best platoon and then the best company in the battalion. My men adored me and were showing off all the time before the other companies. They didn't bring me flowers. They killed Germans for me instead and drilled like angels. It was an intoxication for them; and for me. And then —

CHARLOTTE. Then you had romantic feelings for Dick.

DAVID. He's never encouraged them. Of course he's the best friend I ever had, and I wouldn't have that spoiled.

CHARLOTTE. Tell me, David, have you ever tried giving way to your . . . to your obsession?

DAVID (*carefully putting down a stymie and playing it with a mashie, answers, not looking at her*). No, of course not. What about you?

CHARLOTTE (*staring gloomily at her nails*). No, of course not!

DAVID. Anyhow, it was all so unsatisfactory that I got desperate and decided to fall in love with a girl.

CHARLOTTE. And you chose Dorothy because she's so like Dick. And because being a doctor she has a superficial hospital hardness and antisentimentality. And because she's rather boyish looking. Right?

DAVID. But, most important, she's very much in love with me. That makes it easier. She confessed it to Dick. I really believe I'm going to fall in love with her.

CHARLOTTE. Is it fair to her? Suppose, when it comes to the point, you feel a wave of disgust for her?

DAVID. Dishonest David is clever enough to hide it if he does. (*Sits down.*)

CHARLOTTE. Look here, David. I'll be quite frank. I have just the same suppressed romantic feelings for Dorothy as you have for Dick.

DAVID. You're jealous of *me*? (*Laughs mirthlessly.*)

CHARLOTTE. I am. My stupid Dorothy got it all wrong: she thought I was jealous of *her*. But I'll tell you something else to square things between us. Your clever Dick's in love with me.

DAVID. O hell, is he? Of course, I knew you were together a lot.

CHARLOTTE. You're jealous of me? (*Laughs mirthlessly too.*)

DAVID. Yes. I mean, no! I'll try not to be if you won't be jealous of me. Are you going to marry him?

CHARLOTTE. When he asks me.

DAVID. He hasn't yet?

CHARLOTTE. He hasn't yet, because I haven't given him the chance. But I know just what he feels for me. Dick's been a damned good friend. If I give him the chance he will. Of course, it's easier for a woman to pretend to have feelings than for a man. The man is expected to do the crude work of loving. The woman's part is more subtle. So the experiment . . .

DAVID (*angry, jumping up*). I refuse to have Dick made the subject of your experiments. He's too good for that. It's a dirty trick.

CHARLOTTE (*angry, jumping up too*). And what about your trick on Dorothy? Look here, you keep away from Dorothy, and I'll keep away from Dick.

DAVID (*scowling*). I'm not quitting now. Besides (*recovers himself*), come back about the dirty trick. You admire Dick, and Dorothy's in love with me. Why should we deny them what they want of us? Besides, I'm hoping it may end happily anyhow.

CHARLOTTE. *I'm* all right with Dick. It's you I'm not sure about. Besides, Dick and I aren't fools. Dorothy is. She's a qualified doctor but she's amazingly ignorant of what a girl of twenty-seven should know. From your point of view, of course, that's a gain. It gives you time to adjust. But I wish — oh, David, I wish you wouldn't marry her. I can't bear to think of her marriage being a ghastly failure. Really it's you and I who ought to get married. Wouldn't it be more honest to try our experiments on each other? You know, I tried to make you fall in love with me once. Shall we?

DAVID. Too cold-blooded. Besides, they'd never forgive us. Besides, I can be — I can try to be in love with Dorothy because she's Dick's sister. And the same with you and Dick, because of Dorothy. Our only hope of becoming normal members of society is to bridge the difficulty like that.

CHARLOTTE. Poor David! Well, good luck!

DAVID. And good luck, poor Charlotte! (*They shake hands.*)

CHARLOTTE. No more jealousies? (*They both sit down.*)

DAVID. But it's a rotten thing to be like us, isn't it?

CHARLOTTE. Yes . . . it's humiliating. I can't even work up that sentimental salt-of-the-earth feeling that you men victims work up for yourselves; as if this misfortune were something to be secretly proud of.

DAVID. Well, after all, Charlotte, there was Socrates and Caesar and Shakespeare and Michelangelo. And on your side, there was Sappho.

CHARLOTTE. Damn that woman! Bridget used to talk about Sappho like that. (*Very bitterly.*) David, sometimes I wish I were just an ordinary old-fashioned prostitute with an honest passion for ordinary, low, ugly, knobbly, hairy men. If you *knew* how the thought of men sickens me! God, I would give my soul to be in love with Dick in the way I am with Dorothy. You see, David, Dorothy's a fool. That's my tragedy. And I have to kid myself all the time that she isn't. Sweet as sugar, but oh, such an almighty fool! Dick's got a mind. He's real.

DAVID. It's just the other way round with me. If Dick were an ordinary, light-hearted, stupid creature like Dorothy, it would be easier for me. I like to boss people I'm in love with, to have them look up to me. But Dick knows I'm a fool and bosses me instead. I don't like it. He overreached himself the other day at the time of that . . . that revolver business. I decided to switch over from him to Dorothy. Dorothy's perfect for me.

CHARLOTTE. You mean she would be, if she weren't a woman. O David! Let's stop talking. If we talk any more we'll change our minds again. There's nobody at the tee. Let's drop balls and start from here again. All square, aren't we?

DAVID. Now for two good shots out of the rough.

(*They drop balls and address them.*)

CURTAIN

ACT II

Scene I

(*An oyster bar in the West End, the following night.* David *and* 'Another' *are sitting at a table together talking in undertones. A waiter comes up from behind* David, *who is seated facing the audience and gives a wink and vulgar grimace at* 'Another,' *whose back is turned to the audience and who never shows his face.* 'Another' *is a youth of seventeen or eighteen dressed somewhat effeminately.*)

David (*to* Waiter). It *is* the first of September, isn't it?

Waiter. Yes, sir, September One. And a very good crop at Whitstable this year. Nice and fat. How many dozen?

David. I'll have one to start with. What about you?

Another. Another, please, mister.

David. Two dozen then. I'll have a pint of Black Velvet. What about you?

Another. Another, please, mister.

David. One for me and another for 'Another.' Also brown bread and butter.

Waiter. And I'm another. (*Again grimaces at* Another.) Very good, sir.

(*Exit* Waiter.)

David. Look here, 'Another,' I oughtn't to be seen in here with you. I've a number of respectable friends. The theatre crowds are just coming out. If anyone comes in here and I kick you, clear out. I'll meet you across the street as soon as I can get away.

Another. What about me oysters?

David. You can take them with you in your handkerchief and swallow them outside.

(Waiter *returns with oysters, Black Velvet, etc.*)

Hell! Here comes someone already. (*Sees him in the mirror.*)

Another. Me oysters! Quick!

(*The* Waiter *holds them out of reach.* 'Another' *grabs at the tray.* Waiter *pushes him away with his foot.*)

Waiter. Nah then, Greedy!

DAVID. Get out; at once!

'ANOTHER,' *whose face can still not be seen, makes a gesture of despair and bolts out through the door at left, back. From right, back,* DICK *slowly enters, smiling.*

DICK. Hul*lo!* David. Surprise. Who was that friend of yours who bolted just now?

DAVID. Oh! casual acquaintance. Odd fellow. Painter, you know. Invited me to have oysters with him and as soon as they arrived dashed off and left me to eat them alone.

(*The* WAITER *has been setting the table. Smiles.*)

DICK. Shy, probably? Saw me coming?

DAVID. Artistic temperament. It doesn't matter. You can manage his helping, can't you?

DICK. Sure. (*Takes* 'ANOTHER'S' *chair, but shifts it round a bit so that he can be seen and heard by the audience.*)

(*A long pause while they eat.*)

By the way, David, Charlotte and I have come to a sort of understanding.

DAVID. I thought something like that was imminent. Feeling happy, oh, so happy?

DICK. Same as usual. Don't be vulgar: I'm not getting married.

DAVID. Not getting married?

DICK. You didn't really think I meant that?

DAVID. Why not? You're in love with Charlotte, aren't you?

DICK. 'In love with.' All right; if you like to put it that way.

DAVID. But . . . er . . . you're not proposing to make her your mistress, are you?

DICK. Mistress! What a magnificently archaic vocabulary you've got! People who are 'in love with' each other, couple and probably live together. That's all there is to it these days. I didn't ask Charlotte to *marry* me. I simply told her what I felt about her.

DAVID. What's wrong with *mistress?*

DICK. It's a dated word; it goes with 'protector.' It belongs to the period before the catastrophe.

DAVID. What catastrophe?

DICK. When the bottom dropped out of things. I told you about that the other day.

DAVID. Oh, that again.

DICK. Yes, that all the time. You seem to think that it's a joke of mine.

DAVID (*waves impatiently*). Doesn't Charlotte want a wedding ceremony?

DICK. Charlotte would say that it didn't matter one way or the other; she might be ready to go through a ceremony for the sake of convenience, that's all. She's rather wanting in that sort of personal morality. But she knows my feelings well enough not to raise the question with me.

DAVID. Personal morality? Do you mean that you have a moral scruple against marrying? What is it? Don't you want to feel bound to her?

DICK. You'll ask me next if my intentions are strictly honourable. Really, David, you're not my sort.

DAVID. Well, what's wrong with marriage as a social convenience? I'm not talking about its sanctity. That's for people like your sister Dorothy. She's the sort of person who'd insist on a church ceremony.

DICK. Once its sanctity goes, I don't see what you mean by its social convenience. Can't you understand that since the catastrophe there's not only no more sanctity, there's no more society either; not *really,* I mean.

DAVID. Oh, that's metaphysics. Be practical for once. Think of hotels. You've got to sign the hotel register. 'Miss Charlotte Arden, Mr. Richard Tompion' — that would look a bit awkward, wouldn't it?

DICK. Hotelkeepers don't believe in the sanctity of marriage any more than you do. They only politely pretend to believe that their clients believe in marriage. I've never met a hotel porter to whom you couldn't say: 'I'm the Emperor Solomon and this is the Queen of Sheba. Please preserve our incognito in the register.' In most hotels you don't even have to take that trouble. What other social convenience besides hotels?

DAVID. Well, there's the possibility of children.

DICK. My good David, what legal or social disqualification do bastards have nowadays?

DAVID. Well, there's the name, for a start.

DICK. A child can be registered in any name it chooses. And?

DAVID. And, and . . . I don't know . . . I had some idea that illegitimacy disqualified you from voting . . . doesn't it?

DICK (*bursts out laughing*). And from sitting in the House of Lords. Go on, David, you're in form.

DAVID (*half smiling, half annoyed*). Well, anyhow, if you live openly with someone who isn't your wife, you can't carry on a lot of the professions. Doctoring — soldiering — politics —

DICK. Or even the Church. The four prime precatastrophic professions — the four that abandoned themselves to an orgy of usefulness during the War to prove that they still had firm ground under their feet. These are debating-society arguments. Got any real ones?

DAVID. Well, if you have a mistress . . .

DICK. Mistress?

DAVID. I don't see why I shouldn't use the word. If you have a mistress, everyone immediately starts thinking of it as purely a sex relation and it must be damned embarrassing. If you're married, once the honeymoon's over, everyone assumes that all the romance is evaporated and it's a sort of business partnership.

DICK. Marriage as an enemy of romance. True.

DAVID. Anyway, Dick. The fact is that there's no sensible argument in favour of marriage, except that it's a universal habit and the only people who live together for long *without* a ceremony are the people who can't be married because one or both are already married to someone else. There *is* a sort of unanimity about marriage — a popular sanctity, if not a divine one.

DICK. What puzzles me, David, is why *you*, of all people, are defending marriage.

DAVID. Well, Dick — er — the fact is, I'm going to marry Dorothy.

DICK. *You*, David? Not really! Sudden metabolism? I can't believe it.

DAVID. Fact, I assure you. Ask Dorothy.

DICK. But wasn't that fellow I saw you with just now . . .

DAVID. By Jove, Dick. There's your father with a woman. They've seen us. Now they're slinking out again!

DICK. What! Protector and mistress. I've heard of her, but never seen her. We mustn't let them escape.

(*Jumps up and after a while returns with* TOMPION *and* ELIZABETTA BEHRENS, *a blonde. They are both in evening dress and* TOMPION *slightly,* MRS. BEHRENS *considerably, drunk.* TOMPION *is on the defensive and ashamed at first.* MRS. BEHRENS *is expansive and thoroughly at her ease.*)

TOMPION (*blustering a little*). Why, fellows, I didn't recognize you. Let me introduce Mrs. Behrens. Mrs. Behrens, my younger son Dick — my friend Casselis — David Casselis the architect.

(DICK *shakes hands noncommittally,* DAVID *nervously.*)

DAVID. I'm going to find the waiter and get him to bring more oysters. (*Takes his hat off the peg and goes out.*)

DICK. I thought you were in Manchester addressing the Students' Fellowship?

(*They sit down,* DICK *in* DAVID's *chair, facing audience, the other two left and right of him.*)

TOMPION. That's right. I *was* supposed to be. But they — at the last moment they wired, postponing it. And I accidentally ran into Elizabetta Behrens — you remember she was a friend of your mother's, Dick. She had room for me in a box at His Majesty's, so I joined her party. Just come out.

DICK. Funny I didn't see you. I was in the stalls.

MRS. BEHRENS. I felt a bit faint halfway through the first scene and Cecil took me out. We had a few drinks at my place. Then we got hungry and came along here. So you're Cecil's son. Funny to think of Cecil with a grown-up son. The one who writes? Let me see: novels, isn't it?

DICK. No. (*Calmly.*)

MRS. BEHRENS. Plays?

DICK. No. (*Calmly.*)

MRS. BEHRENS. Oh, then short stories: of course.

DICK. No. (*Same tone.*)

MRS. BEHRENS. Dick-may-I-call-you-Dick, you're very secretive. What *do* you write, then?

DICK. Oh, writings.

MRS. BEHRENS. Then I'm dying of curiosity to read your writings. Cecil, why haven't you ever shown me any?

DICK. My father's more or less illiterate. But they are all exposed for public sale. I can't prevent you from buying them if you must.

MRS. BEHRENS. Cecil, your Dick is very amusing.

TOMPION. He gets a bit of a bore after a time. He's typical of his generation. No manners. No respect. Stupendous conceit. Dick, where's David?

DICK. Slunk off. He had a pal waiting outside.

TOMPION. Never even sent the waiter. David's another beauty. Hi, waiter!

MRS. BEHRENS. I like Dick's directness. I'm going to ask him questions. I'm going to learn things.

(WAITER *comes up.*)

TOMPION. A good champagne and two dozen oysters!

WAITER. Very good, sir.

(*Exit.*)

MRS. BEHRENS (*leaning over to* DICK *and clasping his hands, which he does not withdraw*). Dick, surely you wouldn't hate me, for your mother's sake?

DICK. You have been introduced to me as her friend; though I don't remember her ever mentioning you to me.

TOMPION. Fact is, Dick, there was a misunderstanding. Your mother was a very jealous woman; got hold of the wrong end of the stick.

DICK. No, Mrs. Behrens, I dislike you for direct personal reasons; I don't carry on family feuds.

MRS. BEHRENS. Oh, this is fine. What reasons? I implore you to tell me. Don't you like my face?

DICK (*looks at her critically, disengaging his hands*). No. Neither your face, your voice, the way you dress, the scent you use, or the questions you ask. I just *don't like* you.

MRS. BEHRENS (*not at all hurt*). Cecil, I'm beginning to believe that your younger son's a genius.

DICK. God forbid. *That* one's a genius (*nodding at* TOMPION).
   (WAITER *enters with oysters and champagne: serves and then exit.*)

MRS. BEHRENS (*claps her hands laughing*). Cecil, I'm convinced of it now. You'll have to look to your laurels. Your son Dick's a great man. Do you know, Dick, genius attracts me in a very peculiar way, particularly when I'm slightly drunk. I always fall in love with man-of-geniuses. Like some women who go all goosey when they see naval uniform. Can't explain it. Just nature working. If I read your writings and find you're a real genius I'll fall in love with you too; however much you hate me. (*Nestles close to him. He does not repulse her.*) Recite me one of your writings. Your best!

TOMPION. Elizabetta, you mustn't behave like that. We're known here.

DICK. Oh, *she's* all right. Have another drink, Elizabetta. (*Pours it out.*) Are you in love with dear old Cecil?

MRS. BEHRENS. Then you *do* love me a little? You're jealous.

TOMPION. Elizabetta. Behave! I insist. Anyhow there's nothing for you there. This generation's no good, no good at all. Dick's typical of it. They don't possess any deep emotions. They don't know what Passion is when they love, any more than they know what Style is when they write. They're soft. They don't hunt hard, drink hard, love hard, work hard, do anything hard.

MRS. BEHRENS. Oh, Cecil, that's very unfair. They fought *very, very* hard in the War!

TOMPION. And they think that gives 'em a right to sag for the rest of their lives. No sense of drama, no religious enthusiasm, no strong religious doubts even. Just nothing. And nine out of ten are perverts. You're one, aren't you, Dick?

DICK (*casually*). Don't know. Never tried. (*To* MRS. BEHRENS.) How long and hard have you loved your honest, hard-riding Cecil? Did you know him when he wore staff-uniform and went to lecture in America on British War Poets?

MRS. BEHRENS. No, that was before my time. Did he look handsome?

DICK. Kingly. He wore his spurs upside down, half the time.

MRS. BEHRENS. We've loved hard for seven years, haven't we, my darling? (*Shifts round to* TOMPION.) That's why Cecil's always so broke. I'm fearfully extravagant.

DICK. I've always wondered where the money went. But you must have been a great comfort to him.

MRS. BEHRENS. Irreplaceably. He puts me in all his books. Can't you recognize me, now you've met me, as the leading female in his *Sussex Cycle?* I'm in every book, slightly disguised, of course. I'm Lavinia in the first, Lavinia's daughter in the second, Phoebe, a little, in the third. Esmeralda . . .

DICK. I've never read *Sussex Cycle*. Is it good?

MRS. BEHRENS. Dick, it's wonderful. Do you honestly mean you haven't? What a feast in store for you. Come round to my flat — number 5, Iddesleigh Gardens, N.W. 3 — and I'll show you the best passages. I have them marked. Cecil and I often gloat over them together, don't we, darling?

(DICK *notes the address.*)

You *will* come, won't you?

DICK. I can't imagine a more amusing way of spending a wet afternoon.

TOMPION. Dick!

DICK. Sir?

TOMPION (*very angry*). Dick, I'm going to raise your allowance by a hundred pounds.

DICK. On what grounds? Don't let me rob Mrs. Behrens.

TOMPION. Because I'm sorry for you. You're pitiful: you can't write, not for little apples you can't. You can't even produce your bad stuff in quantity. And apparently it's your only livelihood.

DICK. True. But why an extra hundred?

TOMPION. With money you can afford to travel. Go to Paris. Go to Australia. Go to Los Angeles. Go any damned place where you please. Buy a bit of life there. Broaden your horizon. Come back a man.

DICK. Father, what's a hundred? Make it another hundred and

fifty. You can't buy much for a hundred, these days. Can you spare it, though? Can he spare it really, Elizabetta?

MRS. BEHRENS. He's an old miser. He got two thousand advance for his last novel. He must have pots put away somewhere. Dick, if you promise to come and read *Sussex Cycle* with me one day soon, I'll see you get it. You won't hate me then, will you?

DICK. Fine. Another drink. Oh, by the way, Elizabetta . . . I have a serious question to ask you . . . do you believe in the popular sanctity of marriage? David Casselis does.

(*They all drink,* MRS. BEHRENS *and* DICK *laughing together,* TOMPION *drunkenly aloof.*)

CURTAIN

SCENE II

(*The library at the Tompions',* DICK *and* CHARLOTTE: DICK *sitting (right) in an armchair.* CHARLOTTE *standing (left) at the magazine table, turning over the leaves, with her back to him.*)

DICK. I've been telling David about you and me and he actually asked when we were going to get married.

CHARLOTTE. And?

DICK. Well, of course, I laughed. But what could you have said to have given him that idea?

CHARLOTTE (*turns round*). I only mentioned *marriage* to David — because — sort of habit I suppose — I know you'd never get *married* to anyone — I just used it loosely for a permanent togetherness of you and me — and you're not angry?

(DICK *is silent.*)

You *do* want me, Dick, don't you? For keeps?

(DICK *does not answer. He gets up from the chair, puts his cigarette in an ash tray, comes very slowly towards her. She looks nervous. He embraces her. After awhile she wriggles free.*)

DICK (*smiles*). All the same, darling, you don't seem to want *me* much.

CHARLOTTE. I've had no practice. Never been embraced by a man before.

DICK. Well, the idea is to be responsive, not just complaisant. Let's try again.

(*She assents, not eagerly.*)

CHARLOTTE. Sorry I can't do better than that, Dick. The fact is, it's an off day for me. I ate something at lunch . . .

DICK. Poor sweetheart. Never mind, there's all the time there is. Going to be all right?

CHARLOTTE. I think so, Dick. Just a bit sick, that's all.

DICK. Come and sit here with me, anyway, and talk?

CHARLOTTE. I'd rather not move, thanks. Sorry to spoil the first moment of romance, Dick. You know I love you, don't you?

DICK. Romance be buttered! Charlotte, dearest, how old are you?

CHARLOTTE. Twenty-seven, and never kissed a man in my life before. Unenterprising, isn't it?

DICK. Oh, look here! Speaking of kissing men, Charlotte; what's David marrying Dorothy for? Is he really changed and all right?

CHARLOTTE. First tell me, do you love me?

(DICK *nods, smiling.*)

Will you *swear* you won't tell David or Dorothy I told you what I'm going to tell you now?

DICK. Swear!

CHARLOTTE. Well, *he's just trying to get over his trouble —* that's all.

DICK. You mean he's not really in love with her?

CHARLOTTE. He likes her. She's in love with him. He wants her to normalize him; he's ashamed to go on any more as he is.

DICK. Who told you?

CHARLOTTE. He did himself . . . Do you really love me, Dick?

(*He nods again.*)

Swear?

DICK. Swear! Why do you want me to go on saying so? What's the doubt about?

CHARLOTTE. I might as well tell you at once and get it over. I'm like David myself, only the opposite.

DICK. You mean you used to be until you decided you were in love with me?

(She does not answer, but smiles.)

Oh! *(A long pause while he looks searchingly at her.)* Now I'm going to ask you questions. Do you really love me, Charlotte?

CHARLOTTE *(in a faint voice).* I . . . I love you very much, Dick . . . better than any man I know . . . I admire you . . . You've been damned good to me.

DICK. To hell with all that. Do you *love* me? Physically, for instance?

CHARLOTTE *(still faint).* I like you to be in love with me, Dick. I want you to be.

DICK *(calmly).* In fact, it comes in the end to this, you're playing the same game with me as David is with Dorothy? That so?

(She does not answer.)

Admit it. It's important.

CHARLOTTE. No, it's not the same, quite. I'm a woman, David's a man. And you said you — you *swore* you loved me.

DICK. Did I?

CHARLOTTE. Just now, Dick; you know you did. I'm offering myself to you, that's all.

(She stands up and holds out her arms for him. He rises and comes towards her, attracted against his will. Suddenly he stops, recovers, retrieves his cigarette from the ash tray, relights it, sits down.)

DICK. I don't accept presents from strangers.

CHARLOTTE. That's too strong, Dick. You can't make a stranger of me.

(Pause.)

DICK. I want to get this straight, Charlotte. Didn't you like me kissing you at all? Not *at all?*

CHARLOTTE. I liked to feel that you were enjoying yourself.

DICK. Not good enough. It disgusted you.

CHARLOTTE. The disgust will wear off.

DICK. I'm not going to give it a chance. It takes two to make a sex life. You'd never be able to do more than politely switch your mind off when I was kissing you. Dentist-chair technique!

CHARLOTTE. But, Dick, if you *really* loved me, you'd help me over my obsession, gradually.

DICK. Never mind whether I really love you or not. What does 'love' mean, anyway? It's a dead-world idea like 'marriage.' All I know is that I'm not going to *live* with you, just because you need me for hygienic reasons.

CHARLOTTE. I'm beautiful. You want me. I won't bind you in any way. In this dead world, why not take gladly what you can get free? Please, Dick! (*Comes closer.*)

DICK. No. What one gets free isn't worth anything.

CHARLOTTE. You can't help yourself.

DICK. *Can't* I?

(*She embraces him.*)

(*He is apparently unmoved.*) Not good enough. Sorry, Charlotte. Run away and practise some more.

CHARLOTTE. You mean that you really don't want me after all?

DICK. Dear Charlotte. I'll be like a sister to you. I always have been, haven't I?

CHARLOTTE. I'm not accustomed to being refused things.

DICK. Well, you can't force me to live with you, can you?

CHARLOTTE. *Can't* I? Look here, Dick. The offer of me, unconditional me, is open till midnight tonight. Then it's withdrawn.

DICK. Well?

CHARLOTTE. If you don't take me, I'll give myself to the first man who'll have me.

DICK. Oh, well! If just *any* man will do to help you over your obsession (or whatever you call it), and that's all you care about — go off now and get just anyone. And thank you for your frankness. Don't trouble to wait until midnight, if you're in a hurry.

CHARLOTTE. Please, Dick. Don't get angry. Be sensible. I like you very, very much. I love everything you do. I honestly believe that once I got accustomed to the strangeness of it I could fall in love with you.

DICK. Talk doesn't help. Cut it out.

CHARLOTTE. Please, Dick, think it over. I really mean that about the offer. It's still open — till midnight.

DICK. Oh, I hope you pick a beauty! Why the Devil aren't you content to remain as God made you?

(*A knock.*)

Oh, come in!

(*Enter* BUTLER.)

BUTLER. Excuse me, Mr. Dick. There's a short, sturdy gentleman at the front door; wearing ready-made clothing. He's highly excited and wishes to see Mr. Tompion. I have assured him that the master is out. But he refuses to credit me.

DICK. Didn't he give his name?

BUTLER. No, Mr. Dick; he says that I am not to mind what his name is.

DICK. Then please inform him that his name is Mr. Richard Pritchard, and that Mr. Richard Tompion is in and would be glad to see him.

BUTLER. Very good, Mr. Dick.

(*Exit.*)

CHARLOTTE. Damn the man coming now. Dick, darling . . . What does he want?

DICK. Oh, he wants to assault my father. I don't blame him.

(*A knock. Enter* BUTLER.)

BUTLER. Mr. Richard Pritchard!

(*Enter* PRITCHARD, *a little, dark, nervous man, in ready-made clothes, a bowler hat held awkwardly, a flower in his buttonhole, a sensitive face. Welsh accent.*)

DICK. Hullo, Pritchard. I've been waiting to meet you. I'm Richard Tompion. This is Miss Charlotte Arden.

(PRITCHARD *shakes hands. His manner is a mixture of anger and nervous apology. He evidently counted on seeing* TOMPION *and had a speech rehearsed.*)

PRITCHARD. Where's Cecil Tompion? I want that rotten fellow. He's grossly insulted me.

DICK. Heavens, he's insulted you too? That's very bad. (*To* CHARLOTTE.) The way these so-called famous men-of-letters carry on is absolutely disgraceful, Charlotte, isn't it? Of course, my father's by far the worst of them all. (*To* PRITCHARD.) How did he insult *you*, Pritchard?

PRITCHARD (*produces a newspaper parcel, tied with red wool, from his pocket, and unwraps the gardening scissors*). Well, now what do you think of that? He sent me that, with his card.

DICK. How's that an insult?

PRITCHARD. A pair of broken bloody garden scissors!

DICK. My poor father's losing his wits. Why garden scissors? It seems rather a poor joke to me. Doesn't it to you, Charlotte?

CHARLOTTE. I don't see it myself.

PRITCHARD. He wrote a long critique of my new book in some foolish new paper. A mock-praising review — I'm not the man to be gulled by his fine phrases. He was laughing at me. Serious, he was!

CHARLOTTE. Yes, I read the review. It was a stinker.

PRITCHARD (*eagerly*). Yes, ma'am. An utterly stinking critique. All about my artless genius and childlike innocence of phrase — me, who's ninety-nine times more of a man and a poet than he.

DICK. Oh, at least ninety-nine times. Practically cent per cent, in fact.

PRITCHARD. Aye, and he had the confounded impudence to hope that, in future, I would prune more in my longer pieces.

DICK. That was a nasty one: coming from him!

PRITCHARD. Aye, and the book was called *The Gardener's Boy*, and see! he sends me these bloody, broken gardening scissors as a symbol.

DICK. It's a dirty shame. Isn't it, Charlotte?

CHARLOTTE. The man ought to be beaten up. If only Mr. Pritchard knew the way he's treated *us!* (*Produces a handkerchief.*)

DICK (*glances puzzled at her, but decides to play the part she has assigned him*). Simply refused to let us marry. Threatened to cut off my allowance if I persisted.

CHARLOTTE. He wants to marry me himself.

PRITCHARD. Well, now, would you believe it!

CHARLOTTE (*into her handkerchief*). And I'll probably let him marry me if I can't marry Dick; I don't care what happens.

PRITCHARD. It's a damned shame!

DICK. Yes, and it's a great disappointment to me. But of course one can't oppose one's father, can one? Especially when one's dependent on him for one's income.

CHARLOTTE. And Dick does love me so.

DICK. And what's worse, all the time he keeps a mistress. You've probably seen her about with him. A beautiful woman with golden hair. Her name's Elizabetta Behrens. A great admirer of your work, by the way, Pritchard. I believe she hates him, really. I know she's afraid of him. He plans to marry Miss Arden and keep Elizabetta on as a side line.

PRITCHARD. What an unmitigated scoundrel! I don't pretend to be a very moral man. But at least I don't go masquerading as a Companion of bloody Honour. (*Passionately.*) Deoul, man! If I had a revolver, now, I'd shoot him like a rat, I would.

DICK. Good for you, sir! There's a revolver hanging up by that table. Would you like it? (*To* CHARLOTTE.) You don't think Mr. Pritchard would really shoot him, Charlotte, do you?

CHARLOTTE. Oh, yes, he would, I think.

(*To* PRITCHARD.) But wouldn't it be much more fun just to frighten him?

(PRITCHARD *has got the revolver down and is gingerly examining it.*)

Shoot the pipe out of his mouth. Put a hole through his silk hat. Give him a real good fright. It's what he needs. It's what he needs badly.

PRITCHARD. Is this his own weapon?

DICK. He claims it: that's the table where he writes.

PRITCHARD. (*grins*). Well, it's mine now, I shouldn't wonder. I'll swap it with him for these broken garden scissors. How do you use it? I've never before had a revolver in my hand in my life, no!

DICK. It's loaded. There's the safety catch. When you press that, it's ready to fire. You just pull the trigger. A steady squeezing motion of thumb and forefinger.

PRITCHARD (*excitedly*). Where'll I find him?

DICK. Probably with his mistress, in a flat, let me see. (*Consults his notebook.*) 5, Iddesleigh Gardens, N.W.3. You'll like Elizabetta Behrens; she's beautiful and also very cultivated. She knows some of your poems by heart. She recited them to me. Of course, she doesn't tell my father about this. I don't know what would happen if she did.

PRITCHARD. I can trust you both not to say a word?

CHARLOTTE. Not a word. And we'll swear the butler to silence too.

PRITCHARD. Most likely it will suffice the circumstances just to frighten him. But I'll keep this revolver handy, all the same.

DICK. Good luck in any case. And remember, don't say a word yourself about having been here.

PRITCHARD. Trust a Welshman! Goodbye, Richard Tompion. And goodbye, Miss Charlotte. (*Puts on his hat to take it off to her.*)

(*Exit.*)

DICK. Oh, so you've chosen my father, have you? Yes, he'll *have* you all right. But why *him?* Surely the world's full enough of men? Why not Pritchard? He'd be better by a long sight. Why not Denman? He's a good solid fellow.

CHARLOTTE (*pale with anger*). Why? Because your father's the man you dislike most in the world. Because when I marry him you'll always see him about with me. Because I *hate* you!

DICK. Charlotte, dear, don't be hysterical. What's this all about, anyway? Why do you *want* a man? Except as a friend, like me. You ought to make a virtue of your natural continence.

CHARLOTTE. That's my business. And I won't have you insulting me any more. You're so ghastly utterly selfish that you won't even accept my sacrifice. I was a fool to tell you about it. I was too decent.

DICK. Oh! sacrifice!

CHARLOTTE. Yes, of letting you enjoy me when I know you want me.

DICK. Well, I'll tell you this: I'm so selfish that it wouldn't be any enjoyment to me to enjoy you or anyone else who didn't enjoy me while I was enjoying them. That's why I don't deal with prostitutes. So you're going to *marry* my father, are you? Red carpet, bridal veil and bouquet, ring, organ, church register, cake, weeping relatives. Why *marry* him? If you want to make me jealous why not just flirt with him? You'd get a rise out of me on that even.

CHARLOTTE. Not final enough. Imagine me as Mrs. Cecil Tompion. Won't you like that?

DICK (*wavering*). I am absolutely, and finally, and irrevocably *damned* if I'm going to be blackmailed into giving in to you.

CHARLOTTE (*pleading*). Dick, dear. Only just a trial. To see if it's possible. A week end somewhere?

DICK (*recovers*). Charlotte, dear. Do you like me very, very much?

CHARLOTTE (*half crying*). Oh, Dick, I've just said I hate you.

DICK. Meaning that you want very, very much to love me, but just can't.

CHARLOTTE. Meaning . . . Oh, Dick . . . How I wish I were an ordinary, ordinary woman!

DICK. But you're not. Face it!

CHARLOTTE. You could help me to be.

DICK. I don't believe it. If you can't help shuddering when I kiss you now, it will be worse later. Let's cut out the physical side altogether. I'll live with you without that, if you like. We've been good friends.

CHARLOTTE (*angry again*). No. If you won't budge, I won't budge. It was a joke about your father, but, by God! I'll do it all the same.

DICK. It seems an unnecessarily disgusting way of committing suicide. Why not try the gas oven instead?

CHARLOTTE. Because I *hate* you. I hate you worse than ever. That's my last word. But I said till midnight, so I'll still give you till then.

DICK (*angry at last*). Goodbye, Charlotte. This is the end. Be a great man's wife and go to hell. It won't hurt me.

CURTAIN

Scene III

(*The tennis court at the Tompions' the following afternoon. Tables and chairs (central), a yew hedge (right). Part of the court can be seen on the left of the stage, with* Tompion *crouched up to the net, facing* Dorothy. Tompion's *partner,* Charlotte, *serves;* Dorothy *mis-hits.*)

Tompion. Oh, well *served,* partner. Magnificent. Game and — ! Want another, you girls? I told you Charlotte and I were invincible, didn't I?

Dorothy. You're always such a bad loser, father, that I'm glad when you occasionally win. Aren't *you* glad, Jane?

Jane. So long as I hit the ball hard once or twice I don't mind either way.

> (*They move off the court (right).* Tompion *actively leaps the net.*)

Tompion. You're as bad as young Dick; he even refuses to play with me now because I go all out to win. I can't understand you young people. You don't take even *games* seriously. Let's have the lemonade. I'm hot. And Jane, help me pull this table into the shade.

> (*They move the table, with the lemonade glasses on it. They sit around on wicker chairs,* Tompion *putting on his sweater, the girls powdering their faces.*)

Dorothy. Father did all the work. You were playing very wildly.

Charlotte. Was I? I'm not surprised. You see, I've a secret. Since this morning.

Dorothy. What is it, dear? Something to make you happy?

Charlotte. I could hardly hold my racquet straight.

Jane. That's the first time I've heard you admit you were happy, for about ten years.

Charlotte. Yes, that's right. You see, I'm going to get married at last.

Dorothy. Married! You, too, Charlotte! You're a dear sweet copycat! Oh, Charlotte, I *am* so pleased. (*Kisses her.*) Father!

> (Tompion *pretends to be busy lacing his shoes.*)

Did you hear that?

TOMPION. Hear what, my dear?

DOROTHY. Charlotte's going to marry Dick!

(TOMPION *grins*.)

JANE. How do you know it's Dick?

DOROTHY. Who else could it be? As a matter of fact, David told me yesterday it was imminent.

CHARLOTTE. Your David's a half-wit. He always gets things wrong. Me marry *Dick!* An utterly selfish person like him!

JANE. Dick selfish! You're crazy, Charlotte. How was Dick ever selfish? He's the best you'll ever get anyway, and I know he's wanted you for months. Who on earth else? You don't know any men besides him, anyway. Not well enough to marry.

TOMPION. Charlotte, my dear, this situation is getting a bit — well — embarrassing. The fact is, Jane, that Charlotte, I trust wisely, prefers maturity to callow youth.

DOROTHY. What on earth do you mean?

CHARLOTTE. I'm going to marry your father, Dorothy.

DOROTHY. Don't be utterly ridiculous. It *is* Dick, really, isn't it?

CHARLOTTE. I'm not joking.

TOMPION. No! honour bright, Dorothy. Charlotte's consented, after a hurricane wooing, to marry me. How do you like your new stepmother, Dorothy?

DOROTHY. Sorry, but I simply can't believe it. It's . . . it's like a sum that you *know* the answer to it is wrong. You can't find the mistake, but you *know* it's wrong. Charlotte, Dick's been in love with you — anyone could see it — since the spring. And now you suddenly go and marry father instead!

CHARLOTTE. If Dick felt like that, he ought to have asked me. He never did. And now your father and I have suddenly found that we're in love with each other. You can't expect me to waste my pity on Dick, can you?

DOROTHY. Oh, Charlotte, that *was* horrid of me. I *do* apologize. I was just confused. Sorry, father. It was so funny to think of the generations getting mixed, that's all.

JANE (*impulsively*). Yes, almost indecent. (*In confusion*.) I mean, I've always thought of Dick and Charlotte together, some-

how, these last six months. Of course . . . Mr. Tompion's very
charming: and still jumping tennis nets.

TOMPION. Thank you, Jane, for championing my cause. Yes,
there's life in the old bard yet.

DOROTHY. Does Dick know?

CHARLOTTE. Not definitely. But I hinted yesterday that I was
in love with your father, so it won't come as a surprise.

DOROTHY. Then he *did* ask you to marry him?

CHARLOTTE. No, not a word about marriage. Truthfully.

DOROTHY (*brightly*).Well, I'm going to cheer him up by telling
him that he needn't be disappointed. You're not much of a loss,
are you, darling? (*Laughs affectionately.*)

TOMPION (*with triumphant indulgence*). Poor old Poet Dick.
But he'll get over it. I always seem to be saying, 'Poor Old Dick'
these days. If it's not about his absurd ways of writing poetry or
his absurd critical views, it's about his gloomy old-old-mannish
outlook on life. I can forgive Charlotte for not wishing to tie up
with a fellow who's old and crabbed enough to be my grandfather. Support me, Charlotte!

CHARLOTTE. Why, of course, Mr. Tompion. I'm absolutely with
you.

TOMPION (*interposes*) — 'Cecil!'

CHARLOTTE. I'm weary to death of the so-called younger generation, Cecil. Especially the writers and their experimental tedi-
ousness. What does it all amount to? What has Dick to show?

JANE. Charlotte, you're a liar. You can't change your opinions
as quickly as that. Only two days ago you told me that Dick was
writing in the only way that it was honest to write nowadays.

CHARLOTTE. Perhaps I did. I felt it my duty to stick up for my
generation. But now that I've identified myself with a really
solid person like Cecil, that's quite unnecessary.

TOMPION. Charlotte's grown up at last, Jane. She sees reason.
Two or three years more and so will you. It wasn't that Charlotte
was taken in by Dick's literary acrobatics. It was just rebellious-
ness against the old tried ways of writing and thinking and behaving. You'd have accepted any charlatanry that was in revolt,

now wouldn't you? (*Tries to draw her on his knees. She stiffens, and with difficulty speaks naturally.*)

CHARLOTTE (*in a low voice*). No, Cecil, dear. Not in public, please!

DOROTHY. I think it's absolutely hateful the way that you two talk of Dick's work — at a time like this, too. I think you might at least leave *that* alone.

JANE. Good for you, Dorothy. I agree. Dick's a good poet, and not in the least a charlatan. You've only got to *look* at Dick to see that. Of course, he's *difficult;* one can't read him lazily like one can Mr. . . . well — say Richard Pritchard's poetry. Obviously it's difficult to write, and so it's difficult to read.

CHARLOTTE. Oh, I agree, Dick's *honest.* But what single poem of his will be found in a popular anthology a hundred years from now?

TOMPION. Oh, I don't know. (*Magnanimously.*) There was that very early poem he wrote before he turned Bolshie. It must be twelve years ago, now. The one about the . . . about fish, wasn't it? I remember it had one or two striking lines in it for a boy of eighteen. That might survive . . .

CHARLOTTE. But seriously, Jane, compared with Cecil's work, what *are* his poems? Look at Cecil's bookshelf of solid, brilliant work — thirty years of it — universally recognized as good. And set Dick's miserable sheaf of potty little limited editions against it. There's no real comparison, is there? After all, bulk counts.

(*She says this with a raise of voice at* DICK, *whom the others have not noticed. He is dressed as if he had just got off his motorcycle; and is crossing the tennis court. He looks haggard but speaks jauntily.*)

DICK. Did you say bulk or bunk? Well, don't trouble to distinguish. Father, my sincerest congratulations.

TOMPION. How did you know?

DICK (*lightly*). I was trying to work this morning; your room is directly below mine, and the noise of love-making floated up. He *does* kiss noisily, Charlotte. You ought to break him of that.

(CHARLOTTE *looks at him with hatred.*)

TOMPION. No ill-feeling, Dick, my boy? You allowed me to steal a march on you, didn't you? Well, all's fair in love and war.

DICK. Yes, I heard that one. It was one of the bayonet-fighting gags taught at the P.T. School at Aldershot. It was called 'The well-known addagy,' and it introduced the butt stroke at the genitals. Congratulations, Charlotte. Has he given you a lovely ring? I bet he has. Diamonds and platinum? Let's see!

(CHARLOTTE *gets up and turns her back.*)

Oh, Charlotte, I *am* sorry. My tactless tongue again. Only an amethyst, set in pearls. For shame!

DOROTHY (*impulsively*). Oh, Dick, dear Dick. I *am* so sorry.

DICK. Yes, it *is* a little hard on her, isn't it? (*Kisses* DOROTHY.) Well, Dorothy, how's your David? (*Mock-earnestly.*) Are you *happy* together?

DOROTHY (*laughs*). Blissfully. He is so sweet to me.

DICK. Keep it up. (*Turns suddenly to* CHARLOTTE, *savagely.*) Are *you* happy, Charlotte?

CHARLOTTE. Blissfully, blast you!

DICK. I hope it keeps fine for you. Are you happy, father?

TOMPION. Dick, old man, don't take it too hard. Shake hands!

DICK. Certainly. (*Shakes hands with both hands.*) Mine are smothered in motorbike grease. I was just going to wash them. How are the 'cinders of middle age,' father? 'Fanned and about to burst into the hottest and most devouring flame of all?' I took Mrs. Behrens' advice the other day and read your latest. I remembered that sentence. It's good, isn't it, Charlotte? Hot! Do you know Elizabetta Behrens, Dorothy? Friend of mother's, admirer of father's.

DOROTHY. Dick! really! I do think . . . (*She glares at him.*)

DICK. A topical reference, though. I've just passed her on my motorbike. She's in a taxi with a revolver, gunning for father.

JANE. Really, Dick? A revolver! Why?

DICK. Ask *him!* She's *his* playmate, not mine.

TOMPION. What fool's game is this, Dick? You didn't mention this engagement to her, did you?

DICK. Yes, casually. I thought she'd be pleased.

TOMPION. She's dangerous, a very dangerous woman. (*Looks round in alarm, rushes into the house.*)

JANE. Oh, I'm so excited. Do you think she's really going to use it?

DICK. Well, this looks like farce rather than tragedy. But of course, that revolver's awfully keen on going off. You noticed it yourself the other day.

JANE. But it's not the same one, is it?

DICK. Why, of course.

(*Re-enter* TOMPION.)

TOMPION. Dick, Dorothy, where's that revolver of Pritchard's? I thought it was hanging over my table.

JANE. Oh, Mr. Tompion, are you going to defend yourself? What fun!

DICK. I'm really awfully sorry, father, but Pritchard called yesterday, when you were out. He said he wanted it back, and Charlotte and I gave it to him. He was very quiet and decent and brought the gardening scissors in exchange. We thought you wouldn't mind.

TOMPION. You gave it back to Pritchard? You young . . . blockhead!

JANE. Charlotte, what *is* all this? Who's this Mrs. Behrens?

TOMPION. Dick, tell Denman not to let *anyone* into the house on any pretext.

DICK. Certainly!

(*Enter* MRS. BEHRENS, *right, from behind yew hedge.*)

Oh, hullo, Elizabetta. What have you got there? Did I leave the garden gate open? My shocking carelessness.

MRS. BEHRENS (*hysterically*). Oh, good afternoon, Dick. I've come to shoot your father.

(*Everyone retreats, leaving* TOMPION *alone, covered by* MRS. BEHRENS' *revolver.*)

TOMPION. Don't! Don't! (*Puts his hands up.*)

MRS. BEHRENS. Why not? Why shouldn't I? You double-crosser! Where's this Charlotte whom you're going to marry? Show her to me.

TOMPION. Elizabetta. Let me explain. I've been unfair to you, Elizabetta. But first put that gun down.

MRS. BEHRENS. Yes, Richard Pritchard told me a few things about you.

TOMPION (*playing for time*). Pritchard? I didn't know you knew him?

DICK. Elizabetta, come! Don't shoot our dear daddy. You'd not leave Dorothy and me orphans!

JANE. No, please don't, Mrs. Behrens, it's not kind.

MRS. BEHRENS (*laughs hysterically*). In half a minute I'm just going to *scatter* him.

DICK. And then we'll never really know how his unfinished novel was to have ended. It'll be another dreary *Mystery of Edwin Drood*. Don't do it, Elizabetta. Or find out about it, first.

MRS. BEHRENS. Damn his novel. He promised to marry me . . . Speaking of the 'sanctity of marriage.' . .

DOROTHY (*coming forward angrily*). Oh, did he? He promised *me* he would *never* marry you; after mother died he promised.

MRS. BEHRENS (*to* TOMPION). You dirty . . . (*takes steady aim*).

(*Dick snatches revolver from her: it goes off in the air.*)
Oh, it's missed!

DICK (*as if talking to a child*). Elizabetta, you might have been hanged for that. It was very imprudent of you. Now tell me, where did you get this gun? Tell me, or I'll call the police! Was it from Pritchard?

MRS. BEHRENS (*crying*). Yes, if you *must* know.

TOMPION. He sent you to murder me?

MRS. BEHRENS. No, he doesn't know I have it. I swear! I . . . I took it from the hip pocket of his trousers early this morning when he was still asleep. He didn't notice.

DICK. You two are friends then, already. That's fine. But in that case, Elizabetta, I think it was rather ungenerous of you to grudge Cecil to Charlotte here; surely one genius at a time is enough?

MRS. BEHRENS. No, that's different. Marriage is quite another thing. Cecil promised to *marry* me.

DICK. Well, what about Pritchard? He's just the sort of man to do the right thing by you. And he's got lots of money put by. He spends very little on himself. He's saving up to marry, he told David, when he finds the right woman. He's a much greater genius than Cecil anyhow. And younger, and has a much nicer face. Ask Charlotte; she'll be the first to agree.

MRS. BEHRENS. Dick, you're a dear. I'm so hot-tempered. It was something about the feel of that gun, too. I hadn't any murderous feelings against Cecil at first, when you told me; but then I went to my room and happened to pick it up and it . . .

DICK. That's all right, Elizabetta. I'll make everyone promise not to tell the police. You all promise, don't you? Yes, of course they do. Let bygones be bygones. Amen.

(*A blank pause.*)

MRS. BEHRENS. Goodbye, then, everyone. I mean everyone except you, Cecil: I hope *you* have a long, nasty life. (*He is silent; she turns to go.*) Oh, Dick, I am so, so grateful to you. (*Comes back and kisses him.*) Come and see us sometime, and we'll have the hell of a celebration. Pritchard thinks no end of your work, he says. He swears that you're the coming man. Isn't that nice of him? Says that you're worth ten of your father.

(*Exit.*)

TOMPION. Charlotte! Can you ever forgive me for this? The fact is, I didn't have time to explain . . .

DICK (*interrupts*). *Do* forgive him, Charlotte. After all, previous love affairs don't count in love, do they?

CHARLOTTE. *All right,* Dick. Well, this is absolutely the end of *you.*

DICK. The end of me? — Why?

CHARLOTTE (*in a fierce aside*). For insulting me, for trying to teach me things that I know already, for repeating my own sour jokes to me as if they were new ones of your own. Do you think I have a scrap of respect left for you now?

DICK. I honestly don't care. But if I have helped to reduce the situation to its lowest terms, that's all to the good.

DOROTHY. Dick, father, Charlotte, I don't know which of you all I hate most. You're just *beastly* to one another. (*Stamps.*) I think *you,* Dick — you're the nastiest. And Jane, you're a bloody-minded little monster. Give me that revolver. *I'm* going to look after it this time. I'm the only one of the whole lot who can be trusted with it.

DICK. Here you are, Dorothy. It's decent of you to take charge. They're dangerous things. I've always said there ought to be a law against revolvers.

DOROTHY (*takes it*). Oh, I'll be glad when I'm married to David and away from you all.

CURTAIN

ACT III

SCENE I

(*Morning room of* DOROTHY *and* DAVID's *new house on the edge of Hampstead Heath. View of the Heath through the window. Interior decorations are of the very advanced 1912 period. London Groupish pictures, Negro and Chinese works of art, Omega-workshop tables and painted chairs. It is January and there is a fire. Hyacinths in bowls.*)

(DOROTHY *writing letters at a desk, right.*)

(*Enter* DICK (*left*). *He looks ill, but his voice is cheerful.*)

DICK. Well, Dorothy?

DOROTHY. Dick! Of all people. Dick! You didn't come to my wedding. Or Charlotte's wedding. Or write to me at Christmas. Where *have* you been? I haven't seen you for a moment since that terrible afternoon on the tennis court. September, October, November, December, January. Nearly five months. Are you all right? You look rotten.

DICK. Yes, I'm all right. I've been working, that's all. It always knocks me out. I've finished the thing now.

DOROTHY. Where have you been? Oh, I'm so glad it was only work. I thought you'd hated me for being so angry with you that day. Or perhaps that you didn't like my marrying David.

DICK. *Were* you angry? I'd forgotten. I've been nowhere in particular since I cleared out from home. I've rooms not far off. (*Waves vaguely.*)

DOROTHY. Father tells me that you've not been drawing your allowance.

DICK. No; that's right. There's a point beyond which one can't carry a bad joke. I've been all right. I sold my camera and some books. And I'm all right for another few months; don't worry. If I want money, I'll ask you for some. Well, how are you?

DOROTHY. Still working. Do you like my new house?

DICK. I suppose it's all right. Modern but beautiful; and so on. Everything going well?

DOROTHY. My practice is increasing. David's work's fine.

Dick. Still blissfully happy?

DOROTHY. David's very, very sweet to me. Of course, he's terribly busy at present on the plans for the church he's to build in Kent. In fact, he often goes to his office at night to work. He says that he can't think while all the office people are about. I want him to bring all the plans and things home to work here, but he says it's too much to cart about.

DICK. Still, Dorothy, you don't look properly *blissful*. Something's wrong. Tell me. Come on. Cough it up in little brother's hand.

DOROTHY. Oh, Dick, you're about the only person I could tell.

DICK. What is it?

DOROTHY. I'm shy about telling even you: well — it's this . . . David's not really right.

DICK. Not right? Isn't he well?

DOROTHY. He's well enough generally, but there's something . . . in our life together . . . A nervous failure, probably, something to do with that wound of his . . . He didn't realize about it before.

DICK (*whistles*). Oh, I *see*. That's damned bad luck, Dorothy. It makes a lot of difference to you?

DOROTHY. Well, you see, what's the use of marriage if you can't have children? It's what the priest reads out in the homily: 'Marriage is ordained for the procreation of children.'

DICK. Can't he be cured?

DOROTHY. Apparently not. I sent him to the best man in Harley Street, but David says he could give him no hope.

DICK. Are you sure that Dishonest David went?

DOROTHY. Oh, Dick, David isn't dishonest with *me*. His dishonesty is only shyness really.

DICK. Well, why not annul the marriage?

DOROTHY. Dick, how *could* you? I do hate you sometimes for the things you say. David's in love with me. He hates being away from me, he says, even when he's at the office.

DICK. Well, I suppose there's nothing to be done. Your profession's no loser, though.

DOROTHY. No, I work harder than ever now. I'm a children's specialist.

DICK. That helps?

DOROTHY. I don't know. It may be making things rather worse for me. Oh, Dick, I must tell you. I'm so envious of women who are having babies. Especially Charlotte; you know we were married in the same week.

DICK (*shaken*). Charlotte having a baby? Are you sure?

DOROTHY. Dick, what's the matter?

DICK. Where do you keep the whiskey?

(DOROTHY *flies to get it.*)

DOROTHY. Oh, poor Dick. I'd forgotten. Are you still in love with her?

DICK (*helping himself*). Most certainly I'm not. But when you suddenly tell me disgusting stories like that and expect me to say the usual things . . .

DOROTHY. *Disgusting,* Dick? — How?

DICK (*to himself rather than to her*). My God! It's monstrous. Imagine carrying spite as far as that. She's the most out-and-out destructionist I know; she's terrific. (*Almost admiringly.*)

DOROTHY. Destructionist? Do you call having a baby 'destruction'? Dick, you're ill.

DICK. What did I say? I've forgotten. Come back, whatever it was! No, Dorothy, I sincerely admire Charlotte.

DOROTHY. I don't think it's anything to admire; I just envy her. I don't understand you.

(*Enter* DAVID, *left.*)

DICK. Hullo, David, here's something Dorothy can't understand.

DAVID (*emotionally*). Oh, Dick, dear, I *have* missed you so. Er — haven't we, Dorothy? Where have you been, old boy? You didn't leave us your address. (*Seizes him by the shoulders.*)

DICK. In a room overlooking some roofs, with a pen, lots of paper, and a big waste-paper basket; not far from here.

(DOROTHY *taps* DAVID *on the shoulder with:*)

DOROTHY. Hullo, darling!

(*They embrace;* DOROTHY *affectionately,* DAVID *perfunctorily.*)

DAVID. Enjoy yourself?

DICK. I didn't notice. I was too busy.

DAVID. There's stacks of letters for you; we couldn't forward them. Shall I get them?

DICK. They can wait a bit longer now they've waited so long. I didn't want them while I was working. How are you?

DAVID. Oh, I'm fine. Very fit . . . What was it that Dorothy couldn't understand, by the way? Another medical problem?

DICK. It was about Charlotte's baby.

DAVID. What about it?

DICK. Oh, I was just talking, as you might say, nonsense to Dorothy. What I really meant was: how *can* reasonable people go on populating the world at this stage? What's the good of just *more* people?

DAVID. Dick's usual line of talk. His retirement from the world doesn't seem to have broadened his sympathies.

DOROTHY. Why *not* more, Dick? There's room in the world for twenty times its present population. And anyone who can afford to have a child and is healthy, ought to. Just to make up for the breeding of the unhealthy.

DICK. A sacred duty to the species? Dorothy, do you really *like* people?

DOROTHY. Yes, I do. Lots of people.

DICK. Crowds and crowds and crowds of people? All those people? (*Includes the audience in a slow wave of the hand.*)

DOROTHY. There are such nice people in every crowd. It's extraordinary how many nice people I meet in the course of a working day.

DICK. Well, that beats me! While I've been working these last months and going out in the evening for a meal and walk, I've found myself getting quite ill just watching people go by. I can't help looking at people, I can't help looking right *into* them, and knowing all about them; and all the time I know it's useless. Nobody's ever worth looking twice at. The chances of seeing anyone worth looking at twice are several million to one. The odds are too great. And now you want more people still.

DOROTHY. What's wrong with ordinary faces? I love looking at people in buses and railway carriages and trams.

DICK. Wrong? What's *right* with them? They are simply the thousand well-known variations on the same worn animal themes — the bull theme — the weasel theme — the stoat — the bitch — the bear — the rat — the rooster — the monkey — the cow — the goat — the sheep theme — even the man theme. I admit that one still sees magnificent specimens of he-man and she-man about. But no proper *person,* no face to look at twice. Only types. Look here, I'll stop. I'm talking too much. I've not talked to a soul for five months, you see.

DOROTHY. Go on. I'm beginning to understand what you mean.

DICK. Well, all right. It's like that with books too, nowadays. No real books — not worth looking at twice. One need only look at a single random paragraph to find the same animal authorship at once — the monkey book — the owl book — father's books are rooster's books — oh, yes, I know! — he's got the clearest cock-o-doodle-doo you ever heard — and his midden is the oldest and fruitiest in the farmyard. But that's nothing. What's that book? (*Takes one off the side table.*) Pritchard's? Yes, he's a collie, a little Welsh collie, the slyest anywhere at weering the sheep and penning them between the hurdles. But he's not a proper person.

DOROTHY. Who *is* a proper person? Am I? Are you? Is David?

DICK. There's never any doubt about a proper one — especially to himself.

DOROTHY. Were there ever any more than there are now?

DICK. I should say not. About the same number always. That's the point. They stay the same few; the others outnumber and outnumber them more and more. Did David tell you what I told him once about the bottom dropping out of things?

DOROTHY. I seem to remember something about it.

DAVID. Yes, I told her.

DICK. Well, perhaps one easy way of describing the catastrophe is to say that it was the moment when the last straw broke the back of reality, when the one unnecessary person too many was born, when population finally became unmanageable, when the proper people were finally swamped. Once they counted; now they no longer count. So it's impossible for a proper person to feel the world as a necessary world — an intelligible world in which there's any hope or fear for the future — a world worth bothering about — or, if he happens to be a poet, a world worth writing for — a world in which there's any morality left to bother about, but his own personal morality: *that* gets more and more strict, of course.

DAVID. So strict that he has no qualms about encouraging his friends and relations to murder one another. Be frank, Dick. Tell Dorothy your homicidal hopes.

DICK. Yes, Dorothy, I'm all for homicide. Of course, I don't go about killing people. Not since the War. But whenever a situation's ripe for homicide, I like hearing the guns go off. In a way the war was good. There was a sort of unconscious realization that the trouble lay in there being too many people. But it was a stupid war, it came too late, it wasn't thorough enough, and two or three proper people were killed in it along with the unnecessaries. And there was another thing too . . .

DAVID (*interrupting*). Don't sidetrack me. Tell Dorothy about the revolver you put into circulation.

DICK. There's nothing to tell. Dorothy's got it safe now. Dorothy's not the person to reduce the population, are you? You want a bigger, better, more dimpled, rosier-cheeked, fatter, ten-pounds-at-birth population.

DOROTHY. Dick, stop it at once!

DICK. Listen, Dorothy. Do you know why the population goes on increasing and increasing in spite of wars?

DOROTHY. It's obvious. People who marry want children.

DICK. And why do they want them? Fear! Fear of the species dying out, translated into smaller pettier fears of nations or families dying out. What's sex? What's sex, David?

DAVID (*mutters*). Don't ask *me!*

DICK. Sex is fear. Loneliness sometimes; that's a fear. Or dullness; that's another. Of fear of personal extinction. Say, generally, fear of death. Copopulation! The other thing I was saying about the war is just that. It wasn't destructive enough; and it was working overtime to repair the damage. Fear. Fear filled the brothels in France. Fear here in England opened an unprecedented market for the one thing that Lord Rhondda couldn't ration.

DAVID. You're exaggerating, Dick.

DICK. I'm not. Those were rabbit days. The owl — the bear — the fox — the sheep — and all the rest of the menagerie — all turned into rabbits. Godalming rabbits. An occasional lion; but all the rest rabbits.

DOROTHY. Why rabbits, Dick?

DICK. Emblem of cowardice, emblem of sexuality, emblem of prolific breeding. Copopulation!

DAVID. Well, I'm all for population. Population swells a doctor's new practice. Population demands new houses for rising architects to design.

DOROTHY. Dick, what *is* this bug you have about a terrible world catastrophe that nobody noticed? David couldn't explain it properly. Is it a joke?

DICK. It *is* a joke in a way. The way things still go on as if nothing had happened. I can't tell you about it, though, if you don't know about it yourself.

DOROTHY. Well, give an example of the change it's made. Any example. Don't hold out on us.

DICK. Well, take Time for instance. In precatastrophic days, afterwards always came after before. Now it doesn't, necessarily, at all. Things are over before they happen, out of fashion before they are in. That's killed all sense of anticipation and climax. As for Space, that's finished, too. You can go round the world from city to city now, always stopping at the same hotel. Or principles of belief. In precatastrophic days you either believed on principle or doubted on principle. Now there's no principle. Once you were a rebel when you were young, and a man of the world when you were middle aged, and a conservative when you were old. Now there's nothing to rebel against or be conservative about. Or any real world to be a man of.

DAVID. Rot, Dick.

> *God is neither dead nor sick*
> *He may amend all yet.*

DICK. Not dead?

DAVID. I'm building a new church with an electric organ and tip-up seats — wired for Talkies.

DICK. They told me in Ireland that He'd been shot by the Black and Tans — resisting arrest — back in 1920.

DOROTHY (*furious*). Dick! You're either mad or very wicked. Stop talking like that or leave this house!

DICK. Sorry, Dorothy. I forgot you were religious. Put it down to the War. They say I've never been the same since my head wound.

DOROTHY (*softening*). Is it only since the War that you can't stand crowds? It's a common complaint among ex-soldiers. Ochlophobia, we doctors call it.

DICK. That's a good word. Ochlophobia. If it were a horse I'd have five bob on it each way.

DOROTHY. You're sorry?

DICK. I didn't mean to upset you, Dorothy.

DOROTHY. Dick, dear, tell me: why are you such a rebel?

DICK. Me a rebel? Don't make me laugh. A rebel is someone with a grudge against the community he belongs to. I've no grudge any longer. I'm simply quit, after a long enough period of conventional usefulness. If this were India there'd be no need to labour the point: it would be enough to announce: 'Ex-captain babu Richard Tompion, B.A., Oxon., has retired from the so-called world to live a life of seclusion and meditation . . .'

DAVID. He has found a dry cave in the hills where he dwells in verminous simplicity, and the local inhabitants, recognizing the authentic smell of holiness and overjoyed at the honour of his presence, daily fill his wooden bowl with tamarind, rice, and ghee. No flowers or letters by request.

DICK. Yes, that's right, David: only this isn't India. You see, Dorothy, a rebel's someone who wants to reform things. I don't. I read in the paper the other day that the chairman of an urban railway company had decided against putting a safety-locking gadget on the carriage doors. He said that only forty-one more people had fallen out on the line while the train was in motion than last year. So it wasn't economically worth while to undertake the heavy expense. If I'd been a rebel I'd have simply boiled with rage at this insult to the community. As it was, I just guffawed. *I* don't care now how many people fall out of trains or what happens to railway dividends.

DOROTHY. Dick, dear. Be serious for once. Honestly; aren't little babies sweet? Aren't they dear little things? You can't think of a baby as population, can you? *Can* he, David?

CURTAIN

SCENE II

(*The same room. Two months later. Curtains drawn. Lamps burning. Late in the evening.* JANE, *restless, picking up a paper, throwing it down, going across to look at the clock. It is ten o'clock. There is a knock at the front door (off). She pulls back the curtain to see who it is, then goes out (left), and comes back with* DICK.)

DICK. What are you doing here, Jane? Dorothy in?

JANE. No, I'm waiting for her. Been here some time. Dorothy hasn't anyone to answer the door at night. The maid sleeps out. I found the side door open.

DICK. Lucky to find you here. I wouldn't have thought of a side door. And it's started to snow.

JANE. I do wish she'd come.

DICK. Something wrong?

JANE. I want to talk to her about Charlotte. You don't mind my mentioning Charlotte, do you? I know you've not seen her since she married; but, Dick, I'm so worried and anxious. She's nearly six months gone now, and won't let a doctor examine her to see if everything's all right. She ought to have gone to a good one months ago. And she won't make reservations ahead in a decent nursing home, or even engage a trained nurse in advance. She says she'll leave it to the local midwife and the family doctor, and she's not going to worry until it starts happening. The family doctor's no earthly use anyhow, and she knows it.

DICK. Can't the proud prospective father control her?

JANE. Dick, don't you realize how she *loathes* that man? (I know he's your father.) I don't blame her: he's *awful*. I simply can't make out why she married him.

DICK. Has she told you that she loathes him?

JANE. No, Charlotte wouldn't tell a soul. Not even me. And yet the funny thing is, the more really utterly loathsome he is, the more she smiles, as if at a joke of her own, and seems to mind him less than when he's being just *rather* loathsome.

DICK. What do you call being really utterly loathsome?

JANE. When he kisses her and calls her his little wife in public to make his stinking literary friends jealous. Or, say, when he talks of the baby as *him,* and says he'll put him down for Harrow the day he's born.

DICK. Harrow? Why Harrow?

JANE. Instead of Eton. More democratic tone, he says. That's how he behaves.

DICK. I believe you: he couldn't afford to send me to a big public school. That was in his struggling days. And now he thinks that that's what's wrong with me, chiefly. He wants to start his new family right this time; and as soon as possible.

JANE. Well, I hope it's a girl. But, Dick, seriously, I *am* so anxious. She's done nothing about buying baby clothes, or anything else. Most women do that as soon as they're sure they're having one. She just sits about and writes letters all day.

DICK. What sort of letters?

JANE. You know me. I'd read over *anyone's* shoulder. I sneaked to look at one of these. They're letters to *you,* Dick.

DICK. I never got any. What are they? Unposted love letters? (*She nods.*)

JANE. Oh, Dick, what possessed her to marry your dreadful father?

DICK. To spite me. I refused to marry her because — well, she had physical difficulties with men and . . .

JANE. But she married your father all right. And she's having a child.

DICK. That proves nothing. Jane, I don't want to discuss my father's married life any more. It's obscene.

JANE. God, neither do I. Only: the one letter of Charlotte to you that I saw didn't seem to show that she had any difficulty in thinking about you physically.

DICK. Jane, understand this: I'm *through* with Charlotte. I shouldn't have let you talk as much as you did.

JANE. If you're really through, what does it matter what I say?

DICK. Oh, if we're just telling each other stories to pass the time till Dorothy turns up, all right. There's a good one about Mrs. Behrens. Did Charlotte tell you that one? She must know it.

JANE. She tells me nothing these days. Let's have it.

DICK. Well, you saw her that day on the tennis court, so I needn't describe her. She and father had an affair while mother was still alive. I think little Elizabetta was an interviewer for the illustrated papers then. My mother didn't like my father's books; she knew they were punk and of course she refused to treat him as a genius. She was good. She wouldn't give an inch to humour his conceit and she never came with him to literary lunches and banquets because she knew how he'd behave. Mrs. Behrens, on the contrary, simply slobbered over him.

JANE. Did your mother mind?

DICK. Mother mind! No. I tell you, mother was *good.* She told me one day, quite casually, that anyone who could play about with Mrs. Behrens wasn't worth a moment's regret. When mother died, he wanted to marry the little bitch. But Dorothy wouldn't let him. She never forgave the insult to mother; funny, because mother herself didn't mind. But Dorothy's like that. In some ways she's rather like father, I'm afraid. Well, he kept her on until last September when Charlotte said she'd marry him — to spite me. That was easy. Charlotte — well — you heard the way she played up to him, and he fell for her at once — principally because he knew that I'd wanted her; it was his supreme chance of humiliating me, he thought.

JANE. Didn't he care for her?

DICK. While she flattered him. As soon as she turned nasty, of course, he tried to get back to Elizabetta. I heard about it from Pritchard.

JANE. Tell me that part, do.

DICK. The joke is that Charlotte and I had originally palmed Mrs. Behrens off on Pritchard — oh, by the way, I forgot — after I first met her, she wrote me three incestuous (technically incestuous) letters. Well, anyhow, Pritchard had his revenge on his rival at last when he came calling. (*Imitates* PRITCHARD'S *accent*.) 'You damned dirty fellow, go back home to your wife! Nobody wants you here.' Then he hit him biff! in the belly and pushed him out of the door. Mrs. Behrens laughed till the tears came; or so Pritchard told me. Collapse of elderly suitor.

JANE. Oh, haven't we got lovely parents! Mine were rotten, both of them. Only perhaps a bit worse, because they were musicians. Dirtier. Charlotte never recovered from them. I did. That's why I'm like I am . . .

DICK. I'll tell you what's wrong with father. He's a period poet, and he's chosen a damned bad period.

JANE. Yes, he's a belated Tennyson who hasn't been able to improve on Tennyson and so would like to be a Byron. But he's ashamed to be a Byron openly, because he's a Tennyson.

DICK. That's right. And he's always looking out for a respectable Missolonghi to lie down in and die.

JANE. I wish to God he'd hurry up and find one . . . Dick!

DICK. What?

JANE. Oh, Dick. I do *hate* people, don't you? That day I held the revolver it was all I could do not to kill off that *stupid* Dorothy and that *dreadful* father of yours and that *hopeless* and *bloody* David. Just to make a little breathing space. Everyone except you and Charlotte, in fact.

DICK. Do you know, Jane, you're the first sensible person I've talked to for years.

JANE. And it seemed so anxious to go off, so intelligent. I'm all for revolvers.

(*Enter* DOROTHY; *she is in furs, and in a state of collapse.*)

DOROTHY. *You,* Dick? I saw a light. I was afraid it might be . . . someone else. How did you get in?

DICK. Hullo, Dorothy. You look bad! What's wrong? Jane let me in. Apparently you left the side door open.

DOROTHY. Oh, is Jane here too?

(DICK *has been sitting by a reading lamp.* JANE *is half hidden from* DOROTHY, *in a big arm chair in the shadow.*)

I'm in terrible trouble, Dick.

DICK. Jane's all right, Dorothy. We're here to help you.

JANE. Something happened to David?

(DOROTHY *nods.*)

Here, have a drink! (*She pours it out.*) Tell us!

DOROTHY (*in a small, childish voice*). Well, you see. I was wrong about David. I mean about his dishonesty being charming. Remember I told you about his little charming dishonesties?

JANE. He's been unfaithful?

DOROTHY (*with almost a laugh*). I don't think you'd call it *unfaithful,* not in a divorce court. I wouldn't have minded *that* so much. But when he was pretending to be working at his office at night, he was doing things so disgusting and so horrible — things I didn't know *existed* — that I couldn't understand at first what it was about; I mean I was so angry I didn't know *what* to think. I took him out for a walk on the Heath and when we came to the part where the football grounds are, I asked him. I showed him the pocketbook I'd found in which all the . . . letters were. I threw it in his face.

JANE. Good for you, Dorothy. What did he do then?

DOROTHY. . . . . He told me all about it; with all the defiance and beastliness of a filthy dishonest person when he's cornered. He just *triumphed* in his filth. So . . .

DICK. So . . .

JANE. Well?

DOROTHY. So I shot him with this. (*Shows the revolver.*)

DICK. Killed him?

DOROTHY (*again with a half laugh*). I'm a doctor. I know where to kill people.

JANE. My God, Dorothy! You've got guts. Meet anyone? Anyone about?

DOROTHY. Not a soul.

DICK. Leave any tracks?

DOROTHY. The ground was hard — frozen mud near some goal posts. And it had just started to snow. It's snowing hard now. I came back a roundabout way.

DICK. What time was it?

DOROTHY. What's the time now? Nearly a quarter past ten? Say, a quarter to.

JANE. Dick and I have been here with you since eight o'clock. They'll be able to work out that he was killed just after the snow started, by the amount of snow under the pocketbook and on his boots. You left it there?

(DOROTHY *nods.*)

DOROTHY. You aren't going to tell?

JANE. Don't be a fool, Dorothy. Have another drink!

DICK. Had he any money on him?

DOROTHY. No; I know, because he took it out of his pockets when he changed for dinner and left it in his dressing room. I found the pocketbook with it.

DICK. Fine. Motive: robbery. Now, Dorothy, do you think you can phone the Anstruthers with a message for David?

DOROTHY (*brightening up*). My voice is all right, I think.

DICK. Say that he went out just before the snow began, when we were all here, and that he told you and me and Jane that he was going there to borrow a book. What book?

DOROTHY. Pritchard's poems. I lent my copy to Lady Anstruther weeks ago. He wanted it back to show you. How's that?

DICK. That's fine. Well, then, say he's not to hurry back if he's there, but wait till it stops snowing. Say that Jane and I will excuse him.

JANE. No, I'll ring up first and say hullo to Lilian Anstruther. That'll make a cast-iron alibi. I'll take the revolver, Dorothy.

DICK. No, Jane. You're too enthusiastic. It's come back to *me,* now.

JANE (*crosses to the phone*). What's the Anstruthers' number, Dorothy? (*Telephone bell rings.*) Damn. Someone else on the line. (*At phone.*) Hullo. Hullo. Yes, this is Dr. Dorothy Casselis' house. Oh. You. Denman, is it? Miss Jane speaking . . . O God, Denman. Has she? Hang on a moment. (*To* DOROTHY *and* DICK.) Everything's happening at once. Charlotte's had a fall. Your bloody father's lost his head; it's Denman speaking. Yes, she's bad. Lots of things broken apparently, and the baby's started; wasn't killed. Here, Dick, take the phone: I can't.

DOROTHY. And now . . . *Charlotte!*

DICK. Pull yourself together, old girl. (*At phone.*) Hullo, Denman. Dick Tompion speaking. Yes, Dr. Casselis is here. She'll come right away. If my father goes on like that, slug him with a sandbag. Yes, with my authority. Fine. That's the spirit, Denman. Yes, they'll both come in her car. (*Rings off.*) And now that Anstruther call. Can you manage it, you two?

JANE (*recovering*). What did you say their number was, Dorothy?

CURTAIN

SCENE III

(DICK'S *bed- and workroom. Three days later. Night. A big table spread neatly with his papers, chiefly foolscap (central). A plain wooden bookcase with a few books (central back), next to window. A smaller writing table (left). A couch, and a door leading to bathroom (right).*

It is a large room with whitewashed walls; no pictures. The furniture does not suggest poverty, only extreme fastidiousness in cutting out inessentials. No washing appliances or clothes visible. The window curtains are heavy and of biscuit colour. They reach to the floor. The only colours in the room are plain — a blue bed-spread, for instance. There is a plain wooden reading lamp at the smaller table and a big light in the centre of the room; a jug of flowers in the middle of the bigger table is the only ornament.

DICK *is sitting at the smaller writing table, left of the stage, facing the wings. He takes the revolver from the desk drawer, ejects the cartridges, glances at the empty cartridge case, puts it on his finger, and wiggles it about; smiles, puts it in his pocket. Gets out the cleaning brush and cleans the barrel.*)

(*A knock.*)

DICK. One moment — who is it?

JANE. Me, Dick. I'm alone.

DICK. Hullo, Jane. Yes, come in. Shut the door. I was cleaning this revolver. Should have done it before, but I've been busy writing again, and interviewing those damned police. They seem to suspect Dorothy. But let them. The alibi's good enough.

JANE. She's not given away anything?

DICK. Not yet. But Dorothy's so damned truthful that I'm a bit anxious. I wish we had someone to hang the murder on.

JANE. Reloading, Dick?

DICK. Yes. Do you want to go gunning with it?

JANE (*shudders*). No, Dick. Charlotte's dying cured me of that for a bit. Shook my nerve . . . Dick!

DICK. Yes?

JANE. Dick, it wasn't an accident, Charlotte's fall?

DICK. People like Charlotte don't have accidents. She threw herself over the banisters all right.

JANE. Dick.

DICK. What?

JANE. It was an *awful* death.

DICK (*does not look at her*). Tell me, if it'll make you feel better.

JANE. Well, the screaming. The pain must have been absolutely unthinkable. And you know how sensitive Charlotte was; even to cut her finger knocked her out. Imagine thirty-six hours of that, with the broken ribs and leg. They couldn't give her mor-phia all the time, because of the baby. Oh, Dick, Dorothy was marvellous. I *do* admire Dorothy. I mean, stupid as hell, but what guts when she's got a job on! She's like you, then.

DICK. When Dorothy's good, she's very good.

JANE. The damned old G.P.! He oughtn't to be practising. He's about ninety and hasn't read any new medical stuff since he qualified in the year Dot. Sort of man who always carried about a little bottle full of live leeches and a rusty cupping knife. He'd lost his head, and had your father carry her up to her bed just bundled anyhow instead of on a stretcher. While the old swine was fussing about trying to put the leg in splints, your father rang up a mental healer. And the mental healer came and sat in a corner of the bedroom with a book and her eyes shut, praying. Charlotte screamed for her to go away. But your father insisted on her staying. Then Denman had the sense to phone Dorothy. Dorothy didn't give a damn for etiquette. She threw everything out of the room and took charge . . . Of course, Charlotte hadn't a chance. But Dorothy saved the baby, of course.

DICK (*bitterly*). Dorothy would!

JANE. I stayed to run the house; your father was useless. You wouldn't believe it, but he made violent love to me while Charlotte was dying.

DICK. That was helpful.

JANE. And your brother Bob was there, too; to make things worse.

DICK. Bob! He was supposed to be cut off with a shilling. What was *he* doing there?

JANE. Your father suddenly got religious and called him up to cry over him and forgive him, and put him back in his will. Why didn't he call you in too while he was about it? To make the sobbing party complete.

DICK. You see, I never let fly at him like Bob did. Bob's old fashioned; he's one of these rebels. I never did my father the honour of rebelling against him. That's why he hates me. Bob's done him two good turns now — first given him the dramatic satisfaction of cutting him off, and now given him the dramatic satisfaction of forgiveness.

JANE. And a third one. Listen. Bob was all upset by Charlotte's screams and only stayed in the house because your father made him. Anyhow, to pass the time he started making violent love to me, too. And your father came in just as I'd slapped Bob's face, and there was a fight. Bob threw a chair. And your father threw a decanter.

DICK. Lively doings. What was the next turn?

JANE. Dorothy came down and gave them both hell. Bob went.

DICK. Pain and fear. I told Dorothy the other day about that. They look for an outlet. Religion first. If religion isn't good enough, then sex. But, Jane, you know you attracted it in those two. Because of the pain and fear; unconsciously.

JANE. Did I? I didn't think of it that way. You're not blaming me? You don't hate me?

DICK. No, indeed I don't. At this moment.

JANE. And one more thing. The same night — last night it must have been — one loses count —

DICK. Keep that for later. I can hear the family coming up the staircase.

JANE. Oh, I can't meet them. Let me go into the bathroom and hide. (*Makes for the bathroom door.*)

DICK. No, someone might want to use it. Behind those curtains. (*She hides.*)

(*A loud knock and the door is flung open.* TOMPION *standing in the doorway with his jaw thrust forward and a horsewhip in his hand. He has a mourning band on his overcoat sleeve.* DOROTHY *is behind him.*)

TOMPION (*solemnly and thickly*). Dick.

DICK (*mimicking the dutiful son*). Sir!

TOMPION. Dick, have you no shame?

DICK. Dorothy, have you noticed what our parent's got in his hand? A real Lyceum horsewhip. If you have any influence on our hard-riding friend, please warn him that he mustn't involve me in his old-world dramas. Tell him that when I fight I fight dirty.

TOMPION. Dirty, yes. Do you know the word *sportsmanship*, Dick?

DICK. Yes. Originally popularized, I believe, by the late Marquess of Queensberry. Now the last dirty word used on Saturday nights in the pubs before the fun starts. (*In Cockney scorn.*) 'Aaow! Sportsmanship!'

TOMPION. 'Shame.' 'Sportsmanship.' Do any of your generation know the words?

DICK. I won't answer for all my generation. Some of them are really hang-overs from yours. No, *I* haven't any shame, if you mean *me*.

TOMPION. I have brought your sister here to tell you in her presence what I have discovered.

DOROTHY. Father, what *is* all this nonsense about? What has Dick done?

TOMPION. Dorothy. You know that my wife, when she was dying, called for your brother, but refused to speak to me?

DOROTHY. Well, I phoned Dick, but he wasn't about.

DICK. At police headquarters, probably. Not that I'd have come.

TOMPION. Never mind that. Do you know what she wanted to say?

DOROTHY. No, how should I?

TOMPION. Read these letters from her to your brother. They were in her desk. (*Hands them to* DOROTHY.) (*To* DICK.) Do you know what she told me before she died?

DICK. I wish I'd heard it.

TOMPION. That she threw herself over those banisters because of you. Because it was *your* child. That she only married me because you had seduced her, and hadn't the pluck to face the consequences. And that even after the marriage . . .

DICK. God, Dorothy! I do admire Charlotte. A fighter to the last. And how she must have hated him!

DOROTHY. Oh, Dick, do deny it. It can't be true?

DICK. What the devil would it matter, anyway, *who* the father of the child was? It's been born, hasn't it? Charlotte's dead, isn't she?

TOMPION (*suddenly sees the revolver, picks it up, dropping the whip, and points it at* DICK). Do you deny it?

DICK. Put that gun down, or I'll hit you.

TOMPION. I'll give you three to deny it. One, two . . .

(JANE *suddenly darts from behind the curtains and stands between* DICK *and the revolver.*)

JANE. Hullo, Dorothy. Hullo, Dick. Oh . . . (*Pretending surprise.*) Hullo, Mr. Tompion!

TOMPION (*taken aback*). Oh, Jane! (*He puts the revolver down on the corner of the table.*)

JANE. Speaking of shameless generations! Do you know that last night, about three hours after Charlotte died, this disgusting old satyr came into my bedroom and tried to play? I gallantly defended my honour with a brass candlestick. (*Knocks up his hat and shows a bruise.*) I got in a good one, too.

DOROTHY. Father! Daddy! You? Jane, you're lying!

TOMPION. It's a conspiracy.

(DICK *looks steadfastly at him.*)

DICK. Are you sure?

TOMPION (*does not answer. There is silence for some moments. Then he picks up the revolver.*) Is that the way to the bathroom?

DICK. Yes, hot, cold and a shower.

JANE. Try the shower!

(TOMPION *walks resolutely into the bathroom.*)

DOROTHY (*laughs nervously*). Oh, Jane, what's he going to do? Gargle? Jane, it *was* a lie, wasn't it?

JANE. No. He's not a very nice little fellow, your father.

(*A shot from the bathroom.*)

DICK. Well, that's that!

(DOROTHY *rushes to the bathroom, looks in, bends down. Returns slowly.*)

DOROTHY. Dead.

DICK (*at the telephone*). Put me through to the police, please. At once. No, I forget the number . . . Thanks. Hullo. Police headquarters? My name's Tompion, Richard Tompion. I want Superintendent Bevans . . . Thanks . . . (*Speaking leisurely.*) Oh, Superintendent Bevans. About Mr. David Casselis' death. Yes, Richard Tompion, the brother-in-law. You questioned me yesterday afternoon. Well, we know the murderer now . . . My father, Mr. Cecil Tompion, the well-known poet and novelist. He's just confessed to my sister, myself, and a friend. Here, hang on. No hurry. I want to tell you. Yes, his wife died yesterday and that shook him, and he confessed. He shot Casselis for his daughter's honour — you know! that pocketbook you showed me, all that unfortunate business; apparently he'd found out about it. No, no good arresting him. Yes . . . He's just committed suicide in my bathroom. Here, hang on, no hurry. Yes, I'll give you the address in a moment. I want to tell you. I don't wonder you suspected my sister. She pretended she didn't know about the pocketbook. My fault: I advised her to deny it. Still, her alibi was all right.

Yes, with a revolver. The same one that killed Casselis — a Webley.

Address: flat 35, Avis Buildings . . . Yes, that's the place. Come along, we won't touch a thing. Goodbye . . . Don't mention it. (*Hangs up.*) Oh, Dorothy, here's the cleaning rod and the first cartridge case and the rest of the cartridges. Plant them in the library — got your car? — and come back here.

DOROTHY (*putting them in her bag*). Oh, Dick, I'm so relieved and happy. I'm actually pleased he's dead. Isn't that awful?

DICK. Happy, are you? What's that? *Happy?*

DOROTHY. I've got Charlotte's baby to look after. Instead of him — (*Points at the bathroom*) having her. Jane, dear, may I have Charlotte's baby for my very own? Oh, please say I may?

JANE. Why, of course, Dorothy. You've earned her.

DICK (*mockingly*). And you'll bring her up as a good Christian, and send her to an expensive school, and shield her from the world? Promise me, Dorothy!

DOROTHY. Oh, Dick, she's so sweet. So *ridiculously* like Charlotte.

DICK. Here, hurry off with those things.

　　(*Exit* DOROTHY.)

　　(*A pause.*)

The extraordinary thing is that it still goes on. (*Makes a circling gesture.*) *And* on. *And* on.

JANE. Oh, Dick, I'm so frightened. Dick, give me a kiss. Before the police come. (*Holds out her arms to him.*)

　　(DICK *appears not to hear her. He still circles with his hand.*)

CURTAIN

The Cult of Tolerance

(1936)

WHEN leaders of a militant faith cannot hope to impose complete conformity of opinion on their political dependents, they resort, if they are wise, to a limited tolerance. Thus Mohammed promised tolerance to all 'men of a Book,' I suppose because he did not wish to disorganize the trade and industry of the regions he had marked out for conversion — to all, in fact, who agreed with him that individualistic thinking was a public danger. His reward was that gifted Jews and Christian heretics took refuge under the Crescent from the intolerance of the Cross, and the backward Arab culture soon vied with the Graeco-Roman in many departments of science and art. Christians granted religious freedom to all and sundry only after a series of bloody wars had shown that the armed forces of Islam and Christendom, as also of Catholicism and Protestantism, were too closely matched for either of them to secure a final victory.

No positive virtue can be granted to a tolerance born of exhaustion; and that indecisive wars have been fought between rival faiths, each claiming the sole prerogative of truth, is no reason for regarding all truth as relative. To do so would be to make truth and fancy equivalent. Yet the relativity of truth is a fundamental tenet of modern liberal thought — the emergence of tolerance as

195

a positive cult — and mathematics, supposedly the purest of sciences, has been adduced in its support. The mathematician postulates experimentally: 'Let twice two equal three; then, etc.'; and the fanciful system that he bases on this equivalence of four and three is held to be just as true, in its way, as the familiar system founded on the multiplication table. Mathematically speaking, then, the religious theory of Islam, which is based on the Koran and the accompanying oral tradition of Mohammed's life, is incontrovertible as truth to the degree that it is consistent in itself; and the same with scholastic, as distinguished from popular, Christianity. Truth is thus travestied as lying merely in the logical correctness of calculations made on a given premiss, all premisses being regarded as ideally of equal value; which is gross materialism, because calculation is mere finger-counting — a physical, not a mental, process.

My personal quarrel with the cultivation of tolerance as a positive virtue is that it classifies poetry, with art and religion, as the ingenious postulation of fanciful worlds, and concedes it no more than entertainment value; to me, poetry is truth-telling. The cruder materialism of a century ago was also antipoetic, but in a different way. The materialists were intolerant of all thought not grounded in sensual apprehension: for example, the simple allegory of Jonah and the whale, showing how men of moral purpose survive conquest and captivity, was derided as rationally inadmissible — a whale's throat is too narrow to admit a man's body. Equally derided was the azoological phoenix, a charming Egyptian symbol for the coincidence, after a cycle of years, of the lunar and solar calendar date, and all similar mythic concepts traditionally presented in concrete, not abstract, terms. Crude materialism is still to be found among the academic psychologists, who assume thought to be fundamentally behaviouristic, subject to certain as yet obscure laws of physical inheritance; and poetry to be an obsessive affection caused by some hormonic derangement — possibly of venereal or alcoholic origin. But it is better to deride the poet as untruthful or mentally sick than to tolerate him as a specialist in artistic or musical entertainment.

The cult of tolerance has been rudely challenged by the new

authoritarians who regard all speculative thinking as wasteful and have gone back to regimentation of thought: only certain agreed premisses are countenanced by them. Improving on the propaganda technique of the 1914-18 war, when intolerance was admitted by democratic governments as a means to victory, they have revived methods that had fallen into desuetude since the times of the Inquisition. Liberal opinion is outraged: the victims and their well-wishers appeal to international justice, free speech, and the rights of man, but without avail because these are among the inadmissible premisses. The authoritarian state is founded on some large, concerted lie which a desperate minority undertake to make pragmatically true in confutation of the various, individualistic, petty lies with which a dispirited majority have been consoling themselves for military collapse or economic backwardness. But to oppose the democratic cult of tolerance to the authoritarian cult of intolerance is merely to marshal many inefficient, unconstructive lies against a single, efficiently destructive one; the only opposition worth making is between plain truth and lies or, more modestly, between sense and nonsense.

The fruit of authoritarian intolerance is cultural monstrosity — for instance, grandiose but depressing state architecture and chauvinistic expulsion from the language of useful foreign loan words. The fruit of democratic tolerance is messiness — for instance, petty bourgeois architecture at once extravagant and mean, and wholesale assimilation into the language not only of foreign loan words but of native solecisms which obscure expression and debilitate thought.

The modern liberal asks, with Pilate: 'What is truth?' Pilate was not, as Bacon suggested, impatient; he was tolerant, in the magnanimous Augustan tradition, of everything but a breach of the peace. Or, at least, like many European liberals today, he cynically used tolerance as a cover for equivocation and corruption. 'What is truth?' he asked. 'Where does it reside? Until you can locate truth in a readily discoverable place, it is surely better for me to keep an open mind in all matters that do not directly concern me as governor-general.'

The Gospels remind us how many irreconcilable attitudes can

be adopted towards a single confused subject. Thus, the orthodox religious attitude: 'The Gospels must be accepted as a final court of appeal in all moral cases.' The unorthodox religious attitude: 'It is the greatest story in the world, but we doubt whether Jesus rose again from the dead.' The rationalistic attitude: 'A story that begins with virgin birth and a travelling star cannot be taken seriously.' The historical attitude: 'The various texts may be collated and examined in the context of contemporary antiquities; an opinion may then be offered on the factual probability of the natural events mentioned in them and on the provenience of the supernatural additions.' The scientific attitude: 'We have no reason either to believe or disbelieve the human narrative, for what it may be worth; as regards the miracles, scientific investigators have been able to account for a few of them, and we prefer to reserve our verdict on the rest.' The Marxist attitude: 'Jesus was a class-conscious proletarian who fell a victim to bourgeois conspiracy.' The National Socialist attitude: 'Jesus was a heroic Nordic whom the Jews murdered because he opposed their plots for the debauchment of the world.' And doubtless a Freudian attitude, in terms of a father fixation, disputed in detail by the followers of Jung and Adler.

Where would the plain truth about the Gospels lie? Surely in an assessment of Jesus's story, once the necessary allowance has been made for discrepancies in the four versions and for the frequent confusion of the language of history and myth, as an account of moral perfection? This, at least, is how it is presented by the evangelists. But the assessment would have to be made, not in terms of what civilizing value the Gospels may have had during any historical period, but in terms of the final adequacy or inadequacy of Jesus's postulates — 'Heavenly Father,' 'sin,' 'sacrifice,' and 'Day of Judgment.'

I am never quite certain what attitude I should adopt towards those who do no more than fancy, or who repeat and believe the fancies of the past and the lies of the present. Should it be a tolerant one? Today the destiny of many millions of people in civilized democratic countries is that they must live and reproduce themselves and die without ever thinking for themselves. They are all 'people of a Book'—a book to which they pay little attention, though it would offend most of them to hear it abused. They do not ask or wish to be told the plain truth about this divine revelation, to which they are supposed to turn every Sunday; and are far more interested in the latest Sunday newspaper, where news is dressed up dramatically and garnished with rumour and invention. The subeditors are highly paid to know what is news, and what is not, and each issue hangs together well enough; if the facts given one Sunday are inconsistent with those of the previous one, they are at least legitimate postulates on which to build a weekly structure of newsworthiness. The tolerationist could have nothing against the logic of the democratic Sunday newspaper; he would even have to admit the entertainment value of the official authoritarian newspaper, though its editorial policy were directed against his own way of life. He would force himself to say: 'Frankly, I detest your point of view, but I would fight to the death for your right to print it.' So liberalism commits suicide.

Do I really mind, should I really mind, what the populace fancy, so long as they remain good human animals (as in the democratic countries), never lifting their heads from the pasture or trough, never aggressively interfering with me? Does it matter to me that journalists provide them with the mendacious nonsense they enjoy, and make a living by doing so? Or that the parish clergy preach a threadbare doctrine in which many of them have no greater belief than the journalist has in his news? Is not the journalist genuinely devoted to his newspaper, the priest to his church? Should I not be tolerant of the populace, as I am of the incurably disgusting habits of pigs and dogs, the noisiness of birds, the reckless sexuality of rabbits, or the stupidity of sheep?

But the populace is not what it used to be—rowdy, drunken, and illiterate. The remarkable result of some sixty years of popular education has been that practically no illiterates are left, and that practically no literates are left either; nearly everyone is semi-literate, as the suburb has superseded the town and the country. And should I not be tolerant of the suburbs? They have reached a surprisingly high level of civilization by a discreet avoidance of all those tracts of debatable ground that separate rival religious or political views. Genuine home pride is found among those who live in jerry-built houses, and true courtesy in buses, streets, and shops; disregard of syntax does not imply moral laxity; acts of violence are rare; there is greater honesty in money transactions and less drunkenness than ever before. Though theirs is the world of fancy, not truth, and though they may not understand or respect my work, can I find it in my heart to hate them?

The title of Julien Benda's *La Trahison des Clercs* was more significant than its contents. To him the treason of the *clercs* — the literates — meant no more than that they had abandoned a wide international culture in favour of a narrow nationalism. But international culture in Benda's sense still continues in a constant exchange of historical or scientific information between learned bodies. Certainly, the national literatures are no longer so closely linked as they were once; because Latin, the scholarly language of Europe for some sixteen centuries, has not proved flexible enough as a medium of sensitive thought, and European writers have had to develop their vernaculars to supplement it. The pace of international culture is that of the slowest thinker, and there are still international literary figures whose unportentous works lose nothing when translated into Latin or even Esperanto. No, the true treason is not that *les clercs,* roughly the University class, have ceased to exchange long Latin letters on humane topics, but that so many of them have degenerated from clerics — the word means 'spiritually chosen' — to mere clerks. Clerks to whom? Not, as once, to a God conceived as the source of all wisdom and truth, but to the great semiliterate, lazy, well-meaning public on whose behalf they undertake to depreciate and make fun of thought. The University renegades have popularized the word 'high-brow' as a caricature of those who still desire to think, and 'low-brow' as a defiant countername for all suburbans who drum on their hairy chests in the jungle of their fancy, or sociably drink tea at the Zoo. It is for these literary demagogues that I ought to reserve my intolerance — in so far at least as I am tempted to go their way myself, in pursuit of easy money. But if I am serious in my profession I shall not be dismayed by even a spectacular decrease in the number of my fellows; a little thought goes a long way.

'Horses': A Play for Children

(1939)

DRAMATIS PERSONAE

HORSES: LILY: *a black riding mare.*
                  BLUNDELL SANDS: *a chestnut race horse.*
                  THE FAVOURITE: *a dapple-grey race horse.*
                  CRIPPLEGATE: *a brown, three-legged race horse.*

PEOPLE: ANNA: *a girl.*
                  HIPPO: *a racingman.*
                  BILL: *a stableman.*
                  THE FAVOURITE'S OWNER
                  JOCKEY
                  LAD WITH TRUMPET
                  TWO STABLEBOYS
                  PAGEBOY

RATS: MOTHER RAT
                  THREE LITTLE RATS

(SCENE: *A stable with eight loose-boxes, numbered from left to right, illuminated by a hanging lamp over box 6 and one almost in the wings over box 1. Above the cribs a wooden beam runs right across the back of the scene, broad enough to walk on. Between boxes 2 and 3 there is a space, filled with hay; hanging*

202

saddles and riding boots; a corn bin, a medicine chest. All boxes are open, with the doors caught back, except boxes 5 and 6. From the far right-hand corner the bandy legs of a sleeping stable-man, BILL, *protrude. He is lying on a heap of straw. Two horses look over the tops of boxes 5 and 6. In box 6* BLUNDELL SANDS, *a tall, nervous chestnut with a white blaze; in 5 is* LILY, *a black cob with a kind face. Other objects in the stable include a weighing-machine and water buckets. There is a heap of hay in box 7.)*

LILY. Horse?

BLUNDELL SANDS. Umph?

LILY. Not asleep yet, horse?

B.S. Not a wink. But look at that stableman fellow! He's been asleep for hours. And they pay him to keep awake and guard me. It's scandalous.

LILY. What's your name, horse? It seems so awkward, just to call you 'horse.'

B.S. My name? Blundell Sands is the name I race under.

LILY. What do they call you in your own stable?

B.S. Well — Sandy, if you *must* know.

LILY. I like 'Sandy.' Blundell Sands is a place, isn't it? Were you foaled there?

B.S. No. (*Pause.*) It's where my owner, the duke, first met his duchess, if you *must* know. What's your racing name?

LILY. I'm not in the profession. I'm a riding pony — hacking and a little hunting. My name's Lily: I belong to a girl with pigtails called Anna.

B.S. (*crossly*). But why *Lily?* Lilies aren't black.

LILY (*quietly*). *I* am.

B.S. (*more crossly*). Yes, but you aren't a lily.

LILY. I didn't say I was. I said that I was *black*. I am.

B.S. Well? I didn't deny that.

LILY. And I'm Lily, that's all.

B.S. You make me tired.

LILY. Let's both go to sleep. I'm tired too.

B.S. That's all very well . . . Oh, look here, Lily — I'm sorry I was so cross. I'm in such a nervous state tonight. That long train journey here and . . .

LILY. Yes — and the Race tomorrow. I know. That's why they put you in here with me — to have someone to talk to if you couldn't sleep.

B.S. I like black mares — they're so kind and so quiet. My mother was a black mare . . . Tell me something, anything, to take my mind off that race, *do,* Lily!

LILY. I can't think of a thing! Honest, I can't.

B.S. You must be able to think of *some*thing. You're just making me crosser than ever— how can I ever race tomorrow? (*Rubs his neck nervously against a post.*)

LILY. Stop thinking about that race! It's absurd. You *know* you'll win it. The others haven't a chance. Bill over there says they only have three legs apiece — except the Favourite — and he's got four legs but no heart.

B.S. (*pleased*). Yes, they're no earthly use, the others. But I don't really feel that I can beat the Favourite even on a good day — and if it rains . . . It's sure to rain before morning. (*Sniffs.*) I can smell rain, I think. When the track is wet I feel as though I had cannon balls glued to my hooves. (*Rubs against the post again.*)

LILY. Nonsense. Forget it, and come out for a little walk with me. Just up and down. It will do you good.

(*They come out and walk slowly up and down.* BLUNDELL SANDS *weighs himself on the scales and shakes his head gloomily, saying:*)

B.S. Lost nine pounds since yesterday.

LILY. Now listen! Every horse feels like you do about a wet track. Horses aren't cows with split hooves especially made for mud. Naturally it's harder for them to run in the wet. There's nothing wrong with your legs, is there? (*They stop to have a look at them. He shakes them, one by one.*) No, of course not. And listen again. I've seen the Favourite gallop. He's fast, in a way, but oh! such a trouble to his jockey! The least thing puts him out. He'll shy like mad at a little piece of silver paper, and run straight back to his stable or to the starting post. If he's out of sorts he sighs and sulks just like a mother's darling. I bet *he's* not asleep yet — he's standing and listening for the sound of rain on the roof. And worrying his head off, and gnashing his teeth.

B.S. Gnashing his teeth? I never heard a horse do that.

(*They return to their loose-boxes.*)

Lily. Well, you see, he was a crib-biter once. He used to bite large chunks of wood out of his crib and gnaw them. The vet said it was giving him stomachache. So they put him in a stainless-steel stable with chromium fittings. He can't gnaw steel — so now he just gnashes his teeth.

(B.S. *bursts out laughing.*)

Lily. It's sad, not funny — like children at school with difficult sums who gnaw the tops of their pencils. They don't really *enjoy* it. Just as you don't really enjoy rubbing yourself like that — you haven't the itch, have you?

(B.S. *stops rubbing himself for a moment, but has to resume.*)

B.S. Sometimes I don't even know I'm doing it. Sorry if it worries you.

Lily. It doesn't *worry* me exactly. But it's a pity — you have such a nice glossy coat — you oughtn't to rub it away like that.

(B.S. *stops rubbing.*)

B.S. (*shyly*). You're so sensible, Lily. I never met anyone so sensible as you.

(*A little* Rat *comes running along a beam and sings:*)

> I had a little mare
> And her name was Puff.
> I sent her to the stores
>   For a half yard of stuff,
> But she bought ice cream
>   And an ermine muff —
> I never had a mare
>   Who had sense enough.

B.S. Oh, these rats — they give me the jumps.

Lily. Run home, little creature, or I'll call the cat.

(Rat *runs home.*)

Now go to sleep, Blundell Sands dear. There's several hours still to go. You'll win the race in a walk, you know, if only you go to sleep.

B.S. You really think I will?

LILY. I know it. I promise you.

B.S. I do *hate* races. I wish I hunted like you. I have an uncle down in Leicestershire — he hunts three times a week. Foxes, you know. I think sometimes of throwing up my career and joining him.

LILY. Dear Sandy.

(*They nuzzle noses.*)

B.S. Good night, Lily.

LILY. Sleep well, Sandy.

(*Their heads disappear. There is a pause, and a squeaking sound. Enter, left, the* MOTHER RAT *and three little ones. They run along the beam until they come to the space between boxes 2 and 3, then jump down on the hay, helping each other with their tails, and run towards the stableman.*)

MOTHER (*as they go*). Come on, my little dears, keep in line, help one another, don't dillydally. There's a *delicious* pair of nicely greased leather gaiters on the floor in the saddle room.

ALL LITTLE RATS. Does it taste good, Mother?

FIRST LITTLE RAT. Does it taste as good as mouldy bread?

MOTHER. Oh, *far* nicer.

SECOND LITTLE RAT. Does it taste as good as rotten eggs?

MOTHER. Oh, *far* nicer.

THIRD LITTLE RAT. Does it taste as good as *really* dead rabbit?

MOTHER. Well . . . almost. But it's better for your teeth.

(*She climbs over the sleeping stableman and they follow-my-leader through a rat hole in the wall behind him and disappear. The stableman groans in his sleep.*)

DAWN

(*Enter* ANNA, *left, dancing anxiously from loose-box to loose-box; looking into buckets, the corn bin, the hay, the medicine chest, the boots, under the weighing-machine. She wears a white jersey, tartan skirt, pigtails, red hair ribbons, white socks, black shoes.*)

ANNA. Oh, my doll, my doll, my best doll — where can she be? I *know* I had her yesterday evening when I came in from my ride with Lily. Oh, I couldn't *bear* to lose her. I've had her all my life. I think I should *die* without her. (*Pauses.*) Or is that really true? Anna, is that true? (*Pauses.*) Perhaps not, after all, Anna. (*Smiles a little, pauses.*) Still. . . .

> (*She looks into the hay in box 7 and pulls out her head with a scream.*)

—Oh, oh! Who *are* you?

> (*Thick sleepy voice from loose-box.*) Me. It's only me.

ANNA. But I don't know your 'me.' Come out and let me see you.

> (*There is a scuffle, yawns, grunts and out comes a very stout man with white-and-tan shoes, baggy check trousers and Norfolk jacket with large pearl buttons, a cricket belt and a large deer-stalker cap. He is dressing as he comes out, adjusting the belt and cap, pulling up his socks, straightening the huge diamond horseshoe pin in his yellow tie. As he speaks to* ANNA *he picks bits of hay from his clothes.* ANNA *stands back, her legs apart, and looks curiously at him.*)

ANNA. I'm Anna. Who are you?

HIPPO. Whatever they call me.

ANNA. What *do* they call you?

HIPPO. Names. Mostly bad ones. I'm not popular.

ANNA. I'm sorry. What shall I call you?

HIPPO. You? (*Looks at her narrowly.*) Oh, *you* can call me Hippo.

ANNA. Is that short for Hippopotamus?

HIPPO. Where's Hippopotamus?

ANNA. Do you mean *'what's* Hippopotamus?'

HIPPO. No, stupid, I asked *where.*

ANNA. Oh . . . At the Zoo, isn't he?

HIPPO. That's right. Go up top of the class . . . Now, what may I have the pleasure of doing for you, my dear?

ANNA. You can find my doll. She's lost.

HIPPO. Certainly.

> (*He goes over to the still-sleeping stableman, lifts him up into a sitting posture, searches him, lets him fall again, searches the straw, puts his arm down the rat hole and pulls*

it back with a little squeak as if he'd been bitten. Then he goes through his own pockets and yanks out a variety of objects — two apples, a pair of braces, a music box which begins to play and which he has difficulty in stopping, and finally from his hip pocket a tall glass of beer which he drinks at one gulp.)

HIPPO. Sorry, my dear! I can't find her anywhere.

ANNA. She was my best doll. If I lose her, I don't know what I'll do.

HIPPO. Are you sure she's somewhere in this stable?

ANNA. Yes. *And I believe you've stolen her!*

HIPPO. Me?

ANNA. Yes, you! I saw you looking in your pockets for her.

HIPPO. Me? I wouldn't steal a sixpence from a drunken sailor.

ANNA. My doll's worth far more than sixpence. She's worth at least a million pounds.

HIPPO. How many sixpences is that?

ANNA. Six into twelve goes two, multiply by twenty, multiply by one million. Answer: forty million sixpences.

HIPPO. You're top of the class already. Up you go into the next. (*He lifts her up playfully onto the gate of* BLUNDELL SANDS' *box.*) I don't believe there are forty million sixpences in the world — do you? It's a terrible lot of sixpences.

ANNA. Oh, yes. A million isn't so much really. It's only a hundred times a hundred times a hundred. And a hundred's nothing. It's only ten times ten.

*(*LILY *looks over the top of her box, gets one leg over, reaches forward and extracts the doll from the flap of* HIPPO's *deerstalker cap with her teeth. She hands it to* ANNA, *who thanks her, hugs her muzzle, and gives her an apple which has rolled on the floor.* LILY *whinnies and disappears.* HIPPO *pretends not to notice. He walks over to the scales and weighs himself.*)*

HIPPO. Good Heavens! I've lost a stone.

ANNA. Out of your nice tiepin? Can I find it for you?

HIPPO. No, not a stone from my pin. I mean fourteen pounds of solid muscle — look!

(ANNA *comes and looks, standing on the scales.*)

HIPPO. Ah, that's better. Now I've gained two stone.

(ANNA *shows him the doll as they get off the scales together.*)

ANNA. Her eyes don't open and shut, you see. But they look at you.

HIPPO. That's nothing. A cat can look at a king. A king can look at a cat. A man can look at a glass of beer (*mysteriously produces another glass and drinks it*), but *that* isn't worth forty million sixpences, nor half a million, neither.

ANNA. But my doll is. (*Pause.*) Hippo, what are you doing here in my father's stables?

HIPPO. Nothing.

ANNA. That's telling fibs. You mustn't tell fibs.

HIPPO. Well; nothing much.

ANNA. Well, what?

HIPPO. The fact is, my dear Anna — speaking to you as a woman of the world: I have a friend (or rather he's only a sort of a friend of a very sort of a friend of mine). And this bloke has bet a lot of money that a horse called Blundell Sands will win the Diamond Cup race tomorrow. Got that so far? (ANNA *nods.*) So when this bloke (the sort of a friend of my very sort of a friend) hears that this Blundell Sands is worn out by his long train journey, and off his feed, and can't sleep, and so on and so forth — *then* he says to himself: 'The Favourite will win after all, and I'll lose all the money I've bet.'

ANNA. How much had he bet?

HIPPO (*counts on his fingers*). Let me see. There was ten thousand guineas, and one thousand pounds, and a monkey, and a pony — that's all. I mean: all that. So he calls this very sort of friend of mine, who was his sort of friend too. He says to him: 'Alf, can you and me do business?' Alf says: 'That's all right between sorts of friends.'

So the bloke says: 'Do you know a stout fellow who will nobble the Favourite? If you do, and he does that nobbling fair and square, so that Blundell Sands wins the race (I expect you know, Anna, the other nags have only three legs apiece), your share of this little business is: the pony, the monkey, one thousand pounds, and a little house in the country — that's very snug, but a little damp. All that.'

ANNA. And so you're the stout fellow?

(HIPPO *sweeps off his deer-stalker cap in a grand gesture and out drop dozens of sixpences.*)

HIPPO. Sixpences. I collect them.

(*The stableman* BILL, *who has red hair and a red face, wakes up at the chink of money.* HIPPO *is alarmed and, after vainly trying to hide under the scales, goes into the space between boxes 2 and 3 and hides under the hay.* ANNA *hides with him.*)

BILL (*yawning and stretching*). Long sleep I've had — long sleep and rum dreams.

(*He picks up a besom and begins to sweep the stable. He knocks at the door of number 6.*)

BILL. Good morning, sir. Time to get up, sir. Fine day for the race, sir. (*Knocks at number 5.*) Good morning, Miss. Nice morning, Miss.

(LILY's *head appears, followed by* BLUNDELL SANDS'. B. S. *yawns and disappears. Suddenly* BILL *stops sweeping and, looking down, says:*)

BILL. Horses above! Look at 'em. About forty million sixpences, more or less. It wasn't a dream after all. I dreamed about forty million sixpences. Someone said it.

(LILY *tilts her head as if in enquiry.*)

BILL. Yes, I dreamed it rained forty million sixpences and I picked 'em all up, as I'm doing now; and I put 'em all in my red handkercher, as I'm doing now; and I says to myself, as I'm doing now: 'Bill, you're going to bet this whole boiling lot on Blundell Sands, to win the Diamond Cup.' And then off I goes to place my bet — as I'm doing now!

(LILY's *head disappears.* BILL *is going out, but stops short at the sight of* HIPPO's *foot. Jerks him out.*)

BILL. Here, what are you doing here, you fat man with the wrong sort of shoes?

HIPPO. Nothing, Mister. Nothing at all.

BILL. Nothing at all?

HIPPO. Well, hardly anything at all.

BILL. For instance?

HIPPO. Well, to be honest . . .

BILL. You can't be honest, not with them clothes.

HIPPO. All right. Well, I was pondering ways and means to nobble the Favourite. This seemed a nice quiet kind of place to do my pondering.

BILL. Sure you was only pondering?

HIPPO. Well, musing a little, and taking a little thought. Do you know Anna? Friend of mine. (*Pulls her out.*)

BILL. Now, whatever are you doing in that hay, Miss Anna?

ANNA. Oh, only hide-and-seek, Bill.

BILL. Are you helping him to nobble the Favourite, Miss Anna? Of course, if you are, that makes all the difference.

HIPPO. Of course she is — we're all friends here. Clever head on her shoulders, Miss Anna has; knows all about geography and mathematics and what not. Tell me, Anna, how exactly does one nobble? Here, have a pear drop before you answer. Sticky, but good.

ANNA. I'm not allowed to accept sweets from racingmen. Mother said so particularly. Bill . . . you tell him how to nobble — I've forgotten.

BILL. I won't. It's against my conscience.

HIPPO. Then give me back my sixpences!

ANNA. Go on, Bill. Give them back. They're his.

HIPPO. Tell me, and you can keep them all.

BILL (*in a confidential whisper, shaking hands on the bargain*). Well, if it is really the Favourite as you want to nobble, and not little old Blundell Sands here — well, then maybe I'll give you a hint or two. First you picks the right stable, then you sneaks in, just the same as you sneaked in here — that's *your* secret how you done it — then you tiptoes up to the Favourite and you coughs gently. He turns round and puts his head over the door, and there you are, you just *nobbles* him, when nobody's looking.

HIPPO. Oh, I *see!* Thank you very much, much obliged, to be sure. Er — by the way — what exactly do you nobble him *with?*

BILL. Well . . . of course, that's left to taste and choice

and discretion and convenience, if you know what I mean. There's some use a hypodermic syringe (*takes one out of the medicine cupboard*) such as this here, filled with California Syrup of Figs; and there's some uses a lump of sugar with three drops on it of hydrochlorotoluoticpic-waxahide — you buys it at any good chemist at twopence a drop; and there's some, of course, uses hypnotism.

HIPPO (*to* ANNA). What's hypnotism, my dear?

ANNA. Hypnotism? Well, it's a sort of magic . . . Suppose you want to make someone believe something that isn't true . . .

HIPPO. You mean telling fibs? Cramming someone? That's easy.

ANNA. No, not that. But suppose I want to make a man believe that he's a horse, when he's really a man — come here, Bill — now watch, Hippo! — I fix him with my eye like this — don't move, Bill! — and I make passes with my hands like this, slowly and slowly (*goes on making passes*), and at last I say to him solemnly like this: 'Abracadabra, you're a horse!'

(BILL *reacts at once to the hypnotism; he goes down on all fours, whinnies, moves into loose-box 7 and is soon rubbing muzzles with* BLUNDELL SANDS.)

ANNA. And he *is*. Isn't he? In a way, I mean.

HIPPO. Too right, he is. My dear Miss Anna, go up to the top of Standard One. It's a miracle, it's marvellous, it's lovely! What shall we make the Favourite be? A snail?

ANNA. No, a crab.

HIPPO. But crabs run fast. I've seen them at Blackpool. I've seen crabs that would beat a lot of horses I've seen.

ANNA. Yes, but they run sideways. The Favourite will never reach the winning post, not running sideways he won't.

HIPPO. You're right. You're right as usual. You're always dead right. Come along quick and we'll do it.

(*Hurries her out, right. She breaks free and runs back.* LILY *and* BLUNDELL SANDS *have both reappeared. She gives them sugar in her palm, and then a lump to* BILL. *He sweeps it into his mouth with his tongue. Magnified noise of crunching.*)

ANNA. Good horse, poor old fellow, then! Like sugar? (*Opens the gate for him.*) Time for your morning gallop, Bill. Out you come, old boy.

(*He comes out prancing and exit left, followed by* ANNA.)

(*A pause.*)

(MOTHER RAT *and her three little ones re-enter out of the rat hole. The little rats are noticeably fatter.*)

MOTHER RAT. Now, children, keep in file, and help one another over the stile. We're all going to the pond to wash our faces.

LITTLE RAT. Oh, need we, Mother? The water's so cold at the pond.

MOTHER RAT. Your whiskers are greasy.

LITTLE RAT. I like them greasy, Mother.

MOTHER RAT. I don't.

LITTLE RAT. I'll lick them clean, Mother.

MOTHER RAT. Don't argue, child. To the pond!

(*They climb up by one another's tails, the way they climbed down before.*)

SONG.   Now then children, keep in file,
        Help one another over the stile!
        One little rat in a velvet hat
        His whiskers sticky with bacon fat;
        Another little rat in little rubber shoes
        His whiskers sticky with tomato juice;
        Another little rat, in scarlet and white
        His whiskers sticky with Turkish delight —
        Over the stile and the rail and the pail
        And help one another up by the tail!

(*Exeunt.*)

LILY. Sandy, darling, are you awake yet?

B.S. Good morning, Lily. I've had a lovely sleep. I dreamed that you and I were hunting foxes together over a wide meadow full of daisies and buttercups. I wonder what that means!

LILY. And the race?

B.S. I could run the Favourite to Scotland and back and give him a week's start.

Lily. That's the way to talk . . . You didn't hear what those people were saying, did you?

B.S. No — who?

Lily. The big rogue in the check suit is going to nobble the Favourite. Bill the stableman and Anna, who rides me, have told him how.

B.S. No, not really! Not really nobble him with a proper nobble, so that he won't be able to run?

Lily. Yes, isn't it wicked? Isn't it unsporting? And all because someone has been betting monkeys and ponies and things on you and now he thinks you can't win.

B.S. It's not only wicked and unsporting — it's an insult to me. I'm surprised at your little Anna.

Lily. I never liked her mixing with the racing crowd. I'd like to take her right away from this place. She's so easily spoilt . . .

B.S. If only we could tell someone in time!

Lily. Let's go and tell the Favourite himself — warn him to be on his guard.

B.S. Yes, that would be the decent thing to do. I like a good, clean race. If the Favourite were nobbled and I only had three-legged horses to run against, it would quite spoil the race for me. I want a good, hard race. I want to win it for your sake. (*They nuzzle affectionately.*)

Lily. Let's go at once.

(*They go out, left, together.*)

(*Re-enter* Bill, *cured, driving* Lily *and* Blundell Sands *before him; they back unwillingly.*)

Bill. Here, back you go, Blundell Sands, sir; back, Lily, old girl! Can't have you straying all over the place like this, as if you was cattle. What for did you want to go out, eh? Wanted to have a squint at the old Favourite? (Blundell Sands *half nods.*) Well, then all you has to do is to stay put. The Favourite's being taken here for safety. The Owner's got a warning as how his horse is going to be nobbled. Favourite's coming here with Cripplegate, that's his stable companion what fought in the War.

(*They exchange looks and quietly return to their stalls, pausing only for a long drink from two water buckets.*)

(*A trumpet sounds.*)

BILL. Here they come, quite a parade, too!

(*Enter: Small scraggy* LAD *in morning coat and bowler hat with trumpet;* STABLEBOY *with velvet cushion and sugar bowl; another with a golden dish containing apples; a third with a suitcase marked* THE FAVOURITE *and three hatboxes; the tall, florid* OWNER *in frock coat, grey top hat, golden watch chain, spats, rolled umbrella; a haggard* JOCKEY, *in red, gold and green, leading the* FAVOURITE. *The* FAVOURITE *is tall, elegant, supercilious, and looks like a rocking horse — grey with black dapples. He wears a sunbonnet and a red, gold, and green saddlecloth decorated with golden palms. Behind him comes a* PAGEBOY, *scattering roses out of a florist's carton.*)

BILL (*To* PAGEBOY *as the* TRUMPETER *pauses to drain the trumpet of saliva.*) Oughtn't them roses to be scattered in front of the nag, not behind?

PAGEBOY. We tried that: it made him plunge like mad. (He don't even like the trumpet.) So, old Cripplegate here — he gets the real benefit of them. See? Come on, Cripplegate, old fellow.

(CRIPPLEGATE, *the* FAVOURITE's *stablemate, comes slowly in by himself, treading delicately among the roses. He is a sad, dirty-brown horse with only one foreleg, a patch over one eye, and a crutch. He hobbles into box 8. The* FAVOURITE *meanwhile stops and inspects boxes 3 and 4, turns away with a sniff, ignores the horses in boxes 5 and 6, examines boxes 7 and 8, finally goes back to box 4.* HIPPO *sneaks into the stable and hides in the hay again.*)

OWNER. Well, he's safe enough here, I suppose. They won't nobble him *here*. We'll bolt the door and bar the windows and our money's in the bank. (*To* BILL, *pointing to* BLUNDELL SANDS.) Hi, you fellow! Is this the animal that thinks he's running against my Favourite?

BILL. Sure. That's Blundell Sands, that is.

OWNER. Well, I don't like his looks.

BILL. You'll like them still less when the race is over.

OWNER. You impertinent clown — I'll trouble you to leave this stable!

BILL. Hark at him! Leave my stable, indeed! You want to nobble my horse, that's your little game, you crooked racingman! But Blundell Sands isn't going to be nobbled, no, not if I has to fight for it. (*Picks up besom.*)

OWNER. Threatening me, are you? Suppose I call the police?

BILL. You can call 'em if you like — it's all the same to me.

(*There is a fight,* BILL *using his besom, the* OWNER *using his umbrella, the* STABLEBOYS *throwing sugar and apples, the* JOCKEY *creeping up timorously behind the* OWNER *and pushing him forward, the* LAD *with the trumpet trumpeting madly.* BILL *is getting the worst of it, when* LILY *pushes open the door and comes out to the rescue, kicking backwards, until the* OWNER *goes down in a heap, the* JOCKEY *under him.* BILL *sweeps them off stage with his besom, and disappears with whoops of triumph. The four horses are left alone.*)

THE FAVOURITE (*in a lackadaisical voice*). Oh, my poor nerves! Oh, what I suffer! (*Shudders.*) First, I can't sleep a wink, thinking about the rain, and then they wake me up, hours before my time, because someone wants to nobble me. (*Shudders.*) And then they bring me to this wretched shed and blow trumpets in my ear, and fight. How *can* I run today, I ask you!

CRIPPLEGATE. You shouldn't be so sensitive, old man, I keep on telling you. Just pull up your socks and snap right out of it. I've stood for all you have, and more, and it didn't trouble me in the least.

THE FAVOURITE. Oh, you! That's different. You fought in the War. I'm highly strung, and thousands of pounds have been bet on me for this race — I feel the responsibilities like a load of bricks on my back.

(HIPPO *crawls out of the hay.*)

LILY (*screams*). Oh, Favourite, take care, take care! He's going to nobble you!

(FAVOURITE *shudders terribly.*)

B.S. Be careful!

(HIPPO *tiptoes triumphantly forward. He rolls up his sleeves, prepares to hypnotize the* FAVOURITE. *Enter* ANNA *from the rat hole and lies on the straw, leaning on her elbows and laughing.*)

HIPPO (*coughs*). Now, what was it that that clever little girl said I had to do, to magic him into a crab? First I fix him with my eye. (*Does so.*) Then slowly, slowly I make passes in front of his face. Then (one moment, if you please). Oh, dear me, what was the solemn magic, what did she say?

(*Pause.*)

— (*Brightly.*) I know — (*Still making passes.*) 'Abracadabra — you're a horse!'

ANNA (*bursts out laughing*). Oh, Hippo, you *idiot!* — you got it all wrong. You should have said: 'Abracadabra, you're a crab!'

HIPPO. But you said 'horse.'

ANNA. I meant 'horse': *you* meant 'crab.'

HIPPO. Why didn't you explain better? (*Makes more passes.*) 'Abracadabra: you're a crab!'

ANNA. It's too late now: he thinks he's a horse.

HIPPO. Well, here's the syringe. (*Gets it.*) This'll do.

ANNA. Haven't you forgotten the California Syrup of Figs?

HIPPO. Too true, I have. And the what's-its-name paxwixahide drops! I'm so absent-minded, it isn't credible. (*Feels through his pockets.*) Here, Favourite, have a pear drop. Sticky, but good.

(FAVOURITE *turns away and begins to bite his crib.*)

— Oh, I expect *your* mother warned you, too, against accepting sweets from racingmen.

(*All the horses nod their heads.*)

— Anna, I'm sunk!

ANNA. Poor Hippo — don't worry — come with me and I'll take you along to the biggest tent on the course and buy you an enormous glass of lemonade.

HIPPO (*blubbering*). But think of it, Anna — think what I've lost — a monkey, a pony, one thousand pounds, and a nice little house in the country.

ANNA. 'Snug but damp,' remember?

HIPPO (*blubbering*). No, 'damp but snug.'

ANNA. You told me 'snug but damp.' If one says 'snug but

damp' one takes good care; but if one says 'damp but snug' one gets awful rheumatism.

HIPPO. I have awful rheumatism, already.

ANNA. Then come along for the lemonade.

(*Exeunt.*)

THE FAVOURITE. Honestly: I ought not to run in this race. I couldn't do myself justice. I'll have myself scratched, I think. I feel so bad. No, no, I won't. I'm a *horse,* not a coward. I'll run just to beat you, you ugly chestnut thing over there! I hate you. I'll run you off your legs! I'll beat you by twenty lengths and a piece of string! (*His voice rises to a bellow.*)

LILY (*gently*). How long is a piece of string?

THE FAVOURITE. Twice as long again.

B.S. (*tartly*). Tie it round your neck until you choke!

LILY. Don't lose your temper, Sandy! Take it easy! What's wrong with you?

B.S. (*after a pause*). I'm just feeling a little hurt, to be honest.

LILY. Hurt? Why on earth are you hurt?

B.S. Well, nobody tries to nobble *me.*

LILY. They'd better not, precious!

(*Re-enter* MOTHER RAT *and little ones, left. She jumps on the beam that runs behind the loose-boxes and the little ones follow her, humming a little tune, the words of which are spoken by the* MOTHER, *and taken up by the little ones.*)

MOTHER RAT. Little ones all together,

> Our money's on Blundell Sands!
> We're going to nobble the Favour-ite
> Do just as I do with your hands.

(*They surround the* FAVOURITE, *who turns round and round in his box, trying to avoid their rhythmically waving paws. But they go on with their hypnotic waving and the melody changes.*)

— Oh, so sleepy, you want to go to sleep,

Hush now! Little rats watch about you keep.

Hushaby, lullaby, pretty dapple grey,

You haven't had a wink of sleep — since yesterday.

Baloo then, laloo then, shoheen and sho lo!

Down drop your hindlegs, off to sleep you go!

B.S. Stop, you rats — it's unsporting. I won't have it! Stop it, I say!

MOTHER RAT. Too late, he's going off fast, he's swaying on his feet. Oh, so sleepy, beautifully sleepy lovely sleepy-peepy-sleep! Bump! There he goes!

(FAVOURITE *slumps down and snores loudly.*)

CRIES OFF. All horses ready for the Diamond Cup! All horses take their place at the starting post — *at* once!

(*Re-enter* OWNER, JOCKEY, LAD *with trumpet,* STABLEBOYS *with saddle, a cup of tea, a whip, a bottle of smelling salts, etc.*)

OWNER. Excellent, excellent! He's snatching forty winks. Just what he needs to help him win. Hi, Favourite, wake up! Time for the race!

(FAVOURITE *snores. He is lying with all four legs in the air.* OWNER *shakes him; no response.*)

OWNER. Here, you lad with the trumpet! Perform. Blow the reveille!

(*He blows the reveille.* FAVOURITE *does not stir. They shout, bang cans, blow the trumpet, whistle, drag him out, jump on him. Re-enter* HIPPO *and* ANNA, *right.*)

OWNER. Oh, great Steeds Below! — I believe he's dead! Let me listen to his breathing.

(*Uses a stethoscope. A tremendous snore jars it out of his hand.*)

HIPPO (*aside, in glee*). Miss Anna, Miss Anna — I've done it, after all — I've done it after all!

ANNA. What, Hippo?

HIPPO. Can't you see, I've *nobbled* him! Now I'll get the monkey and the pony and the thousand pounds in crisp bank notes, and my little house in the country — damp but damp — I mean snug but snug. And I'll live happily ever after. Come and keep house for me, Anna.

ANNA. No. But I'll see you off at the station if you like.

(*Exeunt; the* OWNER *left in despair.*)

MORE CRIES. Come on now — no time to waste — *all* horses out for the race!

(BLUNDELL SANDS *and* LILY *emerge from their boxes, pause to bow to the audience, and exeunt left.* CRIPPLEGATE *hobbles after them.*)

OWNER. I'm going to lodge a protest. This race is foul, foul I say! They have nobbled the Favourite — *my* Favourite! Come along, boys. I won't stand for this!

(*Exit with his crowd. Long snores from the* FAVOURITE. *The* RATS *come in and dance round him. Distant cheering. At last the door opens and they scurry away. Re-enter* CRIPPLE-GATE, *wearing a garland around his neck and a crown round his head. The* FAVOURITE *gives a terrific snore and wakes up, scrambles to his feet.*)

THE FAVOURITE. Where's everyone? Isn't it time for the race yet? I took a nap.

CRIPPLEGATE. The race is over.

THE FAVOURITE. Over? Over, you say? And nobody thought of waking me up? Words fail me! I cannot understand . . .

CRIPPLEGATE. They did their best . . . You were in such a sweet, deep sleep.

THE FAVOURITE (*in a tearful voice*). It's shocking. I'm disgraced for ever. Oversleeping on the day of the Diamond Cup! Oh, dear! Oh, my dear! So of course that ugly brute Blundell Sands won?

CRIPPLEGATE. No.

THE FAVOURITE (*astounded*). No what?

CRIPPLEGATE (*humbly*). No, *sir!*

THE FAVOURITE. Well, if he didn't, who on earth did?

CRIPPLEGATE. I did. I was the fastest three-legged horse on the field. They gave me these. (*Looks at garland and crown happily.*) Our Owner got the Cup.

THE FAVOURITE. *You* beat Blundell Sands?

CRIPPLEGATE. He didn't run. He said that it was unsporting to run, after you'd been nobbled.

THE FAVOURITE. Nobbled, was I? That accounts for it. That

makes me feel better. So Blundell Sands refused to run? Is that true?

CRIPPLEGATE. Of course it's true.

THE FAVOURITE. That was grand, that was white, that was English! What a splendid fellow he must be! I had no notion. I misjudged him. I wronged him. I'm proud to have met him. Where is he now? Fetch him at once. I want to rub muzzles with him.

CRIPPLEGATE. Oh, he's far away by now, over the moors. He has an uncle who hunts — you know, jumps gates and fences in search of foxes — somewhere down in a place called Leicester-shire. Well, he and that pretty little black mare have gone off together to the uncle. He's taken the stableman with him as a rider, and she's taken Anna. I wish them all the best.

THE FAVOURITE. And so do I. (*Cheers.*)

(*Re-enter everyone. All cheer.*)

CURTAIN

Colonel Blimp's Ancestors

(1942)

FOR centuries there has been an unbroken succession of Colonel Blimps. Recently in *The Times* two announcements, covering three generations, appeared on the same page:

> BLIMP — At his residence, Limphalt Manor, Wessex, after a brief illness, Colonel Hereward Marmaduke Blimp, D.S.O., M.V.O., J.P., late Umpty-third Regiment, Royal Patagonians, aged 85. Funeral on Friday, 13th. Flowers by request. Indian papers please copy.
>
> BLIMP — To Daphne, née Crimp, wife of Lieut.-Colonel Marmaduke Hereward Blimp, Royal Patagonians — a son. Indian papers please copy.

The oxheaded Saxon strain has always been dominant in the Blimp family. Qualities of shrewdness, wit, humanity, logic, resourcefulness that intermarriage with more gifted neighbour races has grafted on our brutish Germanic stock have never been noted in a Blimp. Historians and geneticists are puzzled to know how the family has survived so long and prosperously. I will try to explain this by a short family record.

In the reign of Ethelred the Unready there lived an old, bald, long-moustached West Saxon nicknamed Hereward Belemphaltet (Hereward with the limp). Since the whole family was subject to gout, the nickname became hereditary and was shortened to Blimp. Hereweard, though an orthodox Christian, admired the pagan Danes as a 'fine soldierly horde of men' and approved of their raids on 'the base-born churls and mercenary monks of Essex.' He said of Danegeld: 'Gad, sir, King Ethelred is right. The more we give the Danes, the less there'll be for them to pillage.' (Translation.)

Hereweard Blimphalt, the thane of 1066, refused to believe in the Norman danger until it was too late to take his company of spearmen to King Harold's help. William the Conqueror, judging him a loyal pro-Norman, let him keep his estate, which was three parts marsh, on condition that he paid a token to the Crown of three marsh mallows every Lady Day. These flowers appear in the Blimp coat of arms. The Blimps are proud of their picturesque old fee, though it reflects no credit on them. The Blimp crest is a mailed hand with a spear at the charge; this emblemizes the Blimp love of shock tactics. The Blimps always charge baldheaded at the five-barred gate, or the enemy's embattled centre: they scorn the indirect approach or the tactics of infiltration, which they think ungentlemanly.

At Crécy (or that is the family tradition), when the flower of French chivalry was first rudely greeted by the boom of wooden cannon, then galled by volleys of cloth-yard arrows, and finally carved up by wild Welsh irregulars with knives, the de Blympe of the day was scandalized. 'By Saint Ethelburga, my liege lord,' he gasped to the fighting Bishop of Wells, whose vassal he was, 'it grieves me right heartily that so gallant an array of Knights should be distressed and bloodily butchered by our base and vulgar commonalty.' (The Blimps have always detested irregulars.) He rescued a couple of Burgundian knights from the slaughter and did very well out of the ransom, which was paid in wine. This was the Blimp who said: 'I swear by God's Body, I would rather my son should hang than study letters!' He himself could not sign his name.

The Elizabethan de Blympe was satirized by Shakespeare as Sir John Falstaff. Shakespeare was rather too kind to him; but of course unadulterated Blimp is not good theatre.

The Jacobean Sir Marmaduke was the first Colonel Blimp. He learned his soldiering in Holland. A letter of his survives, dated Dec. 13, 1641, from The Hague:

Honoured ffather:
Trewely, let mee travell whair I will, soe I go not to Hell, a more baser countrie than thiss for a jentill man to live I cannot find. I have bin much crost in my advancement by the jelosies of divers other offecers of this Regt. I besitch you send mee a nagg for I am so lame of the gowt I cannot march. And pitty your dewetiful sonn,
                                        Marmaduke Blimp

(The Blimps have always ascribed their failure to rise in the service to the jealous machinations of their brother officers.) The Civil War broke out in 1643, and Sir Marmaduke was given a company in a Royalist infantry regiment. He fought in several indecisive battles and refused to take the New Model Army seriously, 'beeing but a parsel of rogues, runagates, madd men and jack-puddens.' He regarded the pike, already obsolete, as the 'queene of the battle.' He held a strong castle near 'Sentellens' (St. Helen's) in 1645 for some weeks, but then unwisely agreed to a parley with a Roundhead colonel at a postern window. This 'currish dogg' plucked him out through the window by the ears; the castle surrendered. (The Blimps always fall for simple stratagems of this sort.) He gave his parole not to fight again and lay low until the Restoration. Most of his money had been lost in the Wars, but in 1671 a Dutch engineer fortunately drained the marshes for the landowners of the district and added several hundred acres of good land to the Blimp estate. Fortunate Blimps!

His son became colonel of the Umpty-third Regiment shortly after its foundation in 1690 by King William III. He had his head removed by a cannon ball at the Boyne, just after making this speech to his officers: 'Gentlemen, see that you show no quarter to these fubsy Irish papishers, seeing they are scarce to be reckoned human. Why, a sober man, well known to me, avouches that lately on the Dublin road, seeing their naked corpses corded together in a cart, three of every five had long bushy tails like to a fox's.' The Blimps still believe all that they hear to the discredit of those whom Kipling has now taught them to style 'the lesser breeds without the Law.'

His son commanded the Umpty-third under Marlborough. Marlborough gave them their nickname (now confirmed by Royal Warrant) of the Royal Patagonians. Someone remarked in his hearing 'the inhabitants of Patagonia are so rude that they cannot reckon numbers beyond three.' Marlborough replied: 'Ods Cock, that is one better than Colonel Blimp and his kind!' (It is true that the Blimps have never been strong at arithmetic and have always relied on a Scotch bailiff for keeping their accounts.) Marlborough did not ask more from Colonel Blimp than he could perform; the Blimps have always been fairly good at close-order parade-ground drill which suited Continental warfare at that time. Marlborough with a few intelligent *aides* could manage the tactical and strategic side of the fighting. It was about this time that the Methuen Treaty with Portugal made port the family drink of the Blimps; and that the aestuary, a primitive Turkish bath, was invented. Colonel Blimp bought one; it is still in the family.

The next Blimp fought at Minden in 1759: mistaking their orders, the Royal Patagonians and five other well-disciplined British regiments marched out unsupported against three times their number of French cavalry and tumbled them to ruin. Colonel Blimp afterwards said to General Phillips of the Artillery: 'Ecod, sir, 'twas not such an encounter as I could have wished, being fought in no proper order. Upon my soul, General Contades did right to withdraw his cuirassiers when we came upon him so unceremoniously. It is not the part of infantry to assault cavalry, but clean contrariwise.'

The next Blimp married the ugly widow of a ship's chandler who had made a fortune by cheating the Navy. (This windfall lasted the Blimps until in 1840 the railway came through their estate and kept them going another hundred years.) The Blimps always marry beneath them and never marry beauties; in consequence they are neither a handsome nor a well-mannered family.

Under this Blimp the Royal Patagonians were led in 1776 against the American revolutionaries. They were cut to pieces at Breed's Hill, reformed, and in 1782 forced to capitulate at Yorktown. '*Mong Dew, Moosoo!*' cried Colonel Blimp, as he handed his sword to General Choisy, a French ally of the Americans: 'I vow it is a pleasure to engage in civilized warfare again after these raggle-taggle catch-as-catch-can bouts with a mob of canting Mohairs and cowardly Buckskins who skulk behind trees and never come to push of bayonet.'

'Parfaitement, mon Colonel,' replied Choisy, not understanding a word of what he said. (As has already been noted, the Blimps are no linguists.)

Space presses: no room for a detailed account of the Peninsular War Blimp whom Wellington tried to cashier for incompetence, but who cleared himself at the court-martial by pleading that he always rode straight to hounds. Nor of the Indian Mutiny Blimp, who was deeply religious and rejoiced that he had 'implemented Jehovah's vengeance on those devilish copper-coloured Pandies by blowing a full company of them from our guns,' and who afterwards wrote to *The Englishman* under the signature 'Britannicus': 'The only people who have any right to India are the British; the so-called Indians have no right whatever.' Nor of his successor, the famous Bath Club Bore of the Eighties, who adulated the Prussian army, and who was enraged when by Act of Parliament commissions were no longer bought, but awarded by merit. ('Merit be damned! Gad, sir, what will become of us old military families?') He is the Blimp of whom Basil Blackwood wrote succinctly in the first World War *Hun-Hunters:*

> In times gone by, or so I've heard,
> He led the gallant Umpty-third
> To somewhere in Afghanistan
> Where they were slaughtered to a man.

At the Bath Club he was perpetually:

> . . . ventilating more of his
> Grievances against the War Office.

A word about the old man who has just died. He scraped through Sandhurst, where he learned drill and how to draw coloured maps, but nothing about geography or military history or field engineering. In the South African War he despised the Boers as much as his ancestor had despised the American revolutionaries, and won a D.S.O. (then a ration issue to C.O.'s and known as the 'Dam Silly Order'). A Boer commando surprised the Patagonian headquarters one dark night in what Colonel Blimp had thought a safe area, and he ended the war in captivity. In 1914 he returned as a dugout to command a Kitchener battalion; in 1915, on his first night in the trenches near La Bassée, he went out with a flashlight to inspect the barbed wire and, fortunately for his men, was put out of action for the rest of the War by a German sentry. He was David Low's Colonel Blimp, whom we all know so well. His son — but his son is still alive and, I regret to say, still on the active list.

The Search for Thomas Atkins

(1945)

THOMAS ATKINS was immortalized on August 31, 1815, in a War Office order. His name will be found on page 78 of a publication entitled *A Collection of Orders, Regulations, etc.*:

> *Form of a Soldier's Book in the Infantry when filled up.* Description, service &c., of THOMAS ATKINS, Private No. 6 Company, 1st battalion, 23rd Regiment of Foot. Where born: Parish of Odiham, Hants. Bounty: £6.
>   Received: THOMAS ATKINS.   X his mark....

Why not the formal: 'Private John Smith, No. 1 Company, 1st battalion, 1st Regiment of Foot,' with a less out-of-the-way birthplace than Odiham? Edinburgh, say, since the 1st Foot are the Royal Scots?

Obviously, because 'Thomas Atkins of Odiham' was a real man.

But who was he, and who immortalized him, and why? In fact, who at the War Office would have been in a position to substitute 'Atkins' for 'Smith' and 'Odiham' for 'Edinburgh'? And who would have ventured, in defiance of the tradition of regimental seniority, to substitute the 23rd Regiment for the 1st?

And who would have had any interest in doing so, probably in July 1815, when the *Form of a Soldier's Book* went to press?

Well, who was adjutant-general of the Army at that time? His august eye must have been the last to scrutinize and pass the order. He was Lieutenant-General Sir Harry Calvert, G.C.B., and here is the first part of his record in the *Royal Military Calendar* for 1820:

> On April 24th, 1778, this officer was appointed 2nd Lieutenant in the 23rd Foot and in March 1779, embarked to join that Corps in North America. On the 2nd of October he was appointed Lieutenant and embarked from New York for the siege of Charlestown. He served during that siege and the ensuing campaigns which terminated with the surrender of Yorktown and was present at the different actions that occurred, with the exception of that of Camden . . .

His regimental service ended in 1785. In 1790 he exchanged into the Coldstream Guards in order to become A.D.C. to H.R.H. the Duke of York. He rose rapidly in the service, becoming adjutant-general in 1799, while still in his thirties.

The *Royal Military Calendar* praises his urbanity. Urbanity is very well, but was he also a man to remember an old soldier? He was. Sergeant Roger Lamb of the 23rd Foot assures us of this in his *Memoir* (Dublin, 1811):

> General Calvert was from the outset of his military life endeared to the men under his command and it ought to be mentioned to his honour that he always appeared pleased on any occasion of benefiting an old soldier for his past services.

Lamb adds:

> The Author has derived peculiar advantage from his kind condescension in recognizing him after a lapse of years since he fought by his side and had the gratification of being particularly noticed by him for soldierly conduct in action.

So far so good. Sergeant Lamb of the 23rd we know, but who was Private Atkins of the 23rd, and why should Calvert have gone out of his way to immortalize him?

As I was turning this point over in my mind, I found myself saying: 'Thomas Fahy of Birmingham, "A" Company, 1st battalion, the Royal Welch Fusiliers.' For by a singular coincidence my own first commission, like Calvert's, was that of a second lieutenant in the 23rd Foot, the Royal Welch Fusiliers. And like Calvert I was sent overseas a few months after joining the Regiment and found myself engaged in a memorably arduous and unpleasant campaign. Now over thirty years have passed, as they had passed for Calvert, and where he wrote 'Atkins,' I write 'Fahy.' For Private Thomas Fahy of Birmingham was my batman, and I would lay long odds that Calvert's batman or orderly was Private Thomas Atkins of Odiham.

After thirty years, you see, one forgets the names of almost every private soldier in one's first command, except that of one's batman. The names of the N.C.O's stick in the memory longer, and that Calvert remembered Sergeant Lamb in 1810 and secured him an outpension of 1/- a day at Chelsea Hospital is not surprising. Lamb, already a sergeant in 1779, had seen him through his first guard-mounting parade at No. 1 Broadway, New York, and was, besides, a man of unusual distinction. He saved Lord Cornwallis from capture at Guilford Court House; carried the Colours at Camden; was appointed regimental surgeon immediately after; twice led escape parties from American prison camps; was cited by Calvert himself for gallantry in the field. It is unlikely that Atkins was of the same calibre; Fahy was not of the same calibre as his comrade Private Frank Richards, D.C.M., M.M., also of my company, and now the author, like Lamb, of two military classics. But I never think of 'Tottie' Fahy without tenderness and pride.

'Of the Parish of Odiham, Hants.' 'Odiham' rings true; though Colonel Calvert of Odiham, who has kindly searched the Parish Register for me, has been unable to find him there. The 'additional company' of the 23rd, a recruiting centre, was stationed at Winchester, a day's march away. Perhaps early in 1779 Harry Calvert as a very young officer, resplendent in new scarlet regimentals with glittering epaulettes, tall white-plumed hat, gold gorget, and white breeches, visited Odiham Market with the drums to beat up recruits. Perhaps he personally swore in Thomas Atkins, a visitor from some neighbouring parish, who had been enticed into enlistment by the recruiting sergeant's flowery set speech:

To all aspiring heroes bold who have spirits above flattery and trade, and inclinations to become gentlemen by bearing arms in His Majesty's 23rd Regiment of Foot — the Royal Welch Fusiliers . . .

followed by a promise of immortal glory, a golden guinea — not yet £6 — and a crown to drink King George's health! (Tow-row-row!)

Granted the logic of this argument, why should Sir Harry have remembered Atkins in July 1815?

This is my guess. The Waterloo despatches, written on June 29, had just come in from Wellington. Calvert would have been one of the very first to read them. I can see him hurrying from the Horse Guards, his breast heaving with emotion, to call on his old friend Colonel Frederick Mackenzie, secretary of the Royal Military College — Mackenzie had been adjutant of the 23rd, and later the D.Q.M.G. at New York. The news of the victory had already reached London, but so far without authentic detail. Mackenzie would want to hear about the 23rd — 'Ay, Fred, they have been heavily engaged, as always, and have lost heavily, as always.'

Sorrowful news of the commanding officer whom both men knew and admired. Game young Ellis who had seen his first active service with the 23rd at the age of fifteen, while his father was in command — gallant Ellis who had led the 23rd throughout the Peninsular War and had been wounded no less than eight times — heroic Ellis struck down at the head of his square in this last overwhelming victory!

A glass of Madeira solemnly drunk to the memory of Sir Henry Ellis, and another to the memory of the numerous officers and men who had fallen with him.

'Where is the Regiment quartered now?' Mackenzie asks Calvert.

Calvert answers, in an unsteady voice: 'They are encamped on the Plain of St. Denis at Paris — Paris, d'ye hear, Fred? You and I have waited four-and-thirty years for this intelligence!'

'Why, Harry, that is the very thing! It takes the bitter taste of Yorktown out of our mouths at last, hey?'

Thirty-four years! Calvert's mind had been harking back to the miserable morning of October 16, 1781, when General Lord Cornwallis, his small army outnumbered by six to one and in desperate straits from hunger, sickness, and lack of ammunition, had ordered a drummer to mount the crumbling parapet and beat a parley. The capitulation that followed was nominally, indeed, to Washington's small, ragged Provincial Army, just down from the North, who had hardly fired a shot for the past two years; but in reality to the numerous and well-equipped French Army under the Comte de Rochambeau, who had officiously intervened in the quarrel between King George and his rebellious subjects.

It had been a notable campaign against the Revolutionary armies of the South. The siege and capture of Charleston; the bloody victories against odds at Camden and Guilford Court House. The dogged pursuit of General Greene's beaten but unbroken forces through the pine barrens of the Carolinas; the bold advance over a series of creeks and broad, flooded rivers into the rich tobacco country of Washington's own Virginia. For months the officers had travelled as light and gone as hungry as the men. They had no tents, no liquor, and their food for days on end was Indian corn rasped into flour on the perforated bottom of a canteen. The usual day's ration for Calvert and Atkins had been five cobs between them — once for two days they had no food whatever. And that wild cavalry raid by the 23rd, mounted on captured blood horses and riding knee to knee with Tarleton's Greens — the raid on the Virginia State Assembly at Charlottesville! That was something to recall. They had carried off seven members, but unfortunately Thomas Jefferson, author of the Declaration of Independence, was not one of them. He had 'escaped with the greatest precipitation.' Memorable fighting at Yorktown itself, where the dismounted companies of the 23rd, whose casualties had reduced them to the weakest corps in the

Army, held Fusilier Redoubt on the extreme right flank and beat off three heavy attacks by Grenadiers of the Comte de St. Simon's brigade. The mounted companies, meanwhile, were engaging the Duc de Lanzun in a cavalry skirmish across the river at Gloucester. After the capitulation the 23rd earned not only the thanks of Cornwallis but the congratulations of St. Simon and Lanzun. They even succeeded in keeping their Colours.

But surrender is surrender and leaves a bitter taste in the mouth of a young officer. One circumstance above all must have galled Calvert's generous spirit. It was this: that though the officers of the 23rd were set free, after giving their parole not to fight again on American soil, the same liberty was denied to the other ranks who, starved, sick and ragged, were presently marched off, under a single officer, Captain Thomas de Saumarez, towards the prisoners' pen at Lancaster, Pennsylvania. Many of them were to die by the way of frostbite and exhaustion.

Contemporary accounts of this separation of the men from their officers are most affecting. I have a notion that young Harry Calvert's eyes were wet when he clapped Private Thomas Atkins on the back, slipped five guineas into his hand, and wished him good luck and a speedy liberation.

' 'Tis hard indeed to be parted from your honour!'

'Ay, Tom, and 'tis hard indeed for me to lose you. You have proved a very bold soldier and an attentive orderly-man.'

'I have no great quarrel with the rebels, your honour. This is their country, not ours. But I hope that God will spare my life to discharge another ball or two at those damned, strutting, soup-meagre Mounseers!'

'We'll drub them yet, my bold fellow! Before we die, we'll drub them East and West around the whole inhabited world!'

Returned from captivity, the 23rd had fought the French again. Fought them in St. Domingo, the Low Countries, Egypt, Denmark, Martinique. Fought them for nearly four years in Portugal and Spain until the false dawn of 1814 broke with their Regiment's triumphant entry into Toulouse. A few months' respite, now Waterloo, the true dawn; and Paris reached at last.

It Was a Stable World

(1946)

THE world was stable — a compact world of manageable size, centrally governed — a Mediterranean world with Imperial Rome as the focus, the smoke of sacrifice reeking from a thousand altars and the heavenly bodies circling in foreseeable fashion overhead. True, there was another world that began at the River Euphrates, the Eastern world into which Alexander the Great had freakishly broken three centuries before. But the Romans had left it alone since they lost thirty thousand men at Carrhae in an attempt to advance their frontiers at Parthian expense. Oriental luxury goods, jade, silk, gold, spices, vermilion, jewels, had formerly come overland by way of the Caspian Sea, and now that this route had been cut by the Huns, a few daring Greek sea captains were sailing from Red Sea ports catching the trade winds and loading at Ceylon. But commercial relations were chancy.

Northward, dense forests swarming with uncivilized, red-haired, beer-swilling Germans; and foggy Britain with its chariot fighters who seemed to have stepped from the pages of Homer; and the bleak steppes of Russia peopled by mare-milking nomad Scythians. Westward, the Ocean, supposedly extending to the point where it spilt over into nothingness. Nobody had thought it worth while to test the truth of the Greek legend that far out

234

lay a chain of islands where coconuts grew on palms and life was indolent and merry. Southward, marvellous Africa, of which only the coastal fringe had been explored; from the interior came rumours of burning deserts, pigmies, camelopards, and marshes full of cranes. Though the Greek scientist Eratosthenes had calculated the distance of the sun from the earth, and the earth's circumference at the equator, with only a small error, his theory of a global world was received with polite scorn by men of common sense; how could there be a Southern Hemisphere? An Egyptian admiral had once been sent out from Suez as a punishment for insubordination, with orders to follow the African coast as far as it went; after three years he had returned by way of Gibraltar, claiming to have circumnavigated the continent. But that was centuries before, and the fellow had been put to death for an impious report that at the Southern Cape the sun had been rising in the wrong quarter of the sky. To the ordinary Roman citizen, the earth was still as flat as the palm of his hand.

'Midmost is safest,' the Romans said — a dull, unadventurous, home-loving race, who hated the sea, preferred walking to riding, and thought banishment from their country scarcely preferable to death. They had become masters of the world against their real inclinations: the incentive to expand had not been patriotism or a self-imposed civilizing mission, as was later alleged, but family rivalry sharpened by greed. The Republican institution of the 'triumph' was to blame. While there was a sacred king at Rome, he won his title by marrying the queen's daughter or younger female relative, not by being the former king's eldest son; but in a prolonged struggle for the succession at the death of King Tullius, all the royal princesses were either defiled or killed. This unfortunate accident — not a burning love of freedom — ended the monarchy. However, in the Republic that took its place, the Senate might honour a commander-in-chief who conquered an enemy state by granting him one great royal privilege: to ride in triumph through Rome, with the captured gods — that is, their sacred statues — carried on carts behind him, himself impersonating and possessed by the scarlet-faced Oak God Mars, patron of shepherds. Republican commanders-in-chief, who were also judges of the Supreme Court, could be appointed only from the nobility, and it was rivalry between these noble families as to which could secure the most triumphs that started Roman imperialism. For the commoners who did the fighting the rewards were loot, glory, decorations for valour, and farm lands in the conquered country upon their discharge.

The technique of expansion was simple. *Divide et impera:* enter into solemn treaty with a neighbouring country, foment internal disorder, intervene in support of the weaker side on the pretense that Roman honour was involved, replace the legitimate ruler with a puppet, giving him the status of a subject ally; later, goad him into rebellion, seize and sack the country, burn down the temples, and carry off the captive gods to adorn a triumph. Conquered territories were placed under the control of a provincial governor-general, an ex-commander-in-chief who garrisoned it, levied taxes, set up courts of summary justice, and linked the new frontiers with the old by so-called Roman roads — usually built by Greek engineers and native forced labour. Established social and religious practices were permitted so long as they did not threaten Roman administration or offend against the broad-minded Roman standards of good taste. The new province presently became a springboard for further aggression.

Rome was now a great jackdaw's nest, with temples and mansions newly built in solid, vulgar, imitation-Greek style — much of it concrete with a thin marble facing — stuffed with loot from more ancient and beautiful cities. Typical scenes of 'the grandeur that was Rome' at the sack of Corinth: a group of smoke-blackened Roman infantrymen squatting on a priceless old master — Aristides's *The God Dionysus* — and shooting craps for possession of sacred chalices looted from Dionysus's temple. Others hacking souvenirs from the most famous relic of antiquity, the stern of the ship *Argo,* which had brought back the Golden Fleece from the Caucasus more than a thousand years before. The Army commander impressing on the transport captains detailed to convey unique works of art back to Rome — 'Mind you, my men, anything you lose you'll have to replace.'

The prisoners captured in these wars became slaves. The chief cause of Rome's industrial backwardness was not a lack of inventiveness, but the remarkable cheapness of highly skilled slave labour. A first-class smith or weaver or potter could often be bought for about the price that a good dairy cow would fetch nowadays, and was not much more expensive to keep. (For that matter, a Greek schoolmaster or a qualified doctor could be bought almost as cheaply.) In the Mediterranean the winter is generally short and mild, and the Romans could import unlimited cheap grain from Egypt, Libya, and Tripoli — it was not for some centuries that overcultivation made a dust bowl of the whole North African coast. Olive oil, dried fish, chick-peas, wine, and fruit were in plentiful supply. Corn mills driven by water power had been known for some generations, yet were little used; it was a principle of industrial economy to keep one's slaves, especially women, in good physical condition by making them do their daily pull at the lever of a hand mill. And though the carpenter had developed into a highly skilled cabinet-maker, three more centuries passed before the principle of the water mill was combined with that of the saw. Still more remarkable, the steam engine had been invented, and a working model had long been on show in the lighthouse at Alexandria, where it was used as a donkey engine. Capitalists were unimpressed: 'Introduce mechanical hauling into industry and encourage the workers to be lazy.' It was in the same spirit that the Emperor Tiberius, Augustus's successor, put to death an inventor who brought him a specimen of malleable and unbreakable glass: the discovery would have thrown the jewellery trade into disorder and depreciated the value of gold bullion.

On the whole, slaves were treated well and encouraged to hard work and obedience by being given occasional tips and allowed to earn money in their off hours. Eventually they could hope to buy themselves free, though still owing certain duties as freedmen to their masters; and their children would be freeborn. It was dangerous to starve slaves or flog them too freely; indeed, gross cruelty to a slave now ranked as a penal offence. This lesson had been learned in the great revolt under the gladiator Spartacus two generations before, which had all but succeeded in making the slaves their masters' masters. Slavery was now regarded by industrialists as a safeguard against the pretensions of the freeborn working classes, who could not compete in price against well-organized and well-financed slave labour. Strikes of workingmen were exceptional: as when the Levite bakers in the Temple at Jerusalem walked out on being refused a hundred per cent rise in pay. The high priest tried to break the strike by importing bakers from the rival Jewish temple at Leontopolis in Egypt, but their shewbread was not up to Jerusalem standard and the strikers gained their demands.

At the apex of the social pyramid, which was still nominally Republican, stood the Emperor Augustus. As leader of the winning side in the Civil Wars, caused by murderous rivalry between noble families, he had been invested with temporary dictatorial powers, religious as well as civil, which he was always hoping to relinquish when the time was ripe; but it never was. Under him in descending order of importance came the remains of the nobility, who formed a rubber-stamp Senate and from whom all high-ranking Army officers and Government officials were drawn; next, the knights, the heads of merchant families, eligible for less distinguished offices; next, the freeborn Roman citizens with full civil rights, including that of voting at the free democratic elections which no longer took place, and exemption from the servile punishment of crucifixion. After these, freeborn foreigners with more limited rights; then freedmen; lastly, slaves.

In the higher income groups the birth rate fell steadily despite bachelor taxes and personal appeals for fertility by the emperor. Few society women could be bothered to bear children in any number and preferred to let their husbands amuse themselves in brothels or with Greek mistresses. The society woman's day was a full one: 'Madam, your warm cinnamon milk, and the bath is ready.' 'Madam, the masseuse, the chiropodist, the hairdresser.' 'The jeweller has called to show madam the Indian emeralds.' 'The chef wishes to ask madam's advice about the wild-boar steaks. He is of opinion that they should hang a day or two longer.' 'Has madam decided after all to attend the wedding of her third cousin, the Lady Metella? It is today.' 'Madam's pet monkey has, I regret to report, been at his tricks again in the master's study. Yes, madam, I have squared the master's secretary and, please, he has undertaken to procure madam a copy of that charming, bawdy little Greek novel that she picked up at Corbulo's yesterday.' 'My Lady Lentula's compliments, and will madam confirm last night's bid of one thousand gold pieces to three hundred against Leek Green in the second race tomorrow?'

There was a constant recruitment of the nobility from the merchant class, and rich commoners who went up into the merchant class were privileged to wear a gold thumb ring and sit in seats reserved for them at the theatre immediately behind the nobility. Morals among the less fortunately born were based largely on social ambition. Conviction for petty felonies disqualified a man from membership in the social clubs of his class; serious felony degraded him. There was also a vague fear that crimes, even when successfully concealed, might be punished in a shadowy Hell with perpetual tortures. Belief in the Islands of Elysium where virtue was rewarded with a life of perpetual bliss was still vague; besides, Homer had made it clear that these abodes were reserved for royalty. Ordinary citizens became twittering ghosts and went down to Hell, and stayed there, except for an annual ticket-of-leave holiday between owlcry and cockcrow when their pious descendants put food out for them to lick at, and themselves kept carefully indoors.

Among the governing classes, superstitious fear of evil omens, ghosts, and bogeys contrasted with the fashionable scepticism about the gods. However, the majesty of law and the sanctity of treaties depended in theory on the official Olympian cult, and so did the complicated system of national holidays and popular entertainments. Jokes at the expense of ill-tempered, lecherous old Father Juppiter, his shrewish wife Juno, and his clever, unmarried daughter Minerva — the Roman trinity — were confined to intimate gatherings. But gods and goddesses, so far from being jealous guardians of family morals, permitted and even demanded periodical orgies of drunkenness and sexual promiscuity as healthy vents for popular emotion. Their images presided at the wild-beast shows, chariot races, gladiatorial fights, dances, plays,

musical entertainments, and displays of juggling and contortion-
ism, arranged in their honour by endowed priesthoods.

There was no system of public education even for the freeborn
except in Greek cities, which still prided themselves on their high
standard of culture, and among the Jews everywhere, for whom
attendance at the synagogue school was now a religious obliga-
tion. Elsewhere, reading, writing, and arithmetic were luxuries
reserved for the governing and mercantile classes with their
stewards, secretaries, accountants, and agents.

The Jews were at once a comfort and a worry to the central
government. Though industrious, law-abiding, and peaceful
wherever they were left alone, they were not merely a nation of
perhaps three and a half millions settled in Palestine under the
rule of Herod the Great, — a petty king appointed by the emperor, — with a tribal god, a temple, and established festivals.
They were also a huge religious fraternity, including a great many
converts of non-Jewish race, whose first article of faith was that
there was only one god, and that intimate contact with goddess-
worshippers was sinful and disgusting. Far more Jews lived outside than inside Palestine, spread about in small or large communities from one end of the Roman world to another, and over
the edge of the world in Babylonia. They were a serious obstacle
to the Imperial policy of encouraging provincials to pay divine
honours to the emperor, but still enjoyed complete religious freedom. The distinction between Semites and Europeans had not
yet been drawn; for the Spartans, who were pure Greeks, officially claimed cousinship with the Jews in virtue of a common
descent from Abraham. There was, however, strong local jealousy
of Jews who had broken into Greek commercial spheres, with
which went resentment of them as spoilsports and religious prigs.

Colour was no problem. If the question had ever arisen — but
it never did — whether the black races were inferior to the white,
the answer would immediately have been found in Homer, who
was quoted as an inspired authority in all matters of general
morality: 'Homer relates that the blessed gods themselves used
to pay complimentary visits to the Blameless Ethiopians.' Colour
was not popularly associated with slavery, since slaves were for the

most part white, and nothing prevented coloured monarchs from owning white slaves if honestly come by. Nor was miscegenation frowned upon. Augustus rewarded his ally King Juba II, a Moor, with the hand of Selene, the beautiful daughter of Cleopatra, the Greek queen of Egypt, and his own late brother-in-law Mark Antony.

The Romans were oddly backward in military development except in the arts of entrenchment, siege warfare, and infantry drill with javelin and stabbing-sword. They never practised archery, even for sport, or formed their own cavalry units, but relied for flank protection of their solid, slow-moving infantry masses on allied lancers and horse-archers, including many coloured squadrons. To join the army usually meant staying with one's regiment until the age of sixty, and campaigning was arduous, especially against active and light-armed foresters or mountaineers. The soldier's load weighed more than eighty pounds, which he had to hump for fifteen or twenty miles a day in all weathers; rations were poor, comforts few, pay irregular, floggings frequent. But peacetime garrison duty in big frontier camps was pleasant enough. A regiment kept the same station for generations, and the camp gradually developed into a city as camp-followers set up shops and booths under the protection of the fortifications and soldiers married native women and built permanent huts. In remote outposts of the Empire time dragged. Last year an inscription was found on the site of a small Roman camp on the Libyan frontier to this effect: 'The Company commander fears that it will be a long time before their promised relief arrives from Rome; meanwhile the Company have made the best of a bad job and hereby dedicate this commodious swimming pool to the Goddess of Army Welfare.'

The swimming pool was a Greek institution. It was from the Greeks that the Romans had learned practically all they knew: law, literary technique, public speaking, philosophy, engineering, music, medicine, mathematics, astronomy, stagecraft and acting, domestic and industrial science, sanitation and athletics. But, with a few noble exceptions, they were all barbarians at heart, and in athletics, for example, showed no innate sense of sportsmanship nor any appreciation of the finer points of play. In the public ring they abandoned the Greek style of boxing with light leather gloves in favour of Keystone Comedy knuckle-dusters studded with iron points with which outsize heavyweights slogged chunks off one another.

No great epidemics of plague, typhus, and cholera, such as ravaged Europe in the Middle Ages, are recorded in this epoch. Well-regulated water supply and sewage systems in cities, official supervision of foodstuffs and wine exposed for sale, and a general determination to enjoy life to the full while it lasted: all these increased popular resistance to disease. Medicine, too, was in a saner state than it reached again until the nineteenth century: cures were effected by tried herbal remedies, fomentations, dieting, exercise, massage, and spa waters. Greek surgeons following in the wake of Roman armies had acquired a better knowledge of human anatomy from battlefield observation than had hitherto been possible from dissection of mummies in the Alexandrian medical school; and dentists undertook fillings and complicated bridgework as well as extractions. Mail and transport services ran smoothly throughout the Empire, the insurance rate for shipping was low, now that piracy had been suppressed, and losses by burglary and fire were infrequent. Bureaucracy had just begun rearing its anonymous head: the Emperor Augustus, grown too old and weary to manage all the official business that falls to a dictator, allowed his ex-slave secretariat to issue minutes, demands, and routine orders under his seal.

Typical success story: M. Fullanus Atrox, grandson of a Sicilian slave, has made money in hogs, invested it in a suburban tile factory and a block of tenements in central Rome. He now sells a half interest in the factory, which is receiving heavy orders from Spain and North Africa, buys a villa near Naples complete with central heating, baths, a picture gallery, formal gardens, stabling, twenty acres of good land, and accommodation for fifty slaves — the very villa where his father once stoked the furnace. He marks the happy occasion by presenting a solid gold salver engraved with poplar leaves to the nearby temple of Hercules —

it will create a good impression locally. At the same time he sends his son to the university at Athens.

It was a stable world. But the farther from the hub one went the uglier grew the scene, especially after Augustus's succession by less humane and energetic emperors. When the poorly paid Roman armies of occupation were quartered in the provinces of Asia Minor and Syria, the rich man was bled but the poor man was skinned. Banditry, beggary, blackmail, and squalor abounded. Conditions were as bad after the death of Herod the Great in the Protectorate of Judaea, where Communism was already flourishing among the ascetic communities of the Dead Sea area, and in the Native State of Galilee. The cost of living in Galilee, during Jesus's ministry, was excessively high. Everything was taxed separately: houses, land, fruit trees, cattle, carts, fishing boats, market produce, salt. There was also a poll tax, a road tax, and taxes on exports and imports. Worse: the collection of taxes was leased to private financiers and subleased by them to contractors who had to buy police protection at a high cost. The Disciples were poor working men with dependents. When they were on the road their annual out-of-pocket account — apart even from money handed out to the distressed — can hardly have been less than three or four thousand pounds sterling. But out they went, two by two, deploring the instability of a world that was based on greed, lovelessness, and the power of the sword. Surprisingly, St. Luke mentions among their financial backers the wife of a high finance officer of the rapacious Native Court.

Caenis on Incest
A.D. 75

(1946)

CAENIS, the Emperor Vespasian's wife by courtesy, was in her study checking an Honours List of new knights when the door burst open and Domitilla, his young granddaughter, came raging in. 'Why, what has happened, child? You're flushed to the neck.'

'I've been dreadfully insulted. Oh, I could *kill* that Astraea!'

'Kill your best friend? What did she do?'

'She's been politely hinting at things for a long time, and just now I ordered her, in the name of all the gods, to speak out plainly. So she asked me — guess what? She had the impertinence to ask me — oh, really, I can hardly bear to tell you — she asked whether I ever sleep with either of my brothers! I was so surprised, I couldn't think of a really crushing answer. I just asked: "Why on earth should I?" And she said: "Oh, I'm sorry. I thought Roman princesses always did." And then she started talking about those loathsome creatures, Caligula and Nero. And then . . . then I lost my temper.'

'Don't be too cross with her, my dear. She meant no harm. In fact, it was almost a compliment. Incest is a divine prerogative, you know.'

'But dear Caenis,' said Domitilla, cooling down a little, *'why,* tell me *why,* did Caligula and Nero and the rest of the Caesars behave in such a ridiculous and revolting way? You can't imagine Grandfather Vespasian having ever committed incest with his sister or his mother, now can you? And incest seems such a dull crime, too. I mean, who in his senses would want to sleep with his own family? One sees too much of them, don't you agree, to make the prospect in the least exciting. What was wrong with them all? You ought to know, if anyone does — I'm told you were once secretary to Antonilla, the last of the family, whom the Emperor Nero killed. By the way, you don't mind my asking, do you?'

Caenis smiled and said slowly: 'I suppose it all started with Julius Caesar and Cleopatra.'

'Really? That sounds promising. Go on.'

'You know that Julius conquered Egypt and liked the place so much that he decided to keep it as a family possession by marrying her? The reason was that the right to be the Pharaoh of Egypt had always been won by marrying the royal heiress, who was the incarnation of the Goddess Isis. This was usually done by her eldest brother, or nearest male relative, who then became an incarnation of the God Osiris; so the throne was always kept in the same male line, except when an invader married the heiress instead. Well, Julius brought Cleopatra to Rome, where he already had a wife, and put her statue in the Temple of Venus. Venus was supposed to be the ancestress of the Julian family — she once had an affair with Aeneas's father Anchises. So this was as much as to say: "Venus, here is a divine cousin of yours come to visit you." '

'What about his Roman wife?'

'Oh, she had to accept the distinction he drew between a human and a divine marriage.'

'But I don't see what this has to do with Nero and Caligula and their revolting ways. Julius didn't commit incest with Cleopatra.'

'No, no. But the marriage gave him ideas. Julius was a student of ancient religion and descended through his mother from Ancus Marcius, one of the ancient kings of Rome. So he knew something that the historian Livy either didn't know or pretended he didn't, which was that in Rome too the title of king — and a king was a sort of god — was won by marriage with the royal heiress, and that the Republic came into existence simply because the female line, in whom the Goddess Carmenta was incarnate, became extinguished by the famous suicide of Lucrece. Julius would have liked to become a Roman king, but there was no royal heiress to marry. So he had to become a god instead, which could be arranged by simple decree of the Senate — who did as he told them. He put the decree through a year before his death. As a god, he was above human law and, like Juppiter, could sleep with any woman, or boy, he pleased.'

'Is it true that his grandnephew Octavian, who afterwards became Augustus, was really his son, as well as his heir, by uncle-and-niece incest?'

'If the rest of the story makes any sense at all, he must have been, though he was born long before Julius was deified. But step by step. Julius's colleague Mark Antony survived him, you remember, and he and Octavian joined forces and defeated Julius's murderers. Then they shared the world between them for some years, until they fell out. The fact was that Octavian, as soon as he had learned that he was Julius's heir and that he and his sister Octavia were both of divine parentage, had counted himself as a god, too, and — as I suppose Julius had intended — founded a new sacred monarchy by a secret divine marriage with her. She was already married, and so was he; but divine marriages are on a higher plane than human ones and can be contracted between already married people without the need of human divorce. In fact, when Octavia became a human widow, Octavian married her to Antony as a mark of confidence. But Antony grew restive and decided to become a god himself by marrying Cleopatra; which was poaching on Octavian's Egyptian preserves. And Cleopatra was pleased to make him her new Osiris and bear him children. However, Antony's new dignity was not recognized by the Senate; Octavian had Rome in his pocket. The last phase of the Civil Wars was a contest between Octavian and Antony as to which of them could press his claim to godhead with the strongest backing of armed force. You see, Antony didn't marry Cleopatra until news reached him of the secret *dodecatheos* ceremony at which Octavian had solemnly proclaimed his divinity. That shocked and alarmed him and he wrote to his own supporters at Rome, protesting against "these new divine adulteries".'

'What's a *dodecatheos?*'

'It's a love banquet of six gods and six goddesses. They used to be held in the Heroic Age, if the legends are to be trusted. Octavian was now calling himself Augustus, "the Holy One," and calling Octavia "Augusta," though these titles were not confirmed officially until after Antony's defeat. The twelve banqueters who impersonated gods and goddesses were all members of Augustus's family, or very close friends of his.'

'I suppose Augustus played the part of Juppiter?'

'No, he was not quite so bold as that. Although, while Augustus was still a six-weeks' old baby, his reputed father had dreamed of him as dressed in the robes of the God Juppiter with a radiant crown and a thunderbolt in his hand, Augustus didn't dare play the part of Juppiter and make Octavia play Juno. He couldn't risk being struck by lightning from heaven. As a child he had once been scared nearly to death by thunder, and now always took cover during a storm with a strip of sealskin wrapped round his thumb: a precaution that his ancestor Anchises had failed to take after his rash affair with Venus. No, he preferred to be Apollo, and make Octavia into Minerva, though of course Minerva is supposed to be a chaste virgin goddess. The parts of Juppiter and Juno were played by the Rex Sacrorum and his wife the Regina Sacrorum, the priest and priestess on whom, at the demise of the sacred monarchy, the monthly public sacrifices to Juppiter and Juno had devolved; they used to be performed by the real king and queen. Agrippa, whose sea victory at Actium later broke Antony's power, was Neptune and ever afterwards flew a sea-green pennant at his masthead. An ex-consul named Ventidius, who had recently triumphed over the Parthians, was Mars. Young Julia, Augustus's daughter by a wife he had divorced nine years before, was Venus; and Livia, his present wife, whom he loved devotedly and who was his right hand in all adminis-

trative and social business, was Vesta, Goddess of the Hearth.
I forget who played the parts of Mercury, Ceres, and Vulcan —
I can look it up for you if you like, but it doesn't affect the story.
At any rate, that was the banquet, all very merry and incestuous
and glorious, but Antony was not one of the banqueters and
resented being left out. Well, when their quarrel was decided at
Actium, Augustus was free to behave as he liked. He was disappointed that Cleopatra took poison and escaped him, because
after displaying her in his Triumph he would have performed a
divine marriage with her — she was still quite young; but he was
able to proclaim himself Pharaoh by decree, I suppose after a
private marriage with little Selene, her daughter by Antony, but
that's only a guess of mine.'

'But why did Augustus never play the god in public, as
Caligula did? Why didn't he even allow the Senate to proclaim
him a god?'

'Julius's assassination had alarmed him, and he was very careful indeed not to incur the jealousy either of god or man. He
lavished gifts on the gods, while living in very meanly furnished
quarters in his palace, dressed unostentatiously, ate below his
station, worked very hard, and throughout his long life kept up
the pretence that the Republic was still in existence — that he was
a simple citizen who happened to combine all the supreme offices
of state in his own person, but one day would resign them all and
give others a chance to rule. Even so, four attempts were made
to assassinate him, and the gods plagued him with a series of
domestic misfortunes.'

'It must have felt queer to be both god and man, with a
different wife in each character.'

'He took it as a joke. Wait a minute, and I'll show you a copy
of a letter that my poor mistress Antonilla gave me. It's from
Augustus as man to Augustus as god . . . In that case over there
. . . This roll; I think I've marked the place. Yes, here it is.
Listen:

'What has come over you, Octavian? Do you object to my sleeping
with a Queen? Isn't she my wife, if I choose to make her so?'

'Oh, so the wicked old man was having an affair with the Regina Sacrorum, who played the part of Juno? I see what Antony meant by "new divine adulteries"!'

'Yes, that's right. And he goes on:

'And is this the first time that I have slept with her? Didn't I sleep with her nine years ago? My dear sir, would you have me remain faithful to my consort Octavia? What about yourself? Are *you* faithful to Livia Drusilla? Get along with you, and I wish you the best of luck! When you get this letter you'll feel like sleeping with Tertulla, or Terentilla, or Rutilla, or Salvia Titisenia, or the whole lot of them. You surely don't think it matters in the least what love affairs you have, do you?'*

'How did Livia feel about it?'

'She didn't much mind Augustus committing adultery, but she hated being the human wife, rather than the divine one. However, she did nothing about it until Augustus chose Marcellus, his son by incest with Octavia, to be his heir, over the head of Drusus, who was her own son by him, though supposedly the son of her former husband. Marcellus was married to Augustus's only legitimate child, his daughter Julia, but was intended eventually to contract a divine marriage with his youngest sister, Antonia Minor, or with this Antonia's youngest marriageable daughter — for you see, the succession was by ultimogeniture — which means that the royal heiress was always the youngest marriageable daughter of the most junior line. Livia knew that if Marcellus became emperor she'd be put on the shelf, and she wanted to go on running the Empire in her own way. So she secretly poisoned him. Augustus felt his death as a terrible blow, because it seemed to be the work of Apollo and Minerva, who always kill by mysterious diseases, not by lightning or any other means — a revenge for their having been impersonated at the *dodecatheos*. Antonia Minor then married Drusus; but unfortunately Drusus did not welcome the career that his mother planned for him — of becoming emperor after Augustus's death and allowing her to be his chief minister of state. He was a red-

* Quoted by Suetonius.

hot Republican; so she had to get rid of him too and refound
her ambitions on her elder son Tiberius, who was not Augustus's
son — and Augustus couldn't bear the sight of him — but who
was more amenable than Drusus. Eventually she managed to
make Tiberius emperor by poisoning or otherwise doing away
with all male descendants of Augustus who seemed at all
dangerous. But that's a long story. She kept a constant close eye
on the royal heiress of the moment and whoever married her,
or had designs on her, signed his own death warrant.'

'How does Julia come in? Augustus was her father and he
had made her a sort of goddess at the *dodecatheos,* hadn't he? I
remember hearing that Livia got her banished for some crime
or other.'

'Thank you for keeping my complicated story straight. Yes,
Julia comes in exactly here. When Marcellus died, Augustus
married her to Agrippa, who had played Neptune on that same
occasion and who was his right-hand man in all military affairs.
She had several children by him. But one son, who died as a
child, and her daughter Agrippina were born in divine incest
between Julia as Venus and her father Augustus as Apollo. Unfortunately Julia didn't inherit her father's caution. She didn't
see why she should distinguish between Julia as Venus and
Julia as woman, and in the end, after Agrippa's death and her
marriage to Tiberius — which Livia insisted on — she played her
ancestress Venus in the old Amazonian style that had been forgotten in Italy for many hundreds of years. Believe it or not,
she performed the sexual act in public, in the Market Place here
at Rome, with a succession of patrician lovers. They say that the
poet Ovid put her up to it.'

Domitilla laughed: 'That certainly was going a little too far.'

'But the public scandal wasn't so serious as the religious and
political implications of her act. Julia was attempting to revive
matriarchal government in its purest form; and Augustus, when
he heard of it, was deeply shocked and frightened too. There
was nothing for it but to banish her for life to a small island
near Elba, though she was his divine wife. So that was the end
of Julia; but Agrippina, her daughter by Augustus, considered

herself a royal heiress born of a quasi-Apollo and a quasi-Venus. Now there were two lines of royal heiresses, which complicated the story even more as time went on. The most dangerous of the two, Livia found, was the Octavia line. Antonia Minor's daughter Livilla was now a young queen bee at whom all the drones in the hive made a dead set. Livia had taken the precaution of marrying her to Tiberius's only son, nicknamed 'Castor,' but when eventually Augustus died and Tiberius became emperor, Augustus's one surviving legitimate grandson, Postumus Agrippa, tried to run away with Livilla as a preliminary to seizing the throne — he could count on half the Army and the whole fleet to support him. However, Livia's spies got to know about the affair in time and Postumus was put out of the way. Later, when Tiberius quarrelled with Livia and went to live in Capri out of her reach, with Sejanus as his viceroy, Sejanus tried to play the same game as Postumus. Livilla was willing enough to marry him and poisoned her husband as a preliminary; but the insurrection failed, and when her part in the plot was discovered, Tiberius had her starved to death. Her only daughter, the new Octavia heiress, was still a child; so Tiberius's chief concern was now with Agrippina, his nephew's widow, the heiress of the Julia line. He refused to let her remarry and kept her under continual surveillance. He told her once:

> And if you are not Queen, my dear,
> Think you that you are wronged?

In the end he found it safest to banish her to the same island on which her mother Julia had died. Her disappearance encouraged someone else to claim the title of royal heiress. This was Quintilia Minor, daughter of Quintilius Varus.'

'The one who lost three Roman legions in the German forests?' asked Domitilla. She felt as though she were drowning in a sea of names and Varus was firm historical ground to her.

'Yes, that one. She thought she had a better claim than anyone else as being the granddaughter of Marcella Minor, Octavia's second daughter, born during her first human marriage but presumably fathered by Augustus. Tiberius accused Quintilla — and her mother and her sister too, for good luck — of high treason and adultery and had them executed. This left no descendants in the direct female line from either Marcella Minor or her sister Marcella Major — I forgot to mention the execution, for adultery and treason, of Marcella Major's only daughter, Apuleia Varilia — so Tiberius felt easier in mind.'

'Do let's go on to Caligula and Nero, Caenis dear,' Domitilla pleaded. 'I can't take in much more.'

'All right then. So in the end the Old Ram, as they called him, was murdered and succeeded by his only surviving nephew, Caligula, who boasted of his mother Agrippina's incestuous birth from Julia by Augustus, and played the god openly. He secured his divine title to the throne by an incestuous marriage with all his three sisters, but showed the greatest interest in Drusilla, the youngest of them. When she died, he proclaimed her the Goddess Panthaea and had her decreed the same honours as Venus. The middle sister, nicknamed Lesbia, was then the Julia heiress; but Caligula banished her and the eldest one, Agripinilla, to an island off Libya so that they should not prove an embarrassment to him. Caligula impersonated not merely one god but all of them, or all except Neptune, with whom he professed to have a war: at one time he went about with a thunderbolt like Juppiter, wearing a golden beard, at another with a serpent wand like Mercury. Sometimes he even pretended to be Venus in a silk dress, with an artificial bosom and women's shoes.'

'What did Caligula look like?'

'Tall, pasty-faced, rather bald, with an awkward gait. He reeked of attar of roses and made a very queer Venus. Well, when he was murdered and his supposedly half-witted uncle Claudius became emperor, Lesbia and Agripinilla were recalled from exile. Claudius was already married to his distant cousin Messallina, who was nearly but not quite the heiress in the Octavia line. She was the granddaughter of Antonia Major, the last female descendant of Antonia Minor being Livilla's daughter Julia Livilla, now old enough to be dangerous. Messallina succeeded in removing Julia Livilla and also Lesbia, the royal heiress in the Julia line, with whom the philosopher Seneca had been having an unphilosophical affair. The remaining Julia heiress, Agripinilla, she dared not touch because Claudius had put her under his personal protection. One day when Claudius was out of town Messallina celebrated a divine marriage with a young nobleman named Silius on whom she intended to confer the Empire. Claudius returned just in time and his freedmen persuaded him to put her to death; after which, of course, he openly married the Julia heiress, Agripinilla — though he had to get a special dispensation from the Senate to excuse this act of incest — because he was warned that, if he did not, someone else would, and take away his Empire. The cream of the joke is that Claudius, being supposedly half-witted, had never been trusted with public office or let into the family secret of the royal heiresses. So he never understood why his relatives were killing one another so consistently, or why he had to marry Agripinilla.'

'Then he *was* half-witted?'

'No, only a little slow at drawing conclusions and easily hoodwinked. Agripinilla eventually poisoned him and put her son Nero on the throne. By this time there were only four female members of the royal line left — I think that's right: Agripinilla, the Julia heiress; Julia Calvina her cousin, granddaughter of Agrippina's elder sister Julilla; the Octavia heiress Octavilla, Claudius's daughter by Messallina; and Messallina's mother Domitia Lepida. Agripinilla persuaded Nero that her own claim through Julia was better than Octavia's and that the only way for him to be emperor in a religious sense was to commit incest with her. He agreed, but he also took the precaution of marrying Octavilla, banishing Calvina on a charge of incest with her brother Lucius Silanus, and executing Domitia Lepida. Agripinilla insisted on running the Empire for him in a way he didn't like; so after an attempt to kill her by poison (but her slaves were too faithful) and by sending her to sea in a collapsible boat (but she had learned to swim like a fish during her exile on that Libyan island, and got ashore easily), he sent a squad of soldiers to kill her, and that was that. Calvina died in exile.'

'Good, so now Octavilla was the only royal heiress left. She was quite young, wasn't she?'

'Not yet twenty and very charming. I knew her very well, of course. But Nero disliked her because her face reminded him of her brother Britannicus whom he had murdered and whose ghost was haunting him. He decided to divorce her and marry a noble-woman called Poppaea. My mistress Antonilla told me that Nero's friend Afranius Burrhus tried to dissuade him by saying ironically: "Divorce her by all means, but give her back her dowry" — meaning the right to marry someone else and make him emperor. But he divorced her and then put her out of the way, arguing that Julius as a god had single-handedly revived the extinct female line of the Goddess Carmenta; and now that it had become extinct again, why shouldn't he found another? He was a god too, and the sacred magic of the previous em-perors, all of whom, except Tiberius, were deified either during their life or immediately after their death, was vested in him; why shouldn't he dispose of it as he pleased? So he married Poppaea and made her a goddess by decree and put her statue in the Temple of Venus. She bore him a daughter to whom he immediately gave the title of Augusta; but she died in infancy. Poppaea was with child again when one night he lost his temper with her because she scolded him for coming home too late from the races. He kicked her in the belly, and so killed both her and his unborn child. But Juppiter had behaved just as badly to Juno once, he reminded himself. Then he grew alarmed at various portents of destruction and decided that his divine ancestors were cross with him and wanted him to marry Claudius's only sur-viving daughter, my mistress Antonilla.'

'Why wasn't she an heiress?'

'Because her mother, Aelia, Sejanus's adoptive sister, had not been royal. But she was at least the daughter of a god on the male side, now that Claudius was deified. However, Antonilla refused the honour, so he said: "Be damned to her then," and had her executed on a charge of high treason. Not long after that, Galba raised a revolt in Spain, and Nero knew himself deserted

≡ PEDIGREE OF THE ROYAL HEIRESSES OF THE JULIAN HOUSE ≡

Marcia m. C. Julius Caesar

Julius Caesar

Julia m. Atius Balbus

Atia m. G. Octavius

Augustus m. Scribonia, then m. Livia, mother of Tiberius and Drusus

Julia m. Marcellus, m. Agrippa, then Tiberius

C. Marcellus m. Octavia Augusta, who then m. Mark Antony, who later m. Cleopatra of Egypt

Antonia Major m. Domitius Ahenobarbus

Antonia Minor m. Drusus

Claudius m. Aelia

Antonilla

Marcella Major M. S. Apuleius

Marcella Minor Marcellus m. Valerius Messala

Barbatus

Apuleia Varilia

Claudia Pulchra m. Quintilius Varus

Quintilia Major

Quintilia Minor

Domitia

Domitia Lepida m. Barbatus

Messallina m. Claudius (q.v.) then Silius

Octavilla m. Nero

Britannicus

Livilla m. 'Castor'   Germanicus

Julia Livilla m. Nero, m. R. Blandus

Gaius   Lucius   Postumus

Drusus

Caligula m. Caesonia

Drusilla Minor

Domitius

Agrippina m. Germanicus

Julilla m. Aemilius

'Ganymede'

Aemilia m. App. Silanus

M. Silanus

L. Silanus

Julia Calvina

Drusilla Major

'Lesbia'

Agripinilla m. Domitius, then m. Claudius

Nero

Nero m. Octavilla, m. Poppaea

Augusta

255

by the gods; he ran off and committed suicide. That was the end of the Caesars; and after the year of three emperors — Galba, Otho, and Vitellius — your grandfather came to the throne. Your grandmother was already dead, and he didn't want to play the god or start any new nonsense with new goddesses; but he needed a common-sense woman to live with, someone capable of helping him with the social side of Empire, and I had the great honour of being chosen by him. Of course, he couldn't marry me honourably — I had no rank — but that was all to the good, really. I *did* understand official business, and I do work pretty hard, and though jealous people spread nasty rumours about me, I must say, Domitilla, that you and your brother Lord Titus have treated me handsomely.'

Domitilla laughed. 'Oh, dear Caenis, I am so glad Grandfather isn't a god! Promise you won't let him be one!'

'I promise. Now run along, child, and make it up with Astraea.'

'I *did* slap her rather hard,' Domitilla admitted.

Está en su Casa

(1946)

'*OLÁ — señor!*'

The sudden summons came from a thin, hook-nosed man in
a baggy white shirt, blue striped cotton trousers, and a black
felt hat, who rose suddenly from behind a mastic bush a few
yards off. I had been sitting for ten minutes or more on the
stone bench of the *mirador,* a lookout platform built on the
cliff edge, idly watching a tall-funnelled Spanish destroyer dis-
engage itself from the horizon and disappear behind the distant
headland to the northeast. Below me was a drop of nearly a
thousand feet to a glaring white stony beach.

I sprang up, startled, and may have answered in English; but
I do not remember. He forced a reassuring smile, spread out both
hands to show that he was unarmed, and said in Spanish: 'Please
forgive my disturbance of your tranquillity. You are an American?'

I answered: 'No, *señor,* you must not judge me by my elegant
straw hat, a gift from a friend in the United States. Judge me
rather by my old shirt and patched trousers. I am one of the
victorious but bankrupt English. What a stifling day, is it not?'

This put him at his ease. 'Yes, it is very hot,' he said. But he
stayed where he was, so I strolled over to him.

'Your first visit to Mallorca?' he asked.

257

'The first time since the troubles started in 1936, when I had to leave my house and lands. And I remember you well, even if you do not remember me. Surely you are Don Pedro Samper, the proprietor of Ca'n Samper on the other side of the mountain spur?'

We shook hands heartily as I went on: 'I visited you once in the company of your neighbour Don Pablo Pons, back in 1935. I needed some really good cuttings to graft on two young apricot trees that had proved to be of poor quality, and Don Pablo informed me that you had the best tree on the island. I had the pleasure of meeting your charming and sympathetic wife. I hope she is in good health?'

'Thanks be to God, we are well, and so are the children.' He apologized several times for not having recognized me, explaining that my sun glasses, the greying of my hair, and the thinness of my face had deceived him. In return he enquired after my health, that of my family, and the condition of my property after ten years' absence. And of course he wanted to hear about the flying bombs in London. The Spanish Press had played up the havoc of the flying bomb until it was difficult for anyone to believe that there could be a single survivor. 'And is it true that in England now potatoes sell at a hundred pesetas a kilo?'

'No, at about one peseta. The farmers are subsidized by the Government.'

'Well, well!' he said. 'Our journalists seem to have been misinformed about many things . . . But, tell me, did those apricot cuttings take?'

'Divinely well. I found a barbaric crop of apricots waiting for me — the branches had to be tied up to prevent them from breaking off — and wonderful-tasting apricots they are. Like orange-blossom honey. I sold a great quantity and bottled the remainder.'

'I am delighted . . . Have you perhaps visited Don Pablo since your return? You must know that he no longer lives in these parts, but has taken a house in Palma?'

'Between ourselves, I have no intention of calling upon him. When I quitted the island at an hour's notice with only a suitcase and a wallet, I left a certain small affair for him to settle on my behalf. He neglected it, and his neglect has cost me a thousand pesetas or more. But I do not intend to recall the matter to his memory; it is already ancient history. And, finding my house in perfect condition, with everything in its place, I have reason to be grateful that his conduct is not characteristic of Majorcans in general.'

'No, indeed! His is a very special case. You know perhaps of my former disagreements with him?'

'You disputed about some irrigation rights.'

'We did indeed.'

'May I ask whether you are still on bad terms with him? In our village I find that the effect of the Troubles has been to end all personal and family feuds and unite the people as never before.'

'*Está en su casa!*, as we say here. He is in his own house; I am in mine.'

'I am sorry. I should be interested to hear the story if it doesn't inconvenience you to tell it.'

'It is a long one. But, Don Roberto — may I first ask a favour of you?'

'Anything that lies in my power.'

'I wish to seat myself on the bench of the *mirador* where you have been. I have been trying to reach it all morning since ten o'clock. Will you help me?"

'But, man, are you lame?'

'Not in my legs. In my belly.'

'You mean that you are scared? Then why go? The view is as good from that rock over there as from the *mirador* itself.'

'My doctor orders it — Doctor Guasp of Soller, a specialist. He knows a great deal about psychology, having studied in Vienna as well as in Madrid. Once I have gone there, he says, and remained calmly for awhile on the bench, making my peace with a certain important saint, my nerves will recover and I shall once more sleep all night. He even offered to come with me, but I was ashamed to put him to the trouble. I said: "No, I will go alone. I am no coward." But now I find that I cannot walk the last few steps.'

He began to stutter and a light sweat broke from his forehead. 'Excuse me,' he said, 'the heat is excessive. You will perhaps take me there in a little while when we have smoked a cigarette or two in the shade of this rock? Meanwhile I will tell you about the irrigation dispute. Have you tobacco?'

'I stupidly left my pouch at home.'

'No matter. Here is good tobacco, and cigarette paper.'

'Contraband?'

'Did I not say it was good tobacco? You cannot buy this sort at any *estanco*. Allow me, you seem to have lost the habit of rolling cigarettes. In England you smoke only Luckies and Camels?'

He began his story between puffs. 'Well, if you know anything of the matter, you will know that I had been for fifteen years the tenant farmer of the estate called Ca'n Sampol, which Don Pablo Pons acquired by his marriage with Doña Binilde.'

I nodded.

'He dispossessed me, though I had an agreement with Doña Binilde's late husband that I was secure in my life-tenancy. Don Cristobal Fuster y Fernandez was a *caballero,* a man of the strictest honour. When he inherited the estate from his brother who was killed in the Rif War, he told me in the presence of his wife: "There will be no changes here. You may cultivate Ca'n Sampol for the rest of your life, friend Pedro. You have transformed the place since you took it over, and I am happy to leave it in your hands." In the island, as you know, a verbal agreement is sufficient between neighbours, and if there is a witness present it becomes binding in law. To ask to have it put in writing is bad manners. We pride ourselves on being men of our word. Well, a catastrophe! In 1934, Don Cristobal died in a road accident, and Doña Binilde fell in love, at the funeral itself, with a profligate adventurer — this same Don Pablo — and married him on the very first day that the law permitted.'

'I did not know that there are restrictions in Spain on immediate marriage in such cases.'

'There is a law that safeguards the rights of posthumous children. Well, as you can imagine, the marriage caused a scandal, and I, for one, did not attend the wedding — out of respect for the memory of Don Cristobal. Not a week later Don Pablo served me notice to quit the farm, which he proposed to cultivate himself.'

'And Doña Binilde?'

'She was infatuated with the man. He could do nothing wrong. And she was angry with me for my coolness towards her. When I appealed to her about the agreement made in her presence between Don Cristobal and me, she answered: "Upon my word, peasant, I can remember nothing. I have a bad head for business matters." '

'But the law protected you?'

'Certainly it did. In those days six years' notice was necessary. But I chose not to take the case to court. It is an uncomfortable position for a man to be tenant to a landlord who has a grudge against him, especially if the wife has instigated it. So I said to him, mildly enough: "Since Doña Binilde has lost her memory for the acts and sayings of the best husband in Mallorca, how can I press the matter? My word is not good enough for you, I see. Well, then, pay me ten thousand pesetas and I will leave on St. Anthony's Day, when I have passed the olives safely through the mill." For it was not a bad olive year.'

' "Ka, man! Why should I pay you ten thousand pesetas?" asked Don Pablo.

' "It is customary to compensate a tenant in lieu of notice. I am asking two years' rent."

' "Two years' rent! How two years' rent? You have ruined the estate by your mismanagement!" he yelled.

'I insisted: "The respected Don Cristobal — may his soul rest in peace — thought otherwise. He knew that I found Ca'n Sampol in a derelict condition and added many thousands to its value. He told me so in the presence of Doña Binilde."

' "I remember nothing of that. I have a bad head for business matters," the lady said very stubbornly. "And, in the Virgin's Name, who are you to decide who is the best husband in Mallorca and who the worst?"

'I should not have believed it possible that a decent woman

could change so, even with the help of peroxide and red nail
varnish; but some women are as accommodating as chameleons.'

'But you got some compensation, surely?'

'Not two *reals*. I will explain. Don Cristobal, like so many
gentlemen of a generous nature, had been slack about keeping
accounts. He had a good memory for sums due, and sums
owing, but disliked committing his memory to paper, and either
demanding, or making out, receipts. Don Pablo was aware of
this peculiarity and therefore asked me to show the rent receipts
for the last few years of my Ca'n Sampol tenancy. Four half-
yearly receipts were missing. So he set those against the two
years' compensation that I asked, and I had no redress, having
always paid in cash, not by cheque, and having no witness to
the payments.'

'What a nasty insect! And then you went to live at Ca'n
Samper?'

'Yes. It had been bequeathed me by my old uncle some three
years before: family property descended from my great-grand-
parents. They had once owned Ca'n Sampol too, though that
was before the big house had been built there in Carlist times.
You have seen Ca'n Samper. It is a small place but the soil is
good, there is plenty of water, and the orchard is valuable.'

'Someone told me a local proverb about its position . . . something about twitching hairs from a beard — I forget.'

He laughed nervously: 'Yes, that is right. St. Peter, we say in
our village, sits on St. Paul's neck and twitches the hairs from
his beard. The proverb refers to the two saints' sharing the same
feast day. St. Peter takes precedence and robs St. Paul of the
glory.

'And in the geographical sense Samper — the name is a contrac-
tion of the Mallorcan words *San Per,* or St. Peter — sits on the
neck of Sampol, or *San Pol,* namely, St. Paul, because of my
farm's situation just above the small western bulge of the Ca'n
Sampol terraces. Yes, *señor,* though not showing any animosity,
I decided to put a tight collar round Don Pablo's neck, a regular
martingale, and pluck out a few bristles from his chin. Meanwhile, my wife and I could live comfortably enough at Ca'n

Samper and enjoy the respect and affection of the village, who soon knew all about the poor trick that Don Pablo had played us. Now we come to the story of the irrigation rights.'

He paused for a minute while he rolled and lighted another cigarette.

' "Water is gold," ' I quoted in the sententious local style which keeps conversation on the move.

' "And land without water is stones and dust," he agreed. Well, while I had been farming Ca'n Sampol, secure in my life-tenancy, I had not made much distinction in my mind between it and my own farm; in fact, I had rather robbed Peter to keep Paul fat. At Ca'n Sampol I had planted a very fine grove of orange trees — Florida seedless navels, brought from Valencia, the first seen in the island. They need a lot of water about midsummer, but if well tended they yield fruit the size of canteloupes and of a marvellous juiciness. Well, St. John's Day came around and Don Pablo's bailiff greeted me in the church porch after mass, and asked me to let down the water from Ca'n Samper every Monday and Friday, if that suited me. And I said, playing the innocent: "Ka, man, why do you want water? You have plenty in Ca'n Sampol. Enough for goldfish ponds and fountains and a turbine for the electric light."

' "Yes," said he, "God be thanked that the greater part of the farm is well watered. But the part separated by the Rock of the Ass from the rest of the terraces, lying directly below Ca'n Samper, does not enjoy the benefit of the spring which rises on the other side of the rock. And that is precisely where you sited the new orange plantation."

' "Of course," I said. "I had almost forgotten that I planted about a hundred Florida navel oranges while I was the tenant of Ca'n Sampol. They no longer interest me." Many people were present and smiled at my words.'

' "But those terraces have a right to the water from Ca'n Samper."

' "Certainly, they have. But only to the residue. Naturally in the winter and spring, when there is plenty of rain, you can have as much as you please, because I cannot possibly use it all, not being a great water-drinker. But in June, July, August, and September I intend to use it all. There will be no residue."

' "Master Pedro, that is a bad thing to say. You should never have planted those orange trees if you intended to starve them."

' "Be reasonable, man! Who is to starve first, myself or the orange trees? Now that I have to make a living for my children from a small place like Ca'n Samper, I must intensively cultivate every square metre of it. I can no longer afford to rob Peter to make Paul fat. If Don Pablo had considered things well he would have built a small reservoir to catch the winter residue."

' "It is a holdup. This is midsummer, and unless you let down the water the trees will die. There is no great depth of soil in the plantation. The roots are touching rock already."

' "No, they will not die, but they will lose their leaves and shed their fruit, and be greatly discouraged until that reservoir is built. A pity, because they are beautiful trees."

' "What are you going to cultivate so intensively this midsummer? This is not the reason for planting vegetables or trees, and your terraces are not by any means fully sown."

' "What is it to you whether I grow twitch grass or coconuts?" That raised a loud laugh.

' "You are ill-advised to quarrel with Don Pablo."

' "I am not quarrelling with him. He is in his own house; I am in mine. If he wishes to buy water, let him come and talk to me, and we will call up a squadron of lawyers from Palma to write the affair down in a manner so clear that neither he nor I can escape our commitments." The occasion, Don Roberto, when you came with him to my house a fortnight later for the apricot cuttings — that was when he finally prevailed on himself to talk to me. As you yourself have recalled, it was St. Peter's Day and my *fiesta;* but it was also St. Paul's Day and his *fiesta.* He brought you with him as a protection, trusting that my courtesy to foreigners would restrain me from making a scandal or slamming the door in his face. You may remember that, while you were chatting with my wife, and showing my little boy your watch that opened with a secret spring and also chimed the hour, I went out with Don Pablo to fetch you the cuttings. He did his utmost to soothe and caress me, pleading that I should let by-gones be bygones, and give him at any rate a loan of the water until it was time to build a reservoir. "Have you no shame, man?" he asked. "Do you wish to lose the esteem of your neighbours? What will the village say if you let my trees die out of spite?" I laughed loudly.

'"I laugh in your face," I said, "your neighbours are laughing behind your back."

'"It is not Christian behaviour," he said. "One would take you for a *chueta**."

'"Distinguished Don Pablo, even Christians disagree at times, and your saint with my saint. For the Hermit of the Moorish Tower, who knows the Scriptures like any priest — he was once on the point of being ordained when he boxed the superior's ears and was thrown out of the Seminary — the hermit, I tell you, Don Pablo, was explaining something of importance to me last Sunday. He said that according to the *Epistle to the Galatians,* St. Paul entered upon a public argument at Antioch with St. Peter, declaring that he was much to be blamed and a regular *chueta,* trying to make everyone else into a *chueta.* But what did St. Peter answer? He refused to be drawn into a scandalous scene (says the Hermit), and instead, like St. Michael when insulted by the Devil, left the matter to be decided by God. And what was the result? He was preferred to St. Paul in all things, and entrusted with the gold and silver keys of Paradise which St. Paul was not allowed to touch, not even with one finger. I am Peter, you are Paul, and the silver key at my belt is water. Call me *chueta,* by all means, but if you want water, pay for it you must."

'So he asked me to name a price. And I said: "It is not much that I ask. Merely a written statement from your wife that I was never behindhand with my rent. That will be worth ten thousand pesetas to me. In return, I will cease to water my young coconut palms and you can have what water you require, sum-mer and winter, and be saved the expense of building a reser-voir." But he refused to do anything of the kind and called me a

---
* A Jew in Christian disguise.

bad name. It was at this point that I made a great mistake, as Doctor Guasp has since pointed out to me. If I had been content to refer historically to the quarrel between the two saints, long ago patched up in Heaven, no great harm would have been done. But before I parted with Don Pablo on this occasion I forgot the hermit's moral about not answering in kind when insulted. I championed my own saint, as was right; but in expressing my disgust of Don Pablo I foolishly sneered at the "Great Apostle to the Gentiles," as Doctor Guasp calls St. Paul, in provocative words that I now deeply regret. Well, as I expected, Don Pablo was thoroughly incensed and fetched me before the tribunal.'

'And you won your case?'

'That was easy. Not only did I have justice and documents and important witnesses on my side, but I happened to be a friend of the prosecuting attorney's secretary, so that I knew in advance exactly what questions would be asked and had all my witnesses well primed, and a series of very cutting replies ready for my own use. Moreover, I had subpoenaed Doña Binilde and she had to take the oath. Despite her love for Don Pablo, she was not going to risk her salvation by committing perjury; I knew that well. So my counsel forced her to admit that, so far as she knew, I had never been in arrears and that her husband had expressed great satisfaction with my labour. The prosecuting attorney protested that these questions were irrelevant, but the judge, who knew of the case beforehand from Doña Binilde's brother, who was very much ashamed of his sister, overruled him. Then my counsel asked me, in cross-examination, whether I intended to bring a countercharge for nonpayment of my compensation.

'I replied: "No. Since there has clearly been a misunderstanding between Don Pablo and his distinguished wife, it will not be necessary. He will obviously pay me, as a matter of personal honour, and shake hands with me in court." Don Pablo grew very red, seeing that the dog was dead, as they say, and came out with the money. We shook hands, and I said in front of everybody: "Many thanks. Now I will see whether I can spare a few bucketfuls of water for your orange plantation. My coconut palms are doing nicely now, and I can perhaps water them a little less intensively. Everyone laughed, including the judge, because the Coconuts of Ca'n Samper were already a byword. But Don Pablo had to pay costs . . . Well, then came the matter of his Large Black pigs; you may have heard of that?'

'They trespassed, did they not?'

'They trespassed gravely, stealing the mast from under my oak trees. I went to the mayor, and served Don Pablo a formal injunction to keep his pigs under restraint, but he told the mayor that he had a legal right to the mast. It was lying on the New Road, which was built to connect the Upper and Lower roads while the two farms were still under the same ownership, and the proprietor of Ca'n Sampol had, he said, a right of free passage through it and could graze his animals on their way through Ca'n Samper. So the mayor brought this message back to me and I said: "If the answer is 'no,' then he must come to the tribunal! And I lay you a hundred pesetas to one that I will win my case." And I won it.'

'Did he not have any grazing rights?'

'Certainly he had. One cannot stop a mule or an ass from snatching a mouthful of grass as he goes along a road to which he has a right. And, to forestall all possible arguments on this head, the deed referring to the New Road — a deed drawn at the time that my grandparents sold Ca'n Sampol — contained a clause making the grazing rights reciprocal: my beasts equally had a right to graze in their passage along the New Road through Ca'n Sampol. But the Ca'n Samper oaks, planted since the deed was drawn, bore acorns of the sweet variety that are sold roasted on the barrows in the market. The ordinary bitter acorns rank legally as "pasture"; these ranked as fruit. So, having disregarded my injunction, he was ordered to pay damages and costs, and undertake that his pigs kept to their sty in future . . . That was another hair twitched from St. Paul's beard. What date was it that you left the island?'

'It was August 2, 1936.'

'A few days only before the catastrophe of the Invasion of Mallorca. I daresay you read all about it in the newspapers. One

Captain Bayo had advertised in Barcelona for volunteers to reconquer Mallorca for the Republican Government, and he arrived, with a few ships and a few thousand Catalans and Valencians and Frenchmen, one Sunday morning at Puerto Cristo on the other side of the island from here. He met with little opposition, and had he chosen to march directly on Palma, the city would have been his. But he did not, or he could not, for his scallywags — and upon my word, though there may have been high-minded and idealistic revolutionaries among them, these were certainly a small minority — his scallywags preferred to loot the shops and cafés and villas of that little seaside place and outraged the feelings of all those who might otherwise have welcomed them and marched in their ranks. Soon they were all drunk, and the acting captain-general of the islands collected the coast guards and civil guards in lorries, and sent them to block the roads. By the time that Bayo had reorganized a part of his force and got them on the move, it was too late. The Italian war planes had flown to the Palma airport, refuelled, and come humming into action. The battle was lost, and much blood was shed, some of it by the peasant women, who came out with butchers' knives to defend their property against Bayo's deserters, scattering them in twos and threes across the Plain.'

'A great disappointment to the Liberals and Socialists of the island,' I remarked. 'Before I left they were saying: "Now that General Goded has failed to secure Barcelona, the rebellion will be over in three weeks." '

'They were disappointed to tears. The precipitate and disorderly Bayo invasion was the worst possible advertisement for their cause, and they had no resistance left when it came to the Terror. The hotheads of the Falange soon got busy on the Reds and hunted them like thrushes. Not merely the few Communists and militant Socialists, not merely the Socialist mayors and councillors and their supporters, but all sympathizers with what was, after all, the legal government. Of this I do not wish to say much except that the military commanders, who were in control, behaved correctly for the most part and discouraged lynch law. But for many months terrible things happened, in revenge for the

terrible things said to have been done to the anti-Republicans
in Minorca, Catalonia, and elsewhere; and as propaganda became
fiercer on both sides, so the acts of revenge became more horrible.
In all, about four thousand men died in Mallorca, for the Nation-
alists were numerically weak and could take no risks of a counter-
revolt. Mallorca with its natural riches, its airfields and seaplane
base must be held at all costs. "To be relentless now," they said,
"is to be merciful in the long run." Trials became tragically brief.
A civil war is like the shaking of a bottle of clear wine. It froths
and grows dark with unsuspected dregs. I tell you, there are men
who die here every month in remorse for their deeds of that day,
though the doctors diagnose tuberculosis or heart trouble.'

'Private feuds become complicated with public causes,' I suggested.

'That is well said. In peacetime, jealousy and rancour pass un-
noticed or find vent in petty ways, but in a civil war it is different.
If a bad man — and every village has one or two bad men, and
many sour old women of the devout sort we call "saints" — had
been worsted in a bargain by his neighbour, or been passed over
in a legacy in favour of a cousin, that was enough. The unfortunate rival would be denounced as a Red who had expressed sor-
row at the news of Bayo's defeat, and off he would have to go
to the overcrowded and unsanitary Castle prison until his case
came up months later. Sometimes he never even reached prison.
He would "resist arrest" or "attempt to escape" and be found
dead by the roadside with a bullet in him, or with a broken neck
at the foot of a cliff.'

'Where were your own political sympathies?'

'I have no politics. I voted for the Socialists at the election which
was the cause of the war, because the candidates for our council
had undertaken to build a new school for the girls and to bring
the telephone to the village. My politics are the same, I suppose,
as any peace-loving man's: I hate disorder, graft, and inefficiency
in government, and I dislike change. But when a thing stinks
it must be thrown away.'

'And Don Pablo?'

'He came out as an ultrapatriotic Right-winger, talking as valiantly and immoderately as the famous "General Manzanilla," the self-appointed Nationalist spokesman, himself. He was so far to the Right that he nearly dipped over the horizon and came to China. Our village is isolated, as you know. No telephone, no telegraph, and at that time we did not even have a Civil Guard stationed there. And nobody had heard of the Falange except from the newspapers. But the priest preached the necessity of rallying to the Church against the miscreants who had murdered children and violated nuns and crucified priests in their own churches and wished to destroy every vestige of decent civilization. So Don Pablo stepped into the breach, as the largest land-owner, and formed a League for Defence against the Reds. He said that since we had no armed forces in the village, we must get help from the Falange Headquarters at Palma. The next thing that we knew, he had two gunmen installed in the barn next to the church, and was soliciting subscriptions to maintain them there at ten pesetas apiece a day until the danger had passed. He collected a large sum with the priest's help, so now we were thoroughly secure. The men were not of the island; the younger was an Aragonese, the elder a Valencian. Well, of course, in times like those, it was not enough for them to sit still and draw their pay. Defence was understood as offence, and since it happened that the Socialist candidates for the local council were all men of property and well-connected — the one who had hoped to be mayor was married to the priest's sister and had freely given a plot of his ground to make an extension of the crowded church-yard — well then, less prominent victims had to be found. There was a harmless one-eyed ancient, a bit silly, but the village bee expert; he boasted that he had been a Socialist since the year of the Second International — whatever that may have been — and that all his bees were Socialists too. He was hauled off to prison with the face of a martyr and died there a few weeks later of peaceful senility. It's now ten years since there has been honey in the village. And the schoolmaster, who was not from these mountains, but a nobody from the Plain, he too suffered. He was altogether too independent and progressive in his views for Don Pablo's taste. He even favoured careers for women and, instead

of attending mass in the parish church, used to go for confession
to a friend of his, a retired priest with an interest in antiques
and literature, who lived five kilometres away. Don Pablo had
him lodged in the "Grand Hotel," as we called the prison, for
six months before his trial came off. He was acquitted, but asked
the Ministry of Education for an exchange of posts, and is now
teaching in Palma, where he has a school of some importance.'

Don Pedro was now coming to the part of the story that made
painful telling. Tears started to his eyes and he had difficulty in
controlling his voice. But he continued: 'After these routine ar-
rests, others followed of a different sort altogether. Bernat Marti,
a schoolfellow of mine, who kept a café and butcher's shop near
the church and was a great wag, was arrested late one night by
the two gunmen, despite the frantic cries of his daughter, a deaf-
mute, and carried off in Don Pablo's car. He was shot in the
back while trying to escape. "A dangerous Red," Don Pablo subsequently reported to the military officer at the Port. But if Bernat
was a Red, then I am a Negro. Truth was that on St. Anthony's
Day, when we have a bonfire and the beasts and cars are blessed
by the priest, it is the custom in our village to make *copeos* — that
is, to say scurrilous rhymes to the accompaniment of an ancient
jig. And on St. Anthony's Day, two years before this, Bernat had
rhymed about the indecent haste with which Doña Binilde had
rushed to the church with Don Pablo. When I heard the news
of his death, I went at once to my cousin Amador, a good fellow
but impulsive. I said to him: "The shameless wretches have murdered Bernat. Take my advice, go off at once to stay with your
brother-in-law, the coast-guard lieutenant, at the other end of the
island."

' "Why should I go? I am no Red."

' "Because you went to the trouble of indirectly warning Doña
Binilde, before she married, of the profligate record of Don Pablo
which you had discovered during your recent visit to the Continent."

' "Ka! I am not afraid of the man. If you suspect him of fram-
ing Bernat, why do you not clear out yourself?" But I could not
convince Amador, and two nights later the gunmen took him off

in Don Pablo's car as he was returning from a game of cards at the café. He tried to escape, they reported afterwards, and fell into the ravine, breaking his neck.'

I asked: 'Well, Don Pedro, and why did you not clear out?'

'For the same reason that my cousin Amador did not: for pride. My reason told me "go"; my pride said "stay." I stayed. So they picked me up the very next night, just before dawn, while I was coming home from Amador's father's house, where I had sat with the family to condole with them, as the custom is. They slowed down the car and shouted: "Jump in, we are going your way." But while the younger drove, the elder kept me covered with his pistol from the back seat. "I have a warrant for your arrest," he remarked casually.

' "It would interest me much to see that," said I. "Before you take me to prison, please have the goodness to conduct me to my house. There I can read the document by a better light than the moon, and also collect bedding, clothing, and food. You understand that I must let my wife know what has become of me and give her instructions about managing my affairs if I should happen to be away for a long time."

' "No, no, we are in a hurry and the New Road would cut our tyres to pieces. You can read the warrant at the prison guardhouse. You are a dangerous Red and supported Socialists in their candidature — "

' "And twice defeated Don Pablo at the tribunal," I interrupted.

' "Not another word," said the elder gunman, "or I shall use the butt first, and then the barrel."

'So I kept quiet and thought only of escape. As we passed the mayor's house, where the car had to slow down to turn an awkward corner, I took a chance. I knew that they would not dare to shoot me in the middle of the village. I slipped off my heavy signet ring and flung it at his bedroom window; by luck my action was not noticed, because the elder gunman at that moment was leaning forward and muttering instructions into his companion's ear. And my aim was good; as usually happens when one is in danger, with no time to reason or calculate. The shutters were open, and the windows too, because it was a very hot night, and my ring flew straight in and rang on the wash basin. The mayor leaped up with a start, lighted a candle, and rushed to the other window. He recognized Don Pablo's car by its make and the beat of its engine as it disappeared down the road to the port; it was a German Opel, nearly worn out. Then he searched the floor and found my ring.

' "Bless my soul!" he cried. "A *P* and an *S*. This is Pedro of Ca'n Samper's signet ring. The assassins have taken him for a ride."

'His wife, now wide awake, though at first she had grumbled at his making such a disturbance when she wanted to sleep, sat up in bed and said: "Man, there is no time to lose. Don't stand there gaping and saying: 'He is taken for a ride.' Hurry into your trousers, never mind your shoes; and unlock the garage, take the car and go after them."

' "I am unarmed," the poor man bleated.

' "You are a great coward. If I could drive I should go myself. Pedro is a good man, besides being your maternal cousin and the godfather of your eldest son. Have you no shame? You have nothing to fear. Drive fast, until you catch them up — yours is the better vehicle — and keep close behind them to make sure that Pedro reaches the prison safely. They will not dare to do anything with witnesses about and will hold their fire until they reach the desolate stretch of road between the *mirador* and the Moorish Tower. For the Virgin's sake, get busy!"

' "Alas, woman," he said, getting into his trousers, "there is not a drop of gasoline in the tank, and it would take me more than five minutes to rouse a neighbour and fill up."

' "In the name of God, have you no sense? Take Tomeu's motorcycle — it is in our garage. You can ride a motorcycle. And if I hear tomorrow that Pedro is dead, I swear to you by all the Saints and Blessed Ones that I will be your woman no longer. You can sleep in the kitchen with the cats." In Mallorca, it is the women who command in the home, just as Solomon prophesied.

'Meanwhile, Don Roberto, you can imagine that I was far from comfortable with the pistol barrel between my shoulders and the car bumping and rattling along the road. We continued to the Port and then turned around the mountain spur by the coast road past your house, and reached Ca'n Bi; then there were no more houses for some kilometres. But I could not see what I hoped to see across the valley as we turned the corner — namely, the head-lights of the mayor's car coming in pursuit. So I addressed the elder gunman: "Friend, here we are in a conveniently desolate place. Before you kill me, will you allow me to address a few words to an old acquaintance of mine?"

' "Where is he?"

' "Far enough from here."

' "What do you mean? Do you want to telephone?"

' "I only want a word or two with my patron saint, St. Peter."

' "He is dead," sneered the younger man. "You will not get through."

' "Shot while resisting arrest?" I asked, mimicking his Ara-gonese accent.

'The elder gunman laughed. "This is a courageous peasant. I am sorry that we have to cancel his account. Very well, Master, we will stop here and you can kneel in peace on the *mirador* yonder and put your call through while I smoke a cigarette. Though, upon my word, I cannot make out why you should take the trouble to telephone one whom you will be confronting in per-son the moment I throw away my cigarette butt." They stopped the car and we got out, and walked to where we are now sitting.

'This is country that I know very well, by day and by night. When I was young I bought myself out of military service with the money I made by smuggling here. I used to hump forty kilos' weight of tobacco up from the beach below us, by way of the cliff track, and take it across the road past the Moorish Tower and away over the mountains. My hope was that perhaps I could break away from my captors and escape down the cliff where, being ignorant of the footholds and handholds, they would be unable to follow me. But they knew their trade and kept me covered with both pistols; unfortunately, too, the moon was very bright and the first signs of dawn were already showing beyond the headland. I tried bribery, but could not interest them. The younger gunman said: "If we took you back alive you would certainly inform the mayor, or the priest, and claim his protection and we should lose not only the money but also the confidence of Don Pablo."

'At this I suddenly solved a problem that had been troubling me for a long time. I cried out: "Chests full of gold! Why did I not think of it earlier? You are a pair of Bayo's deserters, and you have hoodwinked the district party-leader and Don Pablo and everyone else into accepting you as Falangist incorruptibles. Well now, that is very funny and I must laugh, even if it is the last joke that I am ever confronted with.'

' "It is very funny, very funny indeed," agreed the elder. "My companion and I took the Falangist badges off a couple of young gentlemen whom we sandbagged in Barcelona during General Goded's visit, and kept them in our pockets in case of need. But get on with your prayer, without unseemly laughter, because the dawn, of which you will not see the corresponding sunrise, is nearly here."

'I was trembling like a valley poplar in the sea breeze, yet would not admit to myself that my last five minutes had come. There was still hope of rescue; for, as I say, I know this region well, and all that normally happens here, day and night. So I advanced alone to the *mirador* and made my genuflexion to the east, as if in church, and then settled down to pray with my head on the bench where you were seated just now. I prayed in a low, clear voice so that the gunmen should hear every word. My brain was working with great clarity, though my body was shaken with spasms.

' "Most blessed and illustrious St. Peter," I prayed, "you who jangle at your belt the great keys of Heaven, the silver and the gold! Most merciful and humane saint, once the chief of sinners — your colleague Paul alone excepted — insomuch as you cursed and swore from first cockcrow to second cockcrow, denying our Saviour Jesus Christ. Deign to listen to one who is neither a great saint nor a great sinner, but a villager of villagers who calls upon you in his extreme hour of necessity. Permit me respectfully to remind your Holiness that your servant has a peculiar lien upon your care. He is called by your name; he was born upon the very day which you share with your colleague St. Paul; he was baptized in the parish church of which you are patron; and for the last ten years, as the senior Pedro in the village, has been your *obrero* — he has been charged with the organization of your annual fiesta, when we glorify your name with a religious service, a candled procession, and with dances, fireworks, a football match, and agreeable diversions for the children in the Plaza."

' "Eloquent, is he not?" interrupted the younger gunman, tossing a pebble at me. "He prays like a bishop's bastard."

' "Leave him alone," said the elder. "This is as good as the graveyard scene in *Don Juan de Tenorio.*"

' "Peter, Peter!" I continued. "Magnanimous Apostle, who alone of the Twelve had the guts of a man and dared draw a sword in defence of your innocent Master, when the gangsters came to arrest him a little before dawn on Holy Friday. Glorious Saint, whose name signified 'The Rock,' upon you I build my hopes, and call upon you with all my heart and soul. It is for no favour at the Celestial Gates that I am pleading: I ask for immediate help. I conjure you, beloved Patron, by the blue waters of the Galilean Lake, and the blue waters that surround our island, until the other day called 'The Island of Calm'; I conjure you, Saint, by the nets that you spread from the boat of Zebedee, your father, and by the nets that we spread from our boats at the Port for *salmonete* and tunny; I conjure you by the silver coin which you found in the fish's mouth, and by the silver coins which I yearly pay towards the upkeep of your Church and the glory of your name — Peter, my Peter, come, be present, appear! Help, Peter, help!" These last words I shouted with such passion that they could be heard a kilometre away.

' "Silence, man!" exclaimed the elder gunman, flinging away his cigarette butt. "Come, Miguel, over the cliff with him."

'But I pointed with my finger: "Lo! Behold!" I cried.

'They looked, and gaped with astonishment, and the younger gunman whimpered like a dog: "Alas! See who comes! You should never have allowed him to pray with such force." Both stood irresolute, and in the silence that ensued I heard the distant crowing of a cock from Ca'n Bi, and the distant *pam-pam-pam* of a fishing boat as it chugged towards the Port with the night's catch. I closed my eyes again, and waited.

' "Hand over those pistols," cried St. Peter, waving his bundle of fishing rods menacingly. He stood nearly two metres high and the keys clanked loudly at his belt as he sprang towards us through the rosemary and mastic, his beard blowing wildly in the dawn breeze. They gave up their pistols like little boys caught in an act of naughtiness. He tossed one over the cliff in a high arc and handed the other to me. "Accompany me back to your car, rogues," he said, "lest I cast the pair of you where I cast that pistol!"

'They stumbled back, the saint not saying a word but flogging them at intervals with his rods while I kept them covered with the pistol. He was red with wrath. When we reached the road there was the mayor, barefooted but with the motorcycle, waiting by Don Pablo's car, and we were three to one. So the mayor left the motorcycle on this side of the wall, and climbed into the car, and drove us straight to the district barracks, where he demanded to see the commanding officer at once. From that moment everything went very well indeed. The commandant knew the saint well, and knew the mayor by name and reputation, and had once bought a cob from me which fortunately had proved as sound and sweet-tempered as I had guaranteed it to be. When the gunmen had made a full confession and had been put into the guardroom, the saint said to the commandant: "Don Pablo of Ca'n Sampol, when he hears of this, will laugh with one side of his face only."

'Believe it or not, that was precisely what happened. When the Civil Guards came later in the day to arrest him, he suffered a sort of paralytic stroke that screwed up the left half of his face in a grin which has not since left him. After he had spent some months in the Grand Hotel, waiting his turn, he was sentenced to death for conspiracy against the life of an innocent man, but by the influence of Doña Binilde's relations, one of whom was the vicar-general of Palma, the sentence was commuted to life imprisonment, and they let him out after three years. *Está en su casa.* And I am in mine. But ever since then I have had recurrent nightmares of the *mirador,* and have felt myself tossed in a high arc over the cliff by a furious saint whom I suppose, by the portfolio of documents at his side, to be St. Paul. It comes upon me just before dawn and afterwards I cannot sleep a wink.'

It is one of the beauties of Mallorcan storytelling that the point is never laboured. Don Pedro counted on my knowledge of local affairs to supply the details which he omitted. The gunmen, being newcomers to the district, were unaware that in the ruined Moorish Tower on the rock pinnacle high above the coast road lives a hermit, who just before dawn every morning — Sundays and important feasts excepted — locks his great nail-studded hermitage door, scrambles through the evergreen-oak glades and olive groves, crosses the road close to the *mirador,* and climbs down by the smugglers' track to his boathouse at the bottom. There he says his matins, attends to his lobster pots in season, collects driftwood, and sometimes gathers samphire from the cliff face, or caper buds for pickling, and goes fishing with rod and line. He is a very tall, strong, quick-tempered man, formerly a sailor, and disdains to wear shoes or sandals. Pilgrims visit his hermitage often, to leave little gifts when they know he will be at home. They kiss the rope that girds his rough brown habit and sometimes consult him about difficult matters with which they do not wish to trouble the parish priest who, they say, is a good man but inexperienced in the ways of the world.

'Come, friend Pedro,' I said. 'You have recovered from your lameness. Up with you to the *mirador!* Lean right over and you will be able to tell Doctor Guasp from what a fall you were saved. Here is my arm.'

'A thousand thanks, friend. If you will pardon me, I can dispense with help.'

He went leisurely up the steps to the *mirador* and leaned over the parapet with bowed head, humbly making his peace with the energetic saint whom he had insulted.

How Mad Are Hatters?

THE mad hatter was not, as most people suppose, a whimsical invention of Lewis Carroll's. Under HATTER, the *Oxford English Dictionary* quotes from a novel published in 1837: 'Sister Sall walked out of the room, mad as a hatter,' and the famous mad tea party was not thrown by the Hatter and the March Hare until 1865. The mad March Hare, too, was well known long before Carroll's day; Skelton had first mentioned him in the reign of Henry VIII.

Jack hares do, as a matter of fact, go noticeably mad in March because that is their courting season, and 'mad as a tup' and 'mad as a buck' also refer plainly to the lunatic behaviour of love-struck males. But are hatters particularly liable to seasonal outbursts of passion? This suggestion is supported by the *Oxford English Dialect Dictionary,* which lists 'like a hatter' as a Scottish and Northern English intensive of doubtful origin and cites the expressions 'off like a hatter,' 'run like a hatter,' and 'fight like a hatter.' There is, by the way, a close connexion between hatters and hares, not mentioned in *Alice in Wonderland:* St. Clement, the patron saint of hatters, is said to have devised the felt hat, and the best hatter's felt is made of hare's fur. May the March madness be contagious? How mad was St. Clement?

But though the harebrainedness of the hatter seems to be a traditional charge, like the cowardice of the tailor:

Four and twenty tailors went to catch a snail;
Even the bravest of them durst not touch her tail.

the thievishness of the miller, or the profanity of the tinker, sta-
tistics prove it to be unfounded. The incidence of lunacy tends
to be highest in bank-managers and children's nurses, and members of similarly wearing and responsible professions. Keepers of
storm-bound lighthouses also tend to go mad from claustrophobia
and the noise of the sea, or from too much Light Programme and
worrying about their wives. Why not 'mad as the Bank of England'? Why not 'mad as the Wolf Rock'? Hatting is neither an
exacting nor a claustral trade and does not figure in the lunacy
returns.

Granted, there are peculiar occupational aberrancies, as there
are occupational deformities. 'Let the cobbler stick to his last' records a temptation to amateur philosophizing: hammering home
points of dubious logic with each row of brads, while the customer, at his mercy, waits for the shoe. And 'mad as a weaver'
was a reasonable Jacobean phrase, referring to a sectarian madness which had lately seized the London weavers. Once the loom
had been set up, the rhythmic monotony of weaving encouraged
them to roar psalms and hymns until they worked themselves
into a hallelujah fervour. They seem to have been religious enthu-
siasts to a man; the most notorious case was that of Richard Farn-
ham of Whitechapel who, in the year 1636, proclaimed himself
the Holy King of Jerusalem prophesied in the Scriptures. He had
converted a fellow weaver, one John Bull of Aldgate, and promised him the office of high priest when they reached the Holy
Land. But I cannot find that any hatters were affected by this
'roaring madness,' or that they ever took up philosophy in a big
way.

'Monsieur Shattillion is mad as May-butter, and what is more,
mad for a wench.'

wrote the Elizabethan dramatist Fletcher. May-butter was an
ointment: ordinary butter set out in the sun until it melted and

turned a whitish colour. The meaning here is plain: Monsieur Shattillion had exposed his brains to the May sun until they went soft. But what hatter would ever go courting without the protection of his most stylish hat?

When I found that 'hatter,' in Australian slang, means a solitary prospector, I thought I had solved the problem. That sort of digger would tend to be both violent and eccentric, whatever his luck with the pans. 'Mad as a hatter in the gold rush' has a fine ring. Unfortunately the word is not recorded until after the publication of *Alice in Wonderland* and even then carries no hint of mental derangement; it is derived from the Dickensian phrase 'his hat covers his family' — that is to say, 'he is alone in the world.'

Still another meaning of 'hatter,' in the North of England, is 'a jumble, a tangle, a confused crowd.' In Cumberland one can speak of 'an atter of nonsense,' and this may indirectly point to the true derivation of 'mad hatter.' Since the North Country *a* is close to *o*, and the dialect forms *hatter, atter, hotter, other,* and *otter* are all recorded in the sense of 'jumble,' it is possible that the other sort of *hatter* and the other sort of *otter* have become confused. Could 'to be off like a hatter' and 'to fight like a hatter' equally mean 'like an otter' and be phrases coined by impassioned otter-hunters? Could 'mad as a hatter' be a Southern mishearing of 'mad as an otter'? Dog otters are said to go mad in their rutting season, like tups, bucks, and hares, and they are normally such shy animals that countrymen who witnessed their ecstatic courtship might well make it proverbial.

I was still teasing away at the problem when a retired Gunner major, my neighbour in the Spanish village where I live, suggested that 'mad as a hatter' might be a soldiers' phrase brought back from the Peninsular War, a misunderstanding of the well-worn Spanish *loco de atar* — 'mad enough to be tied up.' I think he has something there. It is remarkable what the English can do in the mistranslation of Spanish — 'The Elephant and Castle' for *La Infanta de Castilla* ('the Crown Princess of Castile') is the most familiar instance — and the hat shops of the early nineteenth century were showing such monstrous creations, for men as well as women, that the barrack-room phrase would have gained rapid currency. It would have been difficult, to begin with, to invent an insaner hat for the Spanish campaign than the tall, furred, brimless busby-bag issued to Wellington's troops. And by 'Sister Sall's' time the Life Guard wore so tall a crested helmet, surmounted by a sausage ornament, that he could not have raised his sword for a downward blow even if the tightness of his coatee had permitted the effort; as for the Lancer, the total height of his cap, with the plume, was an arm's length, and its square top was nearly as wide as his shoulders.

However, 'What sort of hat did Tosti wear when Tosti said good-bye?' Hatters are no madder than the customers at whose orders they design lofty belfries for bats, snug bonnets for bees, or funereal black Homburgs for little blue-faced City gremlins. But like male nurses in mental homes, and for much the same reason, they are treated with a certain superstitious reserve when off duty.

Pharaoh's Chariot Wheels:
A Study in Iconotropy

(1949)

SINCE the time of Christopher Marlowe, the first modern critic to cast doubts on the Exodus story, an immense literature of challenge and justification has grown up around it. Now it is generally agreed by all but stubborn fundamentalists that the story as it stands is not nearly so old as the time of Moses, that a close grasp of Egypto-Palestinian geography and history is needed to make any real sense of it, and that certain demonstrable anachronisms suggest that either the editors or the epic poets on whom they drew for their well-rounded prose narrative were wanton liars. I confess that it is these anachronisms that interest me most; wherever they occur in an ancient legend there is always a religious or political reason for them well worth ferreting out.

It would be tedious to recapitulate the various conflicting views of scholars on the date and route of the Exodus. The most reasonable is that not long after the expulsion from Egypt, in 1580 B.C., of the Hyksos kings, the leaders of an invading horde who had come down from the north about 1800 B.C., several thousand oppressed Israelites, mostly of the tribe of Joseph — the familiar twelve-tribe system probably dates only from the time of Solomon — decided to escape from Avaris, afterwards Pelusium, the most easterly city of the Delta coast. They waited for the full moon of the Spring Festival, when the Egyptians would be busy with their own religious celebrations, and then, instead of taking the single well-patrolled high road to Palestine (this is expressly stated in *Exodus xiii. 17*), chose a more difficult but less frequented route to the east — along the narrow, sandy spit separating the near-by Lake of Reeds from the Mediterranean.

They managed to travel a good distance before the hue and cry was raised and, when Egyptian troops came in pursuit, a sudden northeast wind, common at that season, drove up a high sea which swamped the track. Some of the pursuers were swallowed in the quicksands still prevalent there, and no further attempt was made to halt the runaways, who now struck south across the desert and entered Midianite territory. Moses, their sacred king — his early history is characteristic of Mediterranean rather than Semitic myth — is said to have had a previous understanding with the Midianites, who were wavering in their allegiance to Egypt; and indeed it seems unlikely that the expedition was undertaken without an assurance of a welcome in their tents. In *Exodus xviii. 12*, Jethro, the priest of Midian, invites Israel to a sacrificial bread-feast, which may be read as celebrating a fusion of the two peoples of Israel and Midian; for three clans of Midian — Ephah, Epher, and Hanoch — are later found incorporated in the omnium-gatherum tribe of Judah.

The Midianites, who are described as sons of Abraham by Keturah and therefore as coreligionists of Israel, grazed their flocks on the slopes of Mount Horeb, 'the Mountain of the South.' In this context it may be assumed that Horeb was Sinai, the enormous peak dominating the junction of the two arms of the Red Sea, since the Red Sea figures in the tradition and the Midianites gave their name to an Arabian town, Madyan, just across the water; though in later chapters of *Exodus,* Horeb was probably Mount Madara, a smaller sugar-loaf peak a good distance to the northeast, not far short of the Dead Sea in Edomite territory. The Midianites seem to have worshipped the Goddess Miriam, identifiable with Cyprian Mari and the Goddess of Amari in Crete; they were evidently of Asianic stock, since the Kenites, who are also described as Midianites, took their name from Agenor or Chnas or Canaan. Miriam, alias 'Leaping Myrrhine,' Marian, or Mariamne, was in fact the sovereign Moon Goddess of the Eastern Mediterranean and Southern Black Sea regions.

The fusion of Israel and Midian must have taken the usual form of a public marriage between the representative of the Midianite Goddess and the sacred king of Israel. In Egypt, he was apparently wedded to 'the Daughter of Pharaoh,' whom I take to be the Goddess Istar of Pharos, then the trading depot of the Confederate Sea Peoples and the largest port in the Mediterranean, whose worship the Hyksos had protected. In the Accadian version of the 'ark of sedge' story, Pharaoh's daughter is frankly named the Goddess Istar. It was she to whom the seven plagues of Egypt must be ascribed, since all of them — the reddening of the Nile, frogs, gadflies, cattle plague, hailstones, grasshoppers, and darkness — were characteristic of a Moon Goddess's vengeance. She had control of water, and red was her orgiastic colour; frogs were sacred to her, because she took the form of the crane, or stork, or heron, which feeds on frogs; so were gadflies (the gadfly occurs in the legend of the Goddess as Io) and she caused cattle plague because the cow was sacred to her — Isis-Io-Hathor herself being a cow; and sent hailstones, because all rain was in her control and hail is the most destructive form of rain, and because it struck down barley and flax, the crops most sacred to her; and grasshoppers, or locusts, because they were sacred to her as the Destroyer;[1] the plague of darkness represented her baleful eclipse. It was to the Goddess Istar as 'Pharaoh's daughter' that King Solomon built a shrine on the Temple Hall next to Jehovah's. In studying the Old Testament, one must continually bear in mind that the monotheistic worship of Jehovah was not achieved until just before, or during, the Babylonian Exile and that the Books of Moses have been carefully, though not carefully enough, edited to disguise the adoration officially paid to his divine Mother and Bride from the earliest times.

[1] According to the Ethiopian *Kebra Nagast,* 'Pharaoh's daughter' used locusts in a charm against King Solomon.

The death of the first born was, apparently, not one of the original series of plagues but a tactful editorial misrepresentation of the custom that had once doomed all first-born Israelite males of royal blood to sacrifice in the Goddess's service; the practice is attested by *Exodus i. 16.* It is recorded in *Joshua v. 7* that Israel ceased to circumcise their sons while in the Wilderness, and we know that circumcision, unknown among either the Mesopotamian Semites or the Sea Peoples, was practised by the Pharonic Egyptians in honour of their Sun God Ra (*Genesis vi. 30*); which suggests that the Israelites escaped from Egypt partly to avoid interference by Egyptian state priests of the new dynasty with their cult of the Goddess of Pharos.

Miriam is described in *Exodus* as Aaron's sister, because divine marriages were usually celebrated between brother and sister: so Hera married her own brother Zeus, and Isis her own brother Osiris, and Sarah (another name for the Moon Goddess, confirmed by inscriptions) her own brother Abraham. Josephus in his *Antiquities of the Jews* says that Hur was Miriam's husband, but this is a mistake: Hur, who is mentioned only twice in *Exodus,* on both occasions in connexion with Aaron and without any indication of sex, was probably Miriam's title as the Goddess of Mount Horeb. The name of Aaron's wife is given in *Exodus vi. 23* as Elisheba, 'God is my health,' which has a spurious ring in the context. Whether Israel had twin sacred kings, as the Argives, Romans, and Corinthians had, or whether Moses and his brother Aaron are doublets of the same person, is doubtful; most likely they are doublets, because Zipporah's second son by Moses was Eliezar, which was also the name of Aaron's son who succeeded him as High Priest. At all events, on his arrival on Midianite territory the sacred king of Israel married the tribal Dove Priestess who represented the Goddess Miriam.

The sacred union is described in two different ways. Moses married Zipporah ('bird'), daughter of Jethro, priest of Midian; 'Zipporah' is the same as 'Zippor,' the Dove Goddess of Moab, King Balek's mother. Or Caleb married Miriam: Caleb ('dog') was Moses's royal clan — the connexion of the Moon Goddess with the Dog Star and the sodomitic Dog Priests, called *kelebites* in Cyprus, is well known. It is likely that Moses was the king's name before marriage, Aaron the new name he assumed at marriage — as Jacob became Ish-rachel, or Israel, at his marriage with the Ewe Goddess Rachel — and that the marriage treaty was a mutual-assistance pact against Egypt.

Later, Israel moved northeastward out of Midianite territory, made an alliance with the Edomites of the Wilderness of Seir, and eventually, some three centuries, not 'forty years,' after the Exodus, when the Hittite Empire was breaking up, entered Palestine from the east under a sacred king who bore the new title of Joshua — 'He will save.' 'Forty years' is not intended literally; it means merely 'a long time.' The dissolution of the tribal alliance with Midian is recorded in the deaths of Miriam and Aaron and in the readoption by Israel of circumcision — presumably as a token of fealty to the Egyptians, who regarded Palestine as their protectorate and still maintained fortresses there; it is also reflected in the story of the war subsequently waged by Gideon against the Midianites (*Judges vi, vii, viii*) in obedience to a divine instruction given to Moses (*Numbers xxv. 17*): 'Vex the Midianites and smite them, for they vex you with their wiles.' This change of attitude towards Midian, and the eventual rejection, at the instance of the Prophets, of the Goddess and all her works, seems to have persuaded the compilers of *Exodus* to disguise the meaning of the tribal feast at Horeb, and to misinterpret the latter half of a sequence of icons preserved in the Temple archives and traditionally held to refer to it.

The misinterpretation of religious pictures or ritual belonging to an earlier faith, in order to establish and justify the new, I call *iconotropy*, and contend that if obviously artificial legends are restored to pictorial form, the original myths which they were invented to hide will often leap to the eye. The sequence in this case may be postulated as follows:

The first icon shows a sacred king, sceptre in hand, guiding his immigrant people, laden with treasure, between two walls of crested waves to a sacred mountain; the bones of a tribal ancestor are displayed in the procession.

A second icon shows a chariot racing along the seashore; another is having its lych pins removed.

A third icon shows the king plighting his troth with the priestess of the mountain and at the same time spurning with his foot a dead king who lies on the sand in the wreckage of his chariot. Horses are plunging among the waves and a man is drowning.

A fourth icon shows the priestess holding a timbrel; with her are a group of female companions, who dance ecstatically. (The timbrel was used for the expulsion of evil spirits on sacred occasions.)

Next, two or three icons may be postulated showing details of the marriage, the anecdotal allusions to which are given a false sequence in *Exodus*. The account of Jehovah's appearance in *Exodus iii. 2-5*, where he orders Moses to take off his shoes, suggests an icon in which the bridegroom is helped to draw on his marriage shoes by an imposing paranymph stationed under a flowering acacia, sacred to the Goddess. The anecdote in *Exodus ii. 16-22* points to the wrestling matches and lighthearted banter between men and women which marked these tribal marriages; here the Goddess has seven Water Priestesses. The marriage feast is mentioned in *Exodus xviii. 12*, but carefully disconnected from the marriage; that it was a sacramental bread feast shows that the Goddess was not only the Moon-Love-Sea Goddess and the Queen of Heaven who wore seven stars in her hair, but also the Barley Goddess.

Another feature of these sacred marriages (as Hocart points out in his classic *Kingship*) was the symbolic murder of the bridegroom, and the icon illustrating this is discernible in *Exodus iv. 24*, where Jehovah attempts to kill Moses at an inn for taking the road back to Egypt after his marriage with Zipporah; the anecdote is clumsy and illogical, since Moses was acting under Jehovah's own orders. It is related in the same chapter, *Exodus iv. 25-26*, that Zipporah then took a flint knife and circumcised Gershom, her elder son by Moses, as a prophylactic charm and let the blood fall on Moses's feet ('feet' is a euphemism for genitals). But since circumcision had been abandoned in the Wilderness, it is more likely that she castrated and killed a child victim as a surrogate for the royal bridegroom; sacrificial knives were always of flint. The suppressed epic tradition peeps out in verse 26: thus she originated the saying 'A bridegroom of the blood'; the use of 'bridegroom' shows that Gershom was not a child of the marriage, which was still in progress. That circumcision in Egypt was a rite connected with marriage (this is mentioned by Philo Byblius) made an editorial misinterpretation of the human sacrifice more plausible.

So the traditional meaning of a sequence of ancient icons — namely, a record of Israel's escape from Pelusium along the sands of the Sea of Reeds into Midianite territory, and the conclusion of a tribal marriage alliance at Horeb where the two arms of the Red Sea join — has been telescoped by the (perhaps) eighth-century compilers of the historical part of *Exodus:* the pursuit by Pharaoh is represented as having been made across the western arm of the Red Sea, and the marriage festivities are transformed into a dance of triumph over Pharaoh and a complimentary banquet given by Jethro to Moses.

At this point we come to the telltale anachronisms. The Song of Miriam, celebrating the overwhelming of Pharaoh's army, differs both in spirit and technique from the genuinely primitive Song of Deborah and is not older than the time of Isaiah. And neither the chariots nor the riderless cavalry horses can, in fact, have been Pharaoh's; chariots and cavalry were not used in the Egyptian army until 1500 B.C., some time after the only date possible for the Exodus, and no subsequent Egyptian record exists of a military disaster involving the drowning of a Pharaoh.

It looks as if an icon has been misread. Were not the horses in the sea really horses sacred to the Midianite Moon Goddess — later filched from her by Poseidon (after whom, by the way, the cape formed by the junction of the two arms of the Red Sea was in Classical times named Cape Poseidonium) — and not drowning, but thoroughly in their element? But that would not account for the racing chariots and the king lying dead in the wreckage of another. Since they cannot belong to the original story, it must be assumed either that the annalists invented baseless and circumstantial lies, which would be a most unusual procedure at that date, or else that they read as referring to the Exodus, of which only a fragmentary tradition remained, a series of ancient icons which had another origin altogether. The Israelites themselves did not use chariots until the time of David and Solomon, who imported them from Egypt, and the icons are therefore unlikely to have been of Israelite origin. Yet the priests would not have worked from foreign sources; they must have been icons belonging to some tribe or clan which had become absorbed into Israel by treaty, like the three Midianite clans, or the tribes mothered by Leah and Rachel's 'bondmaidens.'

Where, then, in Eastern Mediterranean legend, was a royal chariot described as wrecked by the seashore? Several such fatalities occurred in ancient Greece: to begin with, there was the Athenian myth of Theseus, Phaedra, and Hippolytus. According to most mythographers, Theseus married Phaedra, daughter of Queen Pasiphaë and King Minos, after his conquest of Crete. At Troezen, a coastal city near Mycenae, she met and fell in love with her stepson Hippolytus, Theseus's son by the Amazon Hippolytë; and when he rejected her advances, she accused him before Theseus of having tried to violate her. Theseus thereupon summoned Poseidon to destroy Hippolytus; and the god duly appeared from the sea in the form of a bull and frightened Hippolytus's chariot horses. They bolted, upset the chariot, and dragged him along the shore until he died. Later, Theseus learned that Phaedra had been lying and, when he charged her with it, she killed herself; then Apollo's son Aesculapius restored Hippolytus to life.

The anecdote here has been borrowed from the ancient Egyptian tale 'The Two Brothers,' on which the (perhaps) ninth-century Jewish author of the Joseph story in *Genesis* also drew. Originally, we may be sure, Hippolytus succumbed to temptation, as Myrtilus did in a cognate legend, and killed Theseus; but because Theseus was venerated at Athens, and Hippolytus had a shrine near the Temple of Justice there, the legend was recast in the interests of public morality.

Hippolytus's name, like that of King Eleusis in the Eleusinian mysteries, is clearly not historical but derived from a ritual on which the legend is based: it means 'He of the bolting horses.' 'Hippolytë' is 'She of the bolting horses' — but some mythographers call her Antiopë ('Facing both ways'), so we can fix the season of the ritual. Antiopë must have been the Greek counterpart of Carmenta, the Italian Goddess of Wisdom who, at her New Year feast in early January, was addressed as Postvorta and Antevorta, 'She who looks both back and forward'; and the legend in which she and Hippolytus figure seems to be cognate with those of Myrtilus, of Glaucus, of Diomedes, of Lycurgus, and of Phaëton, all of whom were youths killed by enraged horses.

Glaucus of Corinth, having offended the Goddess Aphrodite (Thetis), died in a chariot accident — or, alternatively, was eaten by mares — on the seashore near Iolcus, at the foot of Mount Pelion, where he had gone to take part in King Pelias's funeral games; and the mares had been infuriated either by eating the aphrodisiac herb hippomanes or drinking the waters of a sacred Boeotian spring. His ghost thereafter haunted his native isthmus of Corinth to the terror of all chariot horses. Glaucus means 'hoary,' and this Glaucus is connected both with the prophetic marine deity Glaucus (formerly, it was said, a drowned Argonaut) who annually paid a beneficent visit with his court of Tritons to every bay and island in Greece and was not easily distinguishable from the God Poseidon, and with the boy Glaucus, son of King Minos and Pasiphaë, who was accidentally drowned in honey and restored to life by Polyidus ('the shape-shifter').

King Oenomaüs of Elis was killed in a chariot race with Pelops the Phrygian, who had arrived in the Peloponnese, which afterwards took his name, from Enete on the southern Black Sea coast, riding at the head of a large immigrant horde. Oenomaüs's charioteer Myrtilus secretly removed the lych pins from his chariot wheels, in the hope of succeeding him as king and marrying his daughter Hippodamia. But his hopes were dashed by the ungrateful Pelops, who took the stolen crown from his head, set it on his own, threw him into the sea, and married Hippodamia himself.

Phaëton was lent the sun chariot of his father, the Sun God Helios, for one day, at the request of his mother, the Ocean Nymph Clymene, but mismanaged it, drove too near the earth, and was destroyed by Zeus with a thunderbolt.

Diomedes was King of the Bistones in Thrace, son of Ares and Cyrene, and owned man-eating mares. When Hercules had seized these mares, as his Eighth Labour, he committed them to the guardianship of his boy friend Abderus, whom they dragged to death. Since, according to Philostratus, horse-racing was omitted at the athletic games periodically celebrated in Abderus's honour, it seems that he had tried to harness them to a chariot. The mythographer Apollodorus records that another Thracian king, Lycurgus, killed his son Dryas in a fit of madness and, the land being therefore cursed by the God Dionysus, 'was bound and destroyed by horses under Mount Pangaeium' — the mountain on which Orpheus had been torn in pieces by wild women at sunrise.

So far as I am aware, no popular ritual corresponding with these legends survived in Classical Greece; but at the Babylonian New Year festivities a chariot with four masterless horses was let loose in the streets to symbolize the chaotic state of the world when the Sun God Marduk was in Hell fighting the sea monster Tiamat. This custom points to a common origin of all these related myths: an end-of-the-year ritual which marked the temporary demise of the sacred king, his supersession for one day by a boy victim, and his subsequent restoration to the throne. The King of Babylon was an incarnation of Marduk, the successor (since the end of the second millennium) of the earlier Sun God Bel, or Enlil, originally the spirit of the solar year. The religious theory was that Bel died annually, engulfed by a huge sea wave. The sea was pictured as the monster Tiamat, on whose back, in early Babylonian art, the Moon Goddess rides; and in primitive times the sacred king, Bel's representative, also died annually — until his reign was prolonged first to a Great Year of a hundred moons and then to a lifetime. Yet he still pretended to die at the close of every year, and it seems that while he was 'in Tiamat's belly,' a boy victim succeeded to the royal couch and, after going

through his shape-shifting dance, was murdered the same evening; and that at dawn on the following day the king was, in theory, spewed up like Jonah (or like Jason, Jonah's counterpart in Orphic art) and brought to life again for another year. Horse chariots do not belong to this early stage of the myth, and in Pelasgian Greece and Thrace the king or the victim was at first torn in pieces by flesh-eating mares — masked priestesses of the Mare-headed Mother intoxicated by hippomanes and other drugs — though later bound with reins at the tail of a chariot and dragged to death. The stories of Diomedes and Lycurgus, read in conjunction with those of Cronos and the infant Achilles, make it plain that a boy victim was annually offered until the king's reign ended and he himself was sacrificed.

The tall white horses of the yearly sun chariot, four in number to represent the four seasons, must be distinguished from the smaller breed that had been sacred to the moon from paleolithic times; but it is clear from the myths that when the Aryans invaded the Eastern Mediterranean, bringing their chariots with them, and settled down as a ruling aristocracy, they consented to reconcile their patriarchal religion with the matriarchal or matrilineal systems they found there. Thus the king would consent to a pretended death at the close of every year as representative of the Sun God, but substituted the less gruesome myth of the chariot crash for that of the cannibalistic, wild, mare-headed, women.

The King of Babylon consented to retire from public gaze during the critical period of the year when he was fighting with Tiamat, but at a later period refused to admit that she swallowed him; on the contrary he claimed, as Marduk, to have netted her and cut her in two with his sword. (There is a mention of this in *Isaiah xxvii. 1.*) Yet he still had to be annually uncrowned, buffeted on the cheek by the officiating priest in memory of his earlier death, and then recrowned. The masterless career of the chariot horses was another concession to tradition. It may be that, as in the Phaëton myth, an annual boy victim was at one time entangled in the reins and dragged to death by the horses, but no record of such a custom survives.

Theseus, of the Hippolytus story, was the leader of the Greek confederacy that sacked Cnossos about 1400 B.C. and conquered Crete. He ritually married the Cretan heiress, whose title Phaedra occurs at Ras Shamra, in Ugarit inscriptions of the early second millennium. She is there styled P'dri, one of the three daughters of Bel; which means that, like Linda, Cameira, and Ialysa, the three daughters of her brother Danaus, she represented the Triple Moon Goddess, whose sovereign powers the new Sun God Bel had usurped.

Reduce the Hippolytus story to pictorial form with the help of material from the related legends. The Moon Goddess makes love to a youth under a myrtle tree (to show, by the symbolism of the Orphic tree alphabet, that the year is in its thirteenth and last month) and persuades him to end the king's life. He engineers a chariot crash as the king drives by the seashore; the king dies, and his body is carried off by a huge sea wave. The youth enjoys a brief triumph. The king's ghost returns newborn from the sea, spewed up in the form of a young bull, resumes man's form, and kills the interloper with a sceptre. (In this scene the returning king is readily mistaken for Poseidon, because his scepter is formalized as a trident thunderbolt and he has a retinue of marine creatures.) The restoration of Hippolytus to life by Aesculapius, a reminiscence of the annual restoration of the Tyrian Hercules-Melkarth by Esmun, is a late addition to the myth — the victim is permitted to die only a mock death, and an animal is sacrificed instead.

(The myth is further confused: the Hippolytus who was given heroic honours at Troezen was not a midwinter king-of-a-single-day, but a typical Spirit of the Waxing Year who alternately slew and was slain by the Spirit of the Waning Year, his dark rival for the Goddess's love. In Italy he was also identified with the hero Virbius, the first of the line of Oak Priests at Nemi, called 'Kings of the Wood,' who are the subject of Sir James Frazer's *Golden Bough*. But that need not concern us.)

Now to return at last to the king in the wrecked chariot lying by the Sea of Reeds, whom Moses spurns with his foot in proof

of victory. We find to our surprise that the same set of icons that underlie the story of the Exodus from Egypt also underlie the legend of Pelops, Hippodamia, Oenomaüs, and Myrtilus. Especially we notice the circumstantial detail (*Exodus xv. 25*), 'And they took off their chariot wheels that they drave heavily,' which belongs to the second icon of the postulated series: Myrtilus secretly removes the lych pins from Oenomaüs's chariot before his race with Pelops. The fourth and subsequent icons of the series show Pelops, the victor, marrying Hippodamia, the Elian heiress, at the foot of Mount Olympus at Olympia, and making a treaty with her people.

It looks then as if the icons on which the *Exodus* narrative is based were originally Greek. This is not so fantastic a conclusion as it seems at first sight. They could have been brought to South Palestine by Achaean immigrants belonging to the Confederate Sea Peoples, whom Rameses II of Egypt defeated in 1335 B.C. at the Battle of Kadesh. According to Homer, King Menelaus of Sparta, who claimed to be descended from Pelops and paid a formal visit to Pharos, was one of their later leaders; and Xanthus, an early Lydian historian, says that Ascalon was founded by Pelops's uncle Ascalos; and, as we know from the *Book of Joshua,* Achaeans were occupying four cities of South Palestine at the time of Joshua's thirteenth-century invasion — they were known as Hivites (Achaivites). Among them (*Joshua ix. 7*) were the men of Gibeon, sometimes known as Nob, the next most powerful city after Ai, who made a treaty with Joshua; by the terms of it they were allowed to take part in the religious rites of the Israelites as foresters of the sacred grove and as drawers of sacred water for the altar. In the prophet Zechariah's time (*Zechariah xi. 13; xiv. 21*) a few of them were still to be seen in the Temple courts making their traditional water jars in honour of the Moon Goddess, greatly to his disgust. Later editors of *Joshua* misinterpreted the story: to disguise what then seemed a discreditable alliance, they pretended that Joshua was tricked by the Gibeonites but spared them on the condition of their accepting a menial servitude. Gibeon (*Agabon* in one text of the *Septuagint*) is perhaps a worn-down form of *Astu Achaivōn,* 'the city of the Achaeans,' and the Gibeonites behaved in a typically Achaean way (*Joshua ix. 3-10*) when they came as suppliants in ragged clothes and explained, veraciously enough, that they were not native Canaanites, like King Sihon the Amorite and King Og of Basan, whom Joshua had killed, but settlers from across the sea. It seems from verse 9 that they also appealed to the ancient Sea Peoples' alliance which Abraham had joined when he gave his sister Sarah to Pharaoh (*Genesis xi. 15*) — when, in other words, the goddess of his tribe ritually married the sacred king of Pharos, usually known as Proteus — and which had not been dissolved by the Exodus;[2] only such a claim would account either for their suppliants' garb or for the honourable reception they were granted.

After the ratification of the treaty the Gibeonites' sacred icons, brought as credentials, were probably laid up in the Sanctuary and, their meaning and origin being forgotten after Saul's treacherous massacre of the Gibeonite priesthood (*1 Samuel xxii. 18*), read as a record of Moses's passage across the isthmus of the Sea of Reeds, laden with Egyptian spoil, his pursuit by Egyptian chariots and cavalry, and his subsequent treaty with Midian. This is to suggest that 'The rider cast into the sea' (*Exodus xv. 1*) was really Myrtilus; that 'Pharaoh' was Oenomaüs; that 'Moses' was Pelops passing across the isthmus of Corinth at the head of his treasure-laden followers; that 'Miriam' was Hippodamia, to whom the white horses in the waves belonged as a representative of the Goddess Thetis — Hippodamia ('tamer of horses') was an Ocean Nymph, the daughter of Sterope, one of the Seven Pleiads who gave fair weather to sailors — and that the 'bones of Joseph' which Moses brought with him (*Exodus viii. 19*) were the Palladium of the Pelopian dynasty, reputedly made of the bones of their ancestor Pallas, or of Pelops himself. The importance of Gibeon as a religious centre even after Saul's massacre — an incident in his war with David — is shown by Solomon's offering his coronation sacrifices there (*1 Kings iii. 4*) rather than at Jerusalem; presumably they were

---

[2] The alliance was commemorated as late as Ptolemaic times by an annual festival which the Egyptian Jews attended on the island of Pharos.

intended for the local Goddess Achaiva ('The Spinner,' a title of Demeter) who owned Nebi Samuel, the highest peak in the district.

A legend directly derived from primitive religious practice, like that of Moses, Pharaoh's Daughter, and the ark of sedge, has an altogether different smell from one iconotropically composed to point a moral and defame an enemy, like that of Lot and his daughters; or to glorify the tribe, like that of Pharaoh's chariotry; or to account for some religious anomaly, like that of the miracle of the quails, which refers to the Israelites' annual quail orgy at Beth-Hoglah in honour of Herkules-Melkarth and the Goddess Istar. In the Historical Commentary at the close of my *King Jesus,* I wrote about iconotropy:

In iconotropy the icons are not defaced or altered, but merely interpreted in a sense hostile to the original cult. The reverse process, of reinterpreting Olympian or Jahvistic patriarchal myths in terms of the mother-right myths which they have displaced, leads to unexpected results. The unpleasant story of the seduction of Lot by his two daughters, which reflects Israelite hostility to Moab and Ammon — tribes reputedly born of these incestuous unions — becomes harmless when restored to its original iconic form: it is the well-known scene in which Isis and Nephthys mourn at the bier of the ithyphallic recumbent Osiris, in an arbour festooned with grapes, each with a son crouched at her feet. The story of Lot and the Sodomites suggests the same ancient icon from which Herodotus derived his iconotropic account of the sacking of Astarte's Temple at Ascalon by the Scythians. He records that 'upon these Scythians and upon all their posterity the Goddess visited a fatal punishment: they were afflicted with the female disease' — that is to say, with homosexuality. But the icon represents a legitimate Dog Priest orgy, against a background of swirling sacrificial smoke. It was to suppress sodomitic orgies that Good King Josiah of Judah (637-608 B.C.) — or Hilkiah, or Shaphan, or whoever the reformer was — inserted into *Deuteronomy xxii* a prohibition against the wearing of women's clothes by men. The pillar of salt into which Lot's wife was turned is presumably represented in the icon by a white obelisk, the familiar altar of Astarte; and Lot's daughter who was abused by the mob is presumably a sacred prostitute of the sort that made Josiah forbid the bringing into the House of the Lord of 'the hire of a whore.' 'The price of a dog,' which goes with this prohibition in the same text (*Deuteronomy xxiii. 18*), evidently means the hire of a Calebite Dog Priest or Sodomite:[3] both fees were devoted to Temple funds in related Syrian cults.

Dr. Raphael Patai, Director of the Israeli Institute of Folklore and Ethnology, though he insists on the importance of the Goddess in Hebrew history, questions the need of supposing an iconotropic origin for the Lot story. He has written to me:

There may be other explanations, one of which is the widespread tendency to attribute the birth of heroes, in this case the tribal ancestors of Ammon and Moab to unnatural, or at least unusual circumstances. The nearest other example I can adduce at the moment is contained in the ancient Arab legend-cycle of the Beni Hillal, in which we are told that Abu Zeid did not allow himself complete coition with his wife, whereupon the tribe came privily to his sister and said that the Beni Hillal must have a son from the loins of Abu Zeid. One night, therefore, she went in secret to her brother's bed and he, not knowing her in the darkness from his wife, lay with her. As he was about to withdraw himself prematurely, according to his habit, she jabbed him with the bodkin that she kept in her hand in readiness. The shock achieved its intent and in the fullness of time she bore a son, who came to be known as Aziz bin Khala (Aziz, son of his uncle) and became a chief hero of the Beni Hillal (cf. Bertram Thomas, *Arabia Felix,* p. 219 et seq.). The similarity between this story and that of Lot is unmistakable: in both cases a hero is tricked by near blood-relations (sister or daughters) into having incestuous sexual relations with them, unknowingly, and the outcome of this union is the birth of a male child, a hero or ancestor of the tribe. I think it is a safe guess that you will find stories of this type in the Greek, Roman and related Oriental literature.

Dr. Patai is one of the shrewdest and least inhibited of Biblical scholars, but disclaims any close knowledge of Western mythology; which, so far as I am aware, contains no similar story. A Western Lot might have seduced his daughter on the death of his wife, as Cinyras of Paphos seduced Smyrna, or Zeus (in the Lesser Eleusynian Mysteries) Persephone, in order to retain the

---

[3] The buildings set aside for the Sodomites in Solomon's Temple are mentioned in *11 Kings xxiii. 7.*

kingship won by marriage with a royal heiress; but she would have had no occasion to trick him into fatherhood. The story in *Genesis* is clearly aetiological: it purports to explain Moab as meaning 'son of my father,' instead of 'The Desired One,' the name of the tribe's goddess mother; and Ammon as meaning 'son of my kinsmen,' whereas this is also probably a goddess's name, 'The Mighty One.' The two goddesses were given 'Daughters of Lot' as a geographical title: they were living in the Lotan country, south of the Dead Sea.

The Beni Hillal story I read as another aetiological myth, reminiscent of the *Genesis* story, invented to explain the title 'Aziz bin Khala.' Evidently the tribal chieftain used to marry his niece or sister in order to keep the matrilineal inheritance in the family, but such a relationship being in Mahometan times regarded as incestuous, the name had to be explained by an ingenious anecdote. The bodkin prick smells of the coffee hearth, not of primitive mythology; but at least this is a more plausible anecdote than that of Lot's daughters who, finding no mates in Zoar because it was so small, were tempted to drug their old father into insensibility. Zoar was big enough to send an army to the Battle of the Slime Pits (*Genesis xiv: 8*). The primitive stories of a hero's peculiar birth, to which Dr. Patai refers, are concerned with ritual objects or creatures such as almonds, pomegranates, fish, bulls, mayflies, serpents, with which the mother is miraculously impregnated; the bodkin prick belongs to another region of the imagination.

The myth of Onan son of Judah (*Genesis xxxviii. 9*), who 'spilt upon the floor' rather than company with Tamar his brother's widow, has a similarly artificial ring: it is offered as a moral anecdote to illustrate the wickedness of circumventing the Levirate Law, even before it was formulated by Moses. But since Onan was killed for his act, and since Onan was the name of a Kenizzite tribe absorbed by Judah, it is possible that the anecdote is deduced from a primitive Canaanite icon: a dying king under a sacred palm tree (Tamar) is ejaculating on the ground, like the antlered king of the famous Domboshawa cave painting in Southern Rhodesia, to promote its fertility, while a priestess lying near by mimics his agony. Tamar was a Canaanite title of Istar, and the further story told of her, that she played the harlot and seduced Judah, from whom she received a signet, bracelets, and his royal staff, suggests a companion icon: the priestess of Istar confers royal insignia on the new king after marriage with him. The kid which figures in the story as a gift from Judah to her would be the usual victim sacrificed at the coronation ceremony.

'Pharaoh's Daughter' was known at Jerusalem as Ashima, the Dove Goddess. The shrine built for her by Solomon adjoined 'The House of Adon,' Jehovah's shrine, and also the much larger 'House of the Forest of Lebanon' sacred to Anatha, the Lion Goddess. The three shrines together formed the Temple, and the Jews of Elephantine in Egypt were still worshipping the same divine Trinity as late as the fifth century B.C. In my *King Jesus* I have made Agabus, the first-century narrator, write:

The Goddess's venerable Temple at Hierapolis, on the Syrian bank of the Upper Euphrates, a region connected in Biblical legend with the patriarchs Abraham and Isaac, is well worth a visit. There, a Sun God, a sort of Dionysus-Apollo-Zeus who rides a bull, is married to his mother the Moon Goddess who rides a lion and grasps a snake in her hand. The Trinity, which is ruled by the Mother, is completed by an ambiguous bisexual deity to whom the dove is sacred. The Temple, which is served by oracular women and eunuch priests, faces east; outside the portals are two enormous phallic pillars like those which stood outside King Solomon's Temple; inside, all is gold and gems and marble. The ritual is a complicated one and includes premarital prostitution for young women, self-castration for young men; for others, intercessions, comminations, hymns of praise, libations, purifications, incense-burning, sacrifices of sheep, goats, and children; holocausts of live beasts hanged from terebinth trees; and oracles taken from sacred fish and sweating statues. The Temple is said to have been founded in honour of the Moon Goddess by Deucalion (whom the Jews call Noah) when the Deluge which had overwhelmed Asia at last subsided. In his honour a sacred ark of acacia wood is exhibited and water is poured down the chasm through which, it is said, the waters of the Deluge were carried away.[4]

[4] The account is drawn from Lucian's essay *De Dea Syria*.

The Canaanites, whom the Israelites conquered and enslaved under Joshua, were devotees of this Goddess. Their remnants still cling to the cult of the terebinth tree, the dove, and the snake, still bake barley cakes in honour of the Goddess, and still maintain the right of every young woman to provide herself with a dowry by prostitution.

Dr. Patai has taken the argument further in his *Man and Temple* (1947). He holds that the Holy of Holies was originally a nuptial chamber in which a sacred marriage was celebrated between representatives of Jehovah and Anatha, like that celebrated by Marduk, on the tree-clad Ziggorath at Babylon, with the most beautiful woman in all the land. He shows that the Ark was a fertility symbol and quotes several early rabbinic legends in this sense, including one which describes how, when Solomon brought the Ark into the Sanctuary, all the trees and cedar beams became green and brought forth fruit: 'Dry wood snuffed the scent of the Life of the World (i.e., the *Shekinah*), blossomed, bore fruit and came to life.' He emphasizes the erotic light-headedness of the women worshippers at the Feast of Tabernacles; and proves that the olive-wood cherubs on the Ark were locked in a sexual embrace, quoting Resh Lagish: 'When the heathen entered the Temple and saw the Cherubs whose bodies intertwined they carried them out and said: "These Israelites whose blessing is a blessing and whose curse is a curse occupy themselves with such things!" And immediately they despised them' — though, as the rabbis plaintively pointed out, the group was far from obscene: it represented God's love for Israel, like the love of Solomon for the Shunemite in the *Canticles*.

Dr. Patai might have added that the Temple incense was originally an aphrodisiac for use in the nuptial chamber. The recipe was this:

Take equal parts of the following ingredients:

(1) Gum of *sturax* — a showy, white-flowered Palestinian tree with five-pointed leaves. Its name is derived from the Greek *stuein,* 'to cause sexual erection.'

(2) Hinge of *murex* shell — still used in Arabia by women in conjunction with other spices as an aphrodisiac scent. The murex

is the Goddess's purple fish. The hinge is used as sympathetic magic to clamp lovers together in sexual union no less tightly than the twin shells.

(3) Gum of *narthex* — the giant fennel (grown in the Greek Islands and Syria) of the Prometheus legend, in the pith of which a spark of sacred fire can be kept alive for a long time.

(4) Gum of frankincense — a fragrant resin consisting of white 'tears' mixed with red. This well-known aphrodisiac was imported into Egypt from Somaliland and Southern Arabia. Its Aramaic name is the same as that used for 'Lebanon' and means 'white.'

Burn all together slowly in a pit under a tent; take off your clothes and drink the scent into the pores of your skin by the sweat-bath method. Or sprinkle on barley cakes and eat.

One last word about 'Pharaoh's chariot wheels.' Before the reformation of Jewish religion ascribed to King Josiah, Jehovah was worshipped for awhile as a form of the God Marduk, and white sun horses, stabled for him on the Temple Hill, were every morning harnessed to a golden chariot which was driven out to greet the rising sun. There are reminiscences of this custom in *Psalms 19, 68, and 84,* in Ezekiel's vision, and in the account of the fiery chariot that took Elijah up to Heaven, as well as the historic statement in *2 Kings xxiii. 11:*

And King Josiah took away the horses that the Kings of Judah had given to the Sun at the entrance to the House of the Lord . . . and burned the chariots of the Sun with fire.

But no tradition survives of a chariot crash staged at the close of the year; and the close affinities of the Exodus legend with the Greek myth of Pelops and Oenomaüs make it unlikely that Pharaoh's chariot wheels are derived from a Babylonian icon illustrating the ritual.

Dead Man's Bottles

(1949)

I WAS more amused than shocked when I first realized that
I was a matchbox- and pencil-pocketer: it seemed a harmless
enough form of absent-mindedness. Why matchbox- and pencil-
pocketers — the aberrancy is quite a common one — should not
also take cigarette lighters and fountain pens, no psychologist has
been able to explain, but in practice they never do. Another odd
thing about them is that, however slow and stupid on other
occasions, they are quick as lightning and as cunning as weasels
when they go into action.

'Sign, please!' the errand boy would call at the door of my flat
in Hammersmith Mall, and when I came out, fumbling half-
heartedly in my pockets for a pencil, he would offer me his.
Then, after scribbling my name on the chit, I would perform
some ingenious sleight of hand — but exactly how and what must
remain unknown, because I never caught myself at it. All I can
say is that he went off whistling, convinced that the pencil was
back behind his ear, while I retired indoors with a clear conscience; and that, when I emptied my pockets before going to
bed, the nasty chewed stub of indelible was there, large as life,
along with other more handsome trophies. As for matches: I
would stop a stranger in the street, politely ask for a light, strike

a match on the box he offered and, after hypnotizing him (and myself) into the belief that I had returned it, thank him and stroll slowly off. I often wonder what a film-take of the incident would have shown.

Pencils are cheap, matches are cheaper still. My friends remained seemingly unaware of my depredations, or at any rate never accused me of them, until one Easter I went to stay at Kirtlington, near Oxford, with one F. C. C. Borley, a Wadham don who lectured on moral philosophy and was an expert on French literature and wine.

Borley was youngish, with an unwholesome complexion, lank hair, and so disagreeable a voice and manner that he literally had not a friend in the world — unless one counted me, and neither of us really liked the other. His fellow dons couldn't stand him, though he had a well-stored and accurate mind, praiseworthy loyalty to the College, and no obvious vices — except to dress like a stage Frenchman and always to be in the right. He gave them the creeps, they said, and agreed that his election had been a major disaster. I had met him by chance on a walking tour in Andalusia, where I nursed him through an illness because nobody else was about; and now I was helping him with the typescript of a book he had written on drinking-clubs at the English Universities. I never pretended to compete with him in vintage scholarship or to share his rhetorical raptures over such and such a glorious port-wine year — Borley always chose to call it 'port wine' — or the peculiar and Elysian bouquet of this or that little known *Château*. And never let on that, in fact, I considered port primarily an invalid's drink and preferred an honest Spanish red wine or brandy to the most cultivated French. The only subject on which I claimed to be knowledgeable was sherry, a wine singled out for praise in the Fellows' grace at Wadham, and therefore not to be lightly disregarded by Borley, even though it meant nothing to his palate.

He had a Savoyard chef called Plessis whose remarkable ragouts and crêmes and soufflés these elegant wines served well enough to wash down. Out of respect for Plessis I never contradicted Borley or listened with anything but close attention to his endless dissertations on food, wine, the French classics, and eighteenth-century drinking habits. In exchange, he accepted my suggested amendments to his book readily enough wherever style, not fact, was in question; but that was because I had left him his affectations and perverse punctuation and everything else that gave the book its unpleasant, personal flavour, and concentrated merely on cutting out irrelevancies and repetitions and taking him up on the finer points of grammar.

Over coffee and brandy one evening, when our work on the book was all but finished, he suddenly unmasked his batteries. 'Fellow drinker,' he said — he had a nauseating habit of calling people 'fellow drinker' at table and 'fellow gamester' at cards — 'I have a crow to pluck with you, and what could be a more suitable time than this?'

'Produce your bird,' I answered, and then in a pretty good imitation of Borley himself: 'When we've plucked, singed, and gutted it like good scullions, and set aside the tail feathers for pipe-cleaners, we'll summon Plessis from his cabinet and leave him to the fulfilment of his genius. I have no doubt but he'll stuff the carrion with prunes soaked in rose water, chopped artichoke hearts, paprika, and grated celeriac — then stew gently in a swaddling of cabbage leaves and serve with hot *mousseron* sauce . . . What wine shall we say, fellow drinker? *Maître Corbeau, 1921?* Or something with even more body?'

But Borley was not to be sidetracked. 'Frankly,' he continued, jutting out his pointed chin with its silly black imperial, 'it goes against my conscience as a host to make the disclosure, but *in vino veritas,* you know: you're a damned thief!'

I flushed. 'Go and count your German-silver teaspoons, check your forged fore-edge paintings, send Mme Plessis upstairs to go through my linen in search of your absurd Sulka neckties. There's not an object in this house that I'd accept as a gift, except some of your sherry — though not all of that. Your taste in furnishings and *objets d'art* is almost as bad as your manners, or your English grammar.'

He was prepared for some such comeback and met it calmly. 'Yesterday, friend Reginald Massie,' he said pompously, 'you stole

every match I possessed. Today I sent to the grocer for another
packet of a dozen boxes. Tonight there's only a single box left,
that one on the mantelpiece . . . Just Heavens, and now 'that
too has disappeared! It was there two minutes ago, I'd stake my
reputation — and I never saw you leave your chair! However,
nobody's come in, so pray hand it over!'

He was trembling with passion. Caught on the wrong foot, I
began emptying my trouser pockets, and out came the matchboxes; but, I was glad to see, no more than seven of them.

'There,' I said, 'count! You lie; I did not take the whole dozen.
Where are the other five? I believe you're a match-pocketer yourself.'

'You were courteous enough to change for dinner,' he reminded me. 'The rest of the loot will be found in your tennis
trousers. And now for the pencils!'

I felt in my breast pocket and pulled out eight or nine. 'The
perquisites of my profession,' I explained lightly. 'Think of the
trouble I've taken in correcting your illiterate English, not to
mention your more than sketchy Spanish. I needed a whole
fistful of pencils. You'd probably have had them all back before
I left.'

'Tell me, how often in your life have you either returned a
borrowed pencil or bought a new one?'

'I can't say offhand. But once, at a Paddington book stall, I
remember . . .'

'Yes, felonious Massie, I can well picture the scene. Just before
the train started you asked the attendant to show you an assortment of propelling-pencils, drew your purse, made a couple of
passes and, hey presto, levanted with the whole tray.'

'I have never in my life pocketed a propelling-pencil. That
would be theft. You insult me.'

'It's about time someone did, fellow drinker! What a petti-
fogging rogue you are, to be sure. Convinced that nobody's going
to haul you into Court for the sake of a penny pencil or a
ha'penny matchbox, you lose all sense of decency and filch wholesale. Now, if you were to set your covetous eyes on something

only a little larger and more valuable, such as, as — let us say this corkscrew — '

'I wouldn't be found dead with that late-Victorian monstrosity!'

' — I repeat, with this corkscrew, I'd have a trifle more respect for you. But you stick to your own mean lay. In the criminal world, *on dit*, William Sikes, the master burglar, looks down his nose at the ignoble sneak thief and tuppenny tapper. William's scorn for you, O lower than Autolycus, would be an easterly blast to wither every flower in the summer's garden of your self-esteem.' He leaned back in his ornate chair, placed the tips of his fingers together and eyed me malevolently.

It is a fallacy that good wine makes one less drunk than bad wine. Borley would never have dared to talk to me like that if he hadn't had a skinful of his special Pommard; and if I hadn't been matching him glass for glass I should probably have kept my temper. I'd once heard him remark after a post-mortem at a North Oxford bridge table: '. . . *And if* the King of Hearts had worn a brassière and pink bloomers, he'd have been a Queen! So what, fellow gamesters?' But there was no *And if* on this occasion.

Frowning, I poured myself another brandy, tossed it over his shirt front, and then tweaked his greasy nose until it bled. I ought to have remembered that he had a weak heart; but then, of course, so ought he.

Borley died ten days later, after a series of heart attacks. Nobody knew about the tweaked nose — it isn't the sort of thing the victim boasts about — and though I think Plessis and his wife guessed from the brandy on their master's clothes that there had been a brawl, they did not bring the matter up. They benefited unexpectedly from the will: a legacy of a thousand pounds, free of death duties. To me, in spite of my disparagement of his wine, Borley left 'the Worser Part' of his cellar — it was another of his affectations to capitalize almost every other word — while 'the Better' was to go to Wadham Senior Common Room. I had also been appointed his sole executor, which entailed a great deal of tiresome work: it fell to me to organize his funeral and act as chief mourner. The bulk of his estate went to a second cousin, a simple-minded Air Force officer at Banbury, who took one look at the Kirtlington house, pulled a comic face, and took the next train back. The will, I should mention, had been a last-minute scrawl on the flyleaf of a cookery book, which was grudgingly accepted for probate because the nurse and doctor had witnessed it and the intentions were clear enough.

I felt a bit guilty about Borley. Once or twice in the course of the next few weeks I had a novel twinge of conscience when I stowed away my day's catch of pencils and matches in the bottom drawer of my desk. Then one day a letter came from Dick and Alice Semphill reminding me that I was to spend a yachting holiday with them in August, and that *Psyche* would be found moored in Oulton Broad on the fifteenth, if that suited me. I wrote back that I'd be there without fail, accompanied by a dozen of Borley's burgundies and clarets which, though the 'Worser Part' of his cellar, were well worth drinking; and a bottle or two of my own Domecq Fundador brandy.

Psyche is a comfortable craft, though rather slow, and the Semphills were glad to see me again. Both of them are mad on sailing. Dick's an architect and Alice and I once nearly got married when we were both under age; we're still a little more than friends. I think that's all I need say about them here.

The first night in the saloon, just before supper, eight-year-old Bunny Semphill watched me produce a bottle of Beaujolais and offered to uncork it. But he found the job too stiff for him, so I had to finish it.

As I was twisting the cork from the corkscrew, I started as though I had been stung. 'Bunny,' I asked, 'where the deuce did this come from?'

He stared at me. 'I don't know, Mr. Massie. I took it from the rack behind you.'

'Dick,' I called, trying not to sound scared, 'where did you get this ivory-handled corkscrew?'

Dick, busy mixing the salad in the galley, called back: 'I didn't know we possessed such a thing. I always use the one on my pocket knife.'

'Well, what's this?' And I showed it to him.

'Never set eyes on it until now.'

Neither, it proved, had Alice Semphill or Captain Murdoch, an Irish Guardsman who was the fifth member of the party.

'You look as though you'd seen a ghost,' said Alice. 'What's so extraordinary about the corkscrew, Reggie? Have you come across it before?'

'Yes: it belonged to the chap who bequeathed me the wine. But the trouble is that it wasn't part of the bequest. I can't make out how it got here.'

'You must have brought it along by mistake. Perhaps it got stuck into one of the bottle covers.'

'I'd have seen it when I packed them.'

'Not necessarily.'

'Besides, who put it on the rack?'

'Probably yourself. You know, Reggie, you do a lot of pretty absent-minded things. For instance, you pinched all our matches almost as soon as you came aboard. Not that I grudge you them in the least; but I mean . . .'

'How do you know? Did you see me pick up so much as a single box?'

'No, I can't honestly say I did. But I was wildly looking for a light and saw your raincoat hanging up and tapped the pockets, and they positively rattled . . .'

'I brought a lot of matches with me. Useful contribution, I thought . . .'

She let that go with a warning grimace. But the corkscrew mystery remained unsolved. I sincerely hoped that I hadn't suddenly become a major thief, as Borley had wished I would. It might land me in a police court — and eventually in a home for kleptomaniacs. I picked up the corkscrew, which I'd have recognized in a million. It was a stout eighteen-eightyish affair, with an ivory handle and a brush at one end, I suppose for whisking away the cobwebs from the necks of 1847 port bottles.

'Who were the people who chartered *Psyche* last week?' I asked.

'The Greenyer-Thoms; friends of Dick's brother-in-law George. He's an estate agent; she paints. They live near Banbury.'

'Aha!' I said, 'that explains it. They must have been at the sale of Borley's effects. The principal legatee is his Air Force cousin, who lives there.'

'Violent T.T. types, the Greenyer-Thoms, both of them,' Alice objected.

'Secret drinkers,' I countered, replacing the corkscrew on the rack. 'That's why they wanted the yacht. It's easy to dispose of the empties; just drop them into the water under cover of night.'

After supper Murdoch asked me jocosely whether he might be allowed to smell the cork of one of my famous brandies. I roused myself from a dark-brown study, fetched a bottle, and reached for the corkscrew. It was not on the rack. I glanced sharply from face to face and asked: 'Who's hidden it?'

They all looked up in surprise, but nobody spoke.

'I put it back on the rack and now it's gone. Hand it over, Bunny! You're playing a dangerous game. I'm foolishly sensitive about that corkscrew.'

'I haven't touched it, Mr. Massie — drop dead, I haven't — I swear!'

'Tap Massie's pockets, Mrs. Semphill,' Murdoch invited. 'They're positively wriggling with corkscrews.'

Dick caught a nose-tweaking glint in my eye. 'Gentlemen, gentlemen!' he cried warningly. Then he pulled out his pocket knife. ' — This will do, Reggie,' he said.

Dick's a decent fellow.

As I silently uncorked the brandy, Bunny went down on his hands and knees and searched among our feet. Then he rummaged among the cushions behind us.

'*Couldn't* it be in one of your pockets, Mr. Massie?' he asked at last.

'Certainly not!' I snapped. 'And for God's sake don't fidget so, child! Go on deck if you're bored with adult conversation.'

'I was only trying to help.'

'Well, don't try so hard.'

Alice didn't like the way I pitched into the boy and came to his rescue. 'I really think he had a right to ask you that,' she said. 'Especially as I can see the end of my best drawing pencil peeping out of your breast pocket.'

'It's not yours, woman; it's mine!'

'Let me umpire this tug of war,' said Murdoch. 'I'm the fairest-minded man in all East Anglia.'

'Keep out of this, Murdoch!' I warned him.

'Oh, forget it, chaps, for Christ's sake!' said Dick. 'If we're going to squabble about matches and pencils on the very first night of our sail . . .'

Under the influence of the Domecq, which everyone praised, we soon recovered our self-possession — but half an hour later, when we had finished washing up and were going on deck, Bunny looked at me curiously.

'Who hung the corkscrew on that hook?' he asked. 'Did you?'

'Captain Murdoch has a devious sense of humour,' I told him, 'and if you find yourself catching it, lay off!' But a cold shiver went through me and I stayed below for a supplementary drink. The blasted thing was dangling from a hook above the galley door. If I had been sure who the practical joker was, I'd have heaved him overboard.

For the sake of peace Dick must have asked the others not to comment on the corkscrew's reappearance, because the next day there was an eloquent silence, unbroken by myself, when I borrowed Dick's knife to uncork another bottle of claret. But for the rest of the holiday I was careful to go through my pockets, morning, afternoon, and night, to make sure that I had left enough matches and pencils lying about for general use. I had a superstitious feeling that, if I did, the corkscrew would stay on its hook. And I was right.

I am a little vague about where we went, or what weather we had; but I know that when the time came to say goodbye, Alice couldn't resist asking: 'Haven't you forgotten your trick corkscrew? It's still hanging up in the saloon.'

'No,' I said. 'It isn't mine and never was. The Greenyer-Thoms left it here. Anyhow, *Psyche* can do with an ivory-handled cork-screw.'

'Thank you,' said Alice quizzically. 'But I don't think Borley intended it for us.'

That evening, back in my flat, I found that in the hurry of my departure I had forgotten to frisk myself for matches and pencils. Among the day's collection I found an outsize box of Swan Vestas boldly marked in ink *John Murdoch, his property; please return to the Guards Club,* and Alice's double-B Koh-i-Noor pencil with her initials burned on it — with a red-hot knitting needle? — at both ends and in the middle. This made me cross. 'Bunny must have planted them on me,' I reassured myself. 'It couldn't have been Murdoch — he went off yesterday morning — and Alice wouldn't have been so unkind.'

'Nice gentlemanly corkscrew you've brought back, sir,' my Mrs. Fiddle remarked as she bustled in with the soup.

'Oh, I have, have I?' I almost yelled. 'Then throw it out of the window!'

She looked at me with round, reproachful eyes. 'Oh, sir, I could never do such a thing, Mr. Massie, sir. You can't buy a corkscrew like that nowadays.'

I jumped up. 'Then I'll have to throw it away myself. Where is it?'

'On the pantry shelf, next to the egg cups,' she answered re-signedly, picking up my fallen napkin. 'But it seems such wicked waste.'

'*Where* did you say it was?' I called from the pantry. 'I don't see it.'

'Come back, Mr. Massie, and eat your soup while it's hot,' she pleaded. 'The corkscrew can wait its turn, surely?'

Not wanting to look ridiculous, I came back and restrained myself until dessert, when I asked her curtly to fetch the thing.

She was away some little time and showed annoyance when she returned.

'You're making game of me, sir. You've hid that corkscrew; you know you have.'

'I have done nothing of the sort, Mrs. Fiddle.'

'There's only the two of us in the flat, sir,' she said, pursing her lips.

'Correct, Mrs. Fiddle. And if you want the corkscrew yourself, you're welcome to it, so long as you don't bring it back here. I should, of course, have offered it to Mr. Fiddle before I talked of throwing it out of the window.'

'Are you accusing me of hiding it with intent to deceive you, Mr. Massie?'

'Didn't you accuse *me* of that, just now?'

The thrust went home. 'I didn't mean anything rude, sir, I'm sure,' she said, weakening.

'I should hope not. But, tell me, Mrs. Fiddle, are you certain you saw a corkscrew? What was it like?'

'Ivory-handled, sir, with a sort of shaving brush at one end, and a little round silver plate set in the other with some initials and a date.'

This was too much. 'That's the one,' I muttered, 'but, upon my word, I never noticed the initials.'

'Well, look again, Mr. Massie, and see if I'm not right,' she said. And then, plaintively, as she retired into the kitchen, with her apron to her eyes: 'But you oughtn't to pull my leg, sir! I take things so seriously, ever since my little Shirley died.'

I poured her a drink, and we made peace.

Next day the corkscrew turned up in the pantry at the back of the napkin drawer. Mrs. Fiddle produced it in triumph. 'Here it is, sir. Now see if I wasn't right about the initials.'

I took it gingerly from her, and there was the silver plate all right. I couldn't understand how I had missed it. *F.C.C.B. 1928,* the silver slightly tarnished.

'Yes, sir, it could do with a nice rub-up.'

I saw no way out of this awkward situation but to earn credit as a practical joker. 'The fact is,' I blustered, 'I bought it at Lowestoft as a present for Mr. Fiddle. I didn't intend you to see it, and that's why I made a bit of a mystery of the whole affair. I meant to keep it for his birthday. First of next month, isn't it?'

'No, sir. Fiddle's birthday was the first of last month. Very kind of you, sir, all the same, I'm sure.'

But she still seemed dissatisfied. 'Fiddle isn't a wine or spirit-drinker, sir,' she explained after a pause, 'and bottled beer comes with screw tops these days.'

'How very stupid of me! All right, let's chuck it out of the window, after all.'

'Oh, no, sir! You might hurt someone passing in the street. Besides, it's a nice article. Keep it for yourself, and give Fiddle a couple of bottles of stout, instead. He'd take that very kindly, though belated. And so would I, if it comes to that, Mr. Massie, sir.'

Late that evening, with a neat package in my hand, I walked along the Mall until I came to Hammersmith Bridge. When no one was about, I hurled it into midstream. What a load off my mind! But that night I dreamed that a nasty looking corpse floating in the water had grabbed the parcel just as it sank and shouted to me to come back and collect my property. He rose dripping from the Thames; it was F. C. C. Borley himself. I turned and fled screaming towards the Broadway, but he came after me. 'It's yours, you damned thief!' he bawled. 'Wait! I've brought it!' And then, as a parting shot, heard indistinctly through the rumble of traffic: 'And the Worser Part (Bins K to T) for Mr. Reginald Massie.' That was the operative phrase in his will.

I awoke with chattering teeth, jumped out of bed, switched on all the lights in the flat, poured myself a stiff drink, and went along to see whether the corkscrew were back again on the pantry hook. Thank God, it wasn't!

I repacked my suitcase and read myself to sleep again.

In the morning when Mrs. Fiddle brought my tea I told her that I had been rung up by another set of yachting friends in South Devon, and was catching the morning train there. I'd send her a wire to let her know when I was returning, and what to do with my letters. This was nothing unusual; I frequently leave home on a sudden impulse.

I booked for Brixham, where I knew that a regatta was in progress. Also, a bachelor uncle of mine lived on the hill overlooking the harbour: an ex-Marine colonel whom I had not seen for years and whose chief interest was British freshwater molluscs. We exchanged cards at Christmas and his were always superscribed: 'Come and visit a lonely old man.' I thought: 'Here's my chance to show a little family feeling; besides, all the pubs are sure to be full because of the regatta.'

Uncle Tim was delighted to see me and discuss his molluscs and his rheumatism. That evening he took me in a taxi to the Yacht Club for an early supper. 'You look depressed, my boy,' he said, 'and not too well in spite of your holiday. You ought to get married. Man isn't meant to live by himself. Marriage would tone you up and give you a motive in life.' He added sadly: 'I put it off too long. Molluscs and marriage don't go together. Children would have played the deuce with my aquarium and cabinets.'

'Oh, they grow up,' I said airily. 'Seven years' patience, and your collection would have been safe enough.'

'You may be right; but the poor little blighters couldn't wait.'

'Who? The children?'

'No, no, stupid! The molluscs!'

'I beg your pardon. But why ever not?'

'River pollution: those confounded chemical manures washed off the soil, you know. A regular massacre of the innocents: whole species destroyed every year.'

I shook my head in sympathy.

'But there's nothing to prevent *you* from marrying, is there?' he persisted.

'I collect matchboxes,' I answered, rattling my pockets gloomily. 'Mine is one of the finest collections in Europe. It would hardly be fair to bring up children among so much incendiary material, would it?'

Presently Uncle Tim, reaching for the menu, said that his rheumatism be damned: with our Dover sole and roast chicken we'd have a bottle of the Club's famous hock, tacitly reserved for resident members. 'I know that you appreciate a sound wine, Reginald,' he said. 'Not many young men do, with all these confounded mixed drinks about. Gin and vermouth — gin and tonic — gin and bitters: that's what it's come to. Even in the Navy.

Pollution, I call it!' He finished enigmatically: 'Whole species destroyed every year.'

'Did you ever come across a youngster called Borley?' he went on. 'Chap I met once, here at the Club. He wore a floppy hat and an absurd tie like a Frenchman; said he was writing a book. A mind like a corkscrew — went round and round, and in and in, and then pop! out would come something wet. But, for all that, he had a remarkable knowledge of wine; and consented to approve of our hock.'

A waiter tiptoed in, cradling the bottle, and ceremoniously dusted its neck with the brush at the end of an ivory-handled corkscrew. 'I've brought it, fellow drinker,' he whispered with a confidential leer.

'Good heavens, boy!' cried Uncle Tim. 'What's amiss? Are you taken ill?'

I had dashed out of the Club, and was half running, half flying, down the slope to the Fish Market. The evening crowds in Fore Street blocked my way, but I swerved and zigzagged through them like an international wing three-quarter.

'Hey, Reggie, stop!' a woman shouted almost in my ear.

I handed her off and darted across the narrow street, where I found myself firmly tackled around the waist.

'For God's sake, Reggie, what's the hurry? Have you murdered someone?'

It was Dick Semphill! I stopped struggling and gaped at him. 'Come into this café and tell Alice and me what's happened.'

I followed him in, still gaping, and sat down. 'What on earth are you doing in Brixham?' I asked, when I found my voice.

'The regatta, of course,' Alice answered.

'But why aren't you up in Lowestoft?'

'That's not till next month. We've been here since Friday. *Psyche's* not distinguished herself yet, but there's still hope.'

'*Psyche?* But she can't possibly have sailed from Suffolk in the time!'

'I don't know what you're driving at. She's not been in the Broads since last year. You're coming up there next month — at least we hope you are — and we're going to have a wonderful time. By the way, you haven't yet told us whether Oulton Broad on the fifteenth suits you.'

'Where's Bunny?'

'At school in Somerset. Murdoch will collect him when he breaks up.'

'Dick — Alice, I believe I'm going off my head.' I told them the whole story from the beginning, even making a clean breast of the matchbox business. They both looked thoroughly uncomfortable when I had finished.

Alice said: 'Obviously, it was a dream, but I can't make out exactly at what point it began and ended. Listen: I'll ring up the Yacht Club and find out if your Uncle Tim's there.'

The phone was close to our table. Presently I heard her say: 'You're sure? Not since last Tuesday? Laid up with rheumatism? Oh, I'm so sorry. No, no message. Thanks very much.'

She put back the receiver. 'It's not so bad, Reggie,' she said. 'You haven't let your uncle down. As a matter of fact, they don't serve meals at the Yacht Club; and the only cellar there is the commodore's personal bottle they keep under the counter. So your dream didn't end until Dick woke you up a moment ago. It was a bit more than a dream, of course; a sort of sleep walk, probably due to worrying about that chap Borley. Lucky we met you. Do you mind turning out your pockets, Reggie, dear? That may give us a clue to how long you've been away from your flat.'

I obeyed dazedly. Out came eight matchboxes of different sorts, seven pencils and, among other odds and ends, the return half of a railway ticket from Paddington, and an unposted letter to Alice herself, written from my flat and confirming the Oulton Broad rendezvous.

'You came down here only this afternoon,' she said, showing me the date on the ticket.

There was also a bulky envelope containing all the documents concerned with my winding-up of Borley's affairs. Alice ran through them. 'I see you duly delivered the wine to the Warden and Fellows of Wadham College,' she said. 'And here's the itemized bill for the funeral at Kirtlington Parish Church. Oh, and a note from Squadron Leader Borley of Banbury, saying that if you'd like any souvenir from his cousin's effects before the auctioneer disposes of them, you're very welcome, but will you please let him know as soon as possible. He wrote on Thursday; I don't suppose you've answered him yet. Hullo, here's a photostat of the will itself! What beastly wriggly writing! Yes, its witnessed by — '

Dick had kept quiet all this time. Now he grabbed the will and read it. 'It's all right, Reggie,' he said. 'You've not gone nuts, and we won't even have to get you psychoanalyzed. You've merely been haunted — by a ghost which it ought to be easy enough to lay.' Then he burst out: 'You dolt, why didn't you take the trouble to find out whether your friend Borley was a Protestant or a Catholic?'

'I did take a great deal of trouble, but nobody knew. Even the College couldn't tell me, so I followed the line of least resistance and had him buried C. of E.'

'Exactly. That's what all the trouble's been about! You see now why in your dream he called you a damned thief?'

'I don't understand.'

'Read the will again. Read it aloud!'

I read:

'I appoint Reginald Massie to be my executor . . . the Better Part of my Cellar (Bins A to J) are for the Warden and Fellows of Wadham College, Oxford. The Worser Part (Bins K to T) are for Mr. Reginald Massie . . .'

'Not *"for Mr. Reginald Massie,"* idiot; if he'd meant you he'd have written "the said Reginald Massie." It's *"for the Requisite Masses"!* Masses for his soul's repose, don't you see?'

The exhumation was not easy to wangle, but I got it fixed up in the end. Then I handed over the wine to the St. Aloysius people at Oxford and they agreed to do the rest. And on Alice's insistence, I wrote to Squadron Leader Borley, asking for the corkscrew as a keepsake. Since he sent it I haven't pocketed a single matchbox or pencil — so far as I know, that is . . .

Occupation: Writer

(1949)

THIS is how I fill in my income-tax return — but cynically because 'writer' has become almost meaningless as a descriptive term since popular education opened the dikes to a shallow sea, and because 'occupation' reminds me that though I am a poet and keep my due distance from the antipoetic world of commerce and bureaucracy, I have earned my living by writing books, mostly full-length novels, for nearly a quarter of a century.

That is a very long time. The odds are heavily against anyone's having enough real, necessary books in him to keep his pen employed for more than five or six years at the outside; unless he is a very slow writer, which I cannot pretend to be. By the law of averages I should long ago have started writing unreal, unnecessary books or frankly taken up journalism.

('Robert Graves is slipping, I fear,' remarks the bookseller to the traveller. 'He's reached the *Collected Essays* stage at last. Pity he couldn't have given us another *I Claudius* instead — I wonder why he never touched the Emperor Nero?' 'A good novel waiting for someone there,' the traveller muses, sucking his teeth.)

I confess that I have been haunted since my school days by Daudet's macabre story of the man with the gold brain — of which he recklessly scraped away bits for his greedy dependants until he died a hollow-skulled imbecile, gold dust and blood under his fingernails. Then why do I make things more difficult for myself by refusing to write the same sort of book twice?

('I wonder he doesn't at least get to work on his autobiography,' continues the bookseller. 'Oh, but he wrote that over twenty years ago,' the traveller reminds him. 'Don't you remember?'

Since when, he has succeeded — *I* have succeeded (I find it difficult at times to identify the bookseller's Robert Graves with myself) in doing nothing in the least newsworthy. Unless providing for a family of seven children is newsworthy; I remember once reading in *The Eugenics Review* that 'writers and mine-owners are two notoriously sterile groups.'

('Well, from now on I shall gradually reduce my Graves' orders,' says the bookseller. 'That's O.K. by me,' the traveller agrees. 'Mind you, I wouldn't go as far as to say that he's written out. But it stands to reason he can't keep it up indefinitely. Even H. G. Wells, you know . . .')

Yes, yes, by God! Even H. G. Wells! Or, for that matter, even Edgar Rice Burroughs. Or even William Shakespeare. Or even my indefatigable brother Charles Graves . . . Or . . . or . . .